BIOGEOGRAPHY
Theoretical and Applied
(Volume-2)

BIOGEOGRAPHY

Theoretical and Applied

(Volume-2)

Dr. T.S. Chouhan

Department of Geography
University of Rajasthan,
Jaipur

Shruti Publications
Jaipur

(Volume-2)

ISBN 978-93-81433-09-6
First Edition : 2013

₹ 1990.00 (2 volume set)

Publishers by

Shruti Publications
50-Ka-6, Jyoti Nagar, Jaipur - 302 005
Phone : 0141-2741653
Mobile: 94140-62585
e-mail : shruti_publications@yahoo.co.in

Typesetting by

Madan Computers, Jaipur

Printed by

Sheetal Printers, Jaipur

Preface

Recently biogeography has emerged as one of the important branch of geography and biology after a long journey of academic dilemma of about two hundred years. During this period biogeographers have done remarkable work and contributed significantly in defining concepts, terminology, aims, pattern approaches and methods of biogegraphy. Thus biogeography has come out as a separate interdisciplinary subject.

As a university teacher, while preparing lecture notes for teaching this subject to graduate and postgraduate geography students of Rajasthan University, I realized the lack of a suitable book on this subject for the use of students in Indian Universities, Accordingly, I conceived and developed the idea of writing a text-cum-reference book containing the theory and the applied aspects of biogeography. The material presented in this book has been divided into two volumes dealing with different aspects of biogeography, i.e. history, nature, scope, principles and different branches of biogeography and their inter-relationships. Each chapter has been provided with relevant and comprehensive review of work of different scientists who have developed ideas and material in different periods from ancient to modern one dealing with contents, trends and changing emphases in biogeography with suitable illustrations.

The author recognize with gratitudes the help drawn from various books on the subject as included in the bibliographical references. I am also grateful to the officials of various government departments and international agencies engaged in environmental planning programmes for their cooperation in providing relevant literature and data for preparation of this book. Our thanks are also due to our teachers, colleagues and friends for their help advice and encouragement in various ways.

I hope the teachers and students of biogeography will find the book useful in their profession.

Dr. T.S. Chouhan

Contents

VOLUME-2

10

Animal Habitats, Adaptations and Migrations

INTRODUCTION

For land animals the word habitat takes on a very different aspect. Most terrestrial animals can tolerate a wide range of variation in the purely physical factors; neither climate nor relief is as a rule in itself of outstanding importance, while, save with burrowing animals, soil exerts little influence. It is indeed in the general case to .the characteristic plant cover and not to details of climate or relief or soil features that land animals must be adjusted in structure, function and habits. In other words, habitat for them is defined not by the physical factors themselves but by their expression in the plant communities present. A particular amount or distribution of rainfall may matter little in itself; it matters enormously in so far as it is reflected in a type of plant community to which the animals present must be adapted.

We have seen that plants tend to form communities which are a direct response to factors of habitat, especially climatic ones. That response again is expressed in the nature and relative numbers of the life-forms in different communities, in the lateral spacing of the plants and in the extent to which they are arranged in tiers. Even defining forest as a close canopy of tall phanerophytes, we find that forests not only vary greatly in their composition, in the density of the tree stands, in the degree to which tier formation occurs but can exist also under a wide range of climate, with e corresponding diversity in character and appearance Similarly, while it is convenient for some purpose to regard the habitat as grasslands communities in which the closing of the canopy is due to herbaceous plants, yet grasslands differ greatly among themselves and again occur in a variety of habitats.

Diversity of plant communities involves diversity of terrestrial habitats for animals and a wide range of anima adaptation. The ocean shows a much greater degree of uniformity, and the contrast has two consequences. In the first place we find that the lands, despite their much smaller area, despite also the presence of purely negative tracts such as those drowned beneath land ice or a permanent snow cover, have a far greater number of kinds of animals than the seas which is at second place from animals habitats distribution point of view. Again, marine animals show little analogy to that wide range of adaptive adjustment to habitat which is so marked in the case of land forms. These adaptations occur especially in connation with the kind o food habitually taken and with the usual mode of movement for, in contrast with marine animals, many of which are either sedentary or float in the water, almost all land animals have well-developed loco-motor organs definitely related to the plant cover-the South American sloth hanging back downwards from branches in the tropical forests and literally unable to put foot to ground, our squirrel almost equally a home in the trees and on the ground, wild horses galloping over the plains, the snake gliding through the grass, and sc on. In the ocean, on the other hand, plants rarely occur in such size and numbers as to exert any special influence, and the animals capable of free movement for the most part either swim in the water or crawl over the sea floor unhindered by the small number of bulky plants present. The two major oceanic habitats are thus that in which the animals are dependent on the solid substratum and that formed by the open water. On the lands, on the other hand, habitat is determined mainly not by the nature of the substratum but by also the plant communities which it bears. Upon those communities depends largely the extent to which free movement is possible and generally all kind of possible movements which is easiest in their life pattern.

These plant communities, again, vary enormously in the amount and nature of the basal food supply which they furnish, in the extent to which this shows seasonal variation and in the degree of its accessibility to plant-feeding animals. It is true that both in the ocean and on the lands the end of the food-chain, and that however numerous the intervening links, is the living, chlorophyll-containing plant cell. But in the ocean the most numerous and most widely distributed plants are single-celled, floating algae drifting with the surface currents, while the remainder consist chiefly of the larger fixed algae which are structurally hardly more complex. The woody and corky tissues which enter so largely into the make-up of many land plants not only are poor in essential food elements but will not yield to the digestive fluids of most animals. Some insects among terrestrial animals, some crustaceans and molluscs among marine ones, seem able to digest wood, but otherwise, like cork, it is practically valueless in this connation. Further, even the softer parts of land plants differ notably both in their food value and in their availability. In consequence, most vegetable feeders among land animals show a delicate adjustment to a particular kind of food, some insects, for example, limiting themselves strictly to the leaves of a single species of plant. Generally, it may be said that associated with the great range of variation of land plant we may find that vegetarian terrestrial animals tend to be adapted to a particular type of diet and thus constrained to frequent the plant communities which yield the food they require.

In sum, then, the kinds of places in which land animals live-that is, their habitats-are determined mainly by the nature of the plant cover, and to that plant cover they are adapted with the prevailing physical factors. But while the plants are fixed, the animals are capable of free movement within the limits set by the nature of their loco motor organs and their demand for suitable food-that is, by their specific adaptations Two interesting topics thus present themselves for discussion in the first place we have to inquire how far it is true that the various kinds of plant communities we have described have each their characteristic fauna, the range of whose members is limited by that of the community. Secondly, there is the more detailed problem of the actual structural adaptations which fit particular animals for the various types of country as defined by their plant cover.

Earth as a whole, following are the dominant as well an important habitats of the earth as a whole—

1. The Equatorial Forest as an Animal Habitat
2. Temperate Grasslands
3. Land Mammals and Plant Communities
4. Water Bodies Habitat - Fresh and salt water bodies

ADAPTATIONS IN ANIMALS

We can hint here only a few major adaptations here and there among the nearly 3,000 species of living mammals because mammals are active, highly organized animals, two problems of feeding present themselves. There is, first, the obtaining of the crude material in sufficient amounts and second, the details of the mechanism by which this is made to yield the substances essential for growth and reproduction as well as to make up for the waste due to the vital processes

As regards the second point, we must note the essential differences between plant and animal tissues. Living plan cells, and this whether the plants are aquatic or terrestrial simple or complex, have a coating of the carbohydrate cellulose round the ported contents. Animal tissues are made up of naked cells and thus bulk for bulk are richer in nitrogenous organic matter and more easily attacked by digestive fluids.

Mammals division is also based on their feeding habits respectively on vegetal and on animal matter than we find that the latter require a proportionately greater bulk of food, for much of the material ingested may pass through their bodies little altered. Whereas, herbivorous forms must have means where by the parts of plants taken are finely ground, thoroughly mixed with the digestive fluids to render their rather scanty nutritive elements soluble, while in this aspect the absorbing surface of the alimentary tract must be extensive. Generally, indeed, vegetarian mammals must either make a very careful selection of the parts of plants consumed so as to include a high proportion of nutritive matter in relation to that which is useless; or, if they are more indiscriminate feeders, they must have elaborate masticatory and digestive organs to deal with rough material. To see that this must be so, one has only to think of the elaborate care with which the squirrel removes every vestige of the outer protective coats of a nut before beginning to chew the kernel, and compare the confidence both in its grinding teeth and in its digestive organs displayed by the elephant. If again we compare either squirrel or elephant with the domestic cat and note what acute senses, agility, intelligence and powerful weapons in the shape of teeth and claws are needed before even such relatively feeble animals as small birds and Rodents can be caught, it becomes clear that the carnivorous habit demands very special adaptations. Once such animals capture their prey, however, the flesh can be 'Noted' without elaborate chewing, for digestion is easy.

Given then the fact that mammals require considerable quantities of proteid, they are faced with the difficulty that for the smaller, less differentiated types, it is difficult to make plants yield a sufficiency of this, while on the other hand, high as is the food value of the flesh and blood of other mammls are what is called omnivorous, and meaning of the term requires a little elaboration.

Most of the small mammals which take storage organs of plants greedily when they can be got, require supplementary sources especially of protein. Of these supplementary sources, that furnished by the class of insects is the most important. There is almost no organic substance, living or dead, whether of plant or animal origin, which does not enter into the diet of some kind of insect, and as a result the insects are the great intermediaries in the food-chains of terrestrial animals. They take up material which is absolutely useless to most other animals and convert it into their own living substance, which is then available. Great numbers of mammals, therefore, both Marsupials and Placentals, even when nominally vegetation take in addition insects, especially insect larvae. Where the larvae are themselves vegetarian the body as consumed by the mammal includes both animal tissues in the strict sense and much semi-digested vegetal food already made partially available. The plump caterpillar has chosen, masticated and swallowed parts of green leaves, and the bird or mammal which swallows it has had part of what would otherwise have been its work done for it and is also getting a mixture of animal and vegetal food. Earthworms, another potential food supply, suffer on the other hand from the disadvantage of containing a large amount o1 an omnivorous mammal that insects will enter into its diet as well as other terrestrial arthropods (millipedes, spiders, etc.)

The smaller weakly armed mammals can also get animal food from the eggs and nestlings of birds, carrion, the remnants of the kill of larger animals and so on. It will be noted, however, that in the general case the omnivorous habit is most easily acquired by mammals which are either arboreal or burrowing, for the resultant modifications of the fore-limbs and body are an important factor. The sensitive finger-like digits of many kinds of arboreal mammals, the sensitive pointed snouts of such burrowers as shrews and other Insectivores are obviously great assets in picking up miscellaneous food substances.

The term insectivorous, it may be noted, whether as applied to the Placental order of Insectivores or to other kinds of animals is somewhat deceptive. Many kinds of mammals eat insects when obtainable, but an exclusive dependence on winged adults, such as occurs in some birds, almost always implies the power of flight. In this sense the chief true insect-eaters are certain of the bats, for mammals live too fast for it to be possible for non-Volant forms to depend on the slow method of stalking adult insects practiced by so many lizards among the cold-blooded reptiles. Here however we have to recall the fact that certain insects, particularly the true ants and the non-nearly-related white ants or termites, show an extraordinary development of the social instinct. Some kinds of both ants and termites construct ant-hills of a size which in relation to that of the individual builders is enormous. These ant-hills are nurseries as well as dwellings, and many of the adults are wingless, wings being present often only during the short pairing phase when the nuptial flights occur. Anthills thus contain an enormous potential of food supply, available provided (1) the protective covering of the "house" can be torn down and (2) there is some means of collecting both the helpless young and the wingless adults as they scatter. In consequence, at various levels in the mammalian sequence, we find forms which are not omnivorous, not insectivorous in the general sense but specifically ant-eaters or termite-eaters. The adaptations present are mainly those which facilitate the two processes already mentioned; teeth are sometimes present and sometimes absent without apparently making much difference, and no special modifications of the alimentary tract seem essential. Such ant-eating mammals occur among Monotremes (Echidna and Proechidna), among Marsupials as in the Dasyure family (banded ant-eater), among Edentates (hairy ant-eaters, pangolins, aard-vark). Even such highly differentiated mammals as some of the bear group, as for example the south-bear of India, seem to depend largely on ants and termites, though the sloth-bear also attacks the nests of the social boss both for the grubs and for the stored honey, and takes also fruits, flowers and other kinds of insects.

Apart from aquatic fish-eating forms the remaining terrestrial mammals, including the larger quadrupeds, are either herbivores, depending on various kinds of fresh herbage, or carnivores, feeding on the flesh and blood of warm-blooded vertebrates, especially members of the Ungulate and Rodent orders, thus in both cases the structural adaptations are numerous and varied.

1. Adaptations in Herbivores

Among mammals the higher Ungulates show the most perfect adaptations to a diet consisting wholly of herbage. Certain of the Diprotodont Marsupials are, however, little inferior in this respect and some of the larger Rodents are at least mainly dependent on such food and correspondingly specialized.

The major features of the dentition have been already outlined, but there are a number of peculiar adaptations in the different groups. Thus the higher even-toed Ungulates are remarkable in having no incisor teeth in the upper jaw, the large lower incisors working against a hardened pad in the upper jaw. Upper canine teeth are also absent while the lower canines resemble the incisors and lie close beside them. That these are adaptive features is shown by the fact that the true pigs, the simplest of the even-toed series, retain the full complement of upper incisors, and have upper canines as well as lower ones, the latter not being incisor-like. Since the pigs take a variety of food it is tempting to regard the loss of the upper incisors as in some way making grazing easier. But this cannot be the case, for the horses, the highest of the odd-toed series, have at once the full number of upper incisors and are as definitely grass-eating as the higher even-toed forms. Here, however, another point is worth noting. In the even-toed series the higher as compared with the lower forms posses bony head appendages (antlers, horns) either in both sexes or in the males only. Apparently it is difficult to obtain from a diet of herbage sufficient lime salts to permit of the calcification of the massive cheek teeth, the head appendages and the bulky skeleton, so that the loss of the upper front teeth may represent a necessary economy of lime.

A tendency to lose either the upper canines or both upper and lower ones is at once more general among herbivorous mammals and more easily explained. In mammals generally these teeth tend to be weapons, and this tendency reaches its maximum in the Carnivores where they are long, strong and sharp. Herbivorous mammals cannot hope to compete with them in this respect and, save in the case of some of the less specialized Ungulates such as the pigs, either depend on flight for escape or have weapons of another type. The suppression of the canines, especially of the upper ones, is a means of attaining this end. In other words, in herbivores generally canines are ineffective as weapons, and inconvenient for animals which do much chewing, and they tend to disappear.

Some considerable examples are being described here. In the Rodents there are no canines in either jaw and hairy pad divides the mouth cavity into an anterior gnawing chamber and a posterior masticatory one. The incisors are large but few, and if cornered the animals can use them to give an ugly bite. The higher even-toed Ungulates cannot give an effective bite, but the antlers or horns combined with the powerful head muscles are used to try to prevent the Carnivores from makirg an approach near enough to use their teeth and claws. The horses, which at least in the males retain the upper canines, use their powerful incisors rather than these in the vicious bite, but their main weapon lies in the powerful hind-limbs armed with the heavy hoofs.

It is however in the characters of the all-important cheek teeth that the herbivorous mammals show the most obvious adaptations. The drier grasses are taken these must be thoroughly chewed, and the problem of maintaining, throughout a life which may be long, efficient, self-setting. The problem is complicated by the fact that one feature of mammals, the limited degree to which the teeth can be replaced, had apparently been fixed before the modern herbivorous forms appeared. Placentals have two successive sets and two only, Marsupials one complete set only. In the Placentals an obvious adaptation is to retain the milk set as long as possible so as to diminish the strain on the adult or second set. This occurs among the Ungulates as a general feature but, rather oddly, not in the same way among the Rodents. There, within the limits of a single family, some forms shed their milk teeth early and others retain them for a considerable period. The living elephants, which have peculiarly massive and complex teeth and are very long-lived, make their cheek teeth last longer by the device of using only one or parts of two at each side of each jaw at any one time. As the functional tooth is worn down it is shed and the next one grows forward to take its place. This is a development of the condition seen in man where the last cheek tooth (wisdom tooth) at each side of both upper and lower jaws normally develops later than the other members of the adult set.

Generally, however, specialization in herbivorous mammals shows itself mainly in the size and complex structure of the cheek teeth. While the details are beyond our scope we may note the distinction between the long-crowned teeth of the hollow-horned ruminants and the short-crowned ones of, e.g., the deer. In the deer the crown is short, the whole depth being exposed from the first and this passing direct into the roots; such teeth wear down readily and make it impossible for the deer to masticate the wiry grasses favoured by the hollow-horned ruminants. It is notable that Africa, south of Mauretania, with its enormous tracts of savanna carrying coarse grasses, has no deer but countless herbs of antelopes; deer tend to frequent areas where the soften kinds of grasses occur or where other kinds of herbage are available.

2. Adaptations in Carnivores

For our purpose the carnivorous mammals are less important than the herbivorous ones. They need not show -such a direct relation to the plant cover; so long as suitable prey is present indeed almost any climatic zone, any type of relief, may serve their purpose. In consequence the range of genera and species tends to be wide. Most of the genera of Ungulates are limited to particular parts of the world land-masses and within these the species tend to be limited to particular types of country. Among the Carnivores the true cats of the genus Felis are all but concerned to the habitat of particular country. Even species such as the lion in the Old World and the puma in the New, range widely, the latter with an extension from British Columbia to Patagonia, showing an astonishing indifference to variations both in climate and topography. Like the grasses and the composites among plants the higher Carnivores seem to have conquered the world and to be able to adapt themselves to almost every kind of physical condition.

Of the three groups included in the terrestrial Carnivores the cat-like forms are the most specialized, this reaching its maximum in the true cats of the genus Felis. These, so far as bodily structure is concerned, may be regarded as the highest of the mammals. Apart from his brain and his sensitive fingers man himself seems anatomically a poor thing beside them, showing little of that perfect adaptation.

Among the adaptations shown by the cats we may note the shortening the lower jaw to give increased leverage and its limited range of movement at the finely moulded articulation to ensure a firm grip on the prey. In the short jaws there is no room for massive grinding teeth, but these are not required. The hindermost cheek teeth are suppressed, the anterior ones have cutting edges to separate flesh from bones, a process assisted by the rasping tongue. The separated shreds of flesh are swallowed with but little chewing and are rapidly and readily digested. The fore-limbs possess five clawed digits and the claws when not in use are drawn back into hoods so that their sharp points are not worn down during walking (contrast the blunt, non-retractile claws of dogs). Since the armed fore-limbs combined with the stabbing canines form the attacking weapons, the range of movement of the former both at shoulder and wrist is great. A striking feature is the enlarged middle ear which is provided with what seems to be a reasonating chamber, giving great acuteness of hearing. The animals' own movements are characteristically silent.

Cats are not social, and though the mother shows great devotion to the young during their period of helplessness and much apparent altruism in bringing them food, later she soon turns against them, for no one locality can support many predatory forms of this type. The play of the young, so obvious in the domesticated cat and directly stimulated by the mother, is of course a training for adult life. There is a very critical period when the mother's guidance is withdrawn and the young have to apply these lessons for themselves, and this before they have come to their full strength. It is at this stage that the struggle for existence occurs in its most acute form and ensure the survival of the fittest stocks.

The dog-like forms lack the saber-edged claws of the cats and the fore-limbs have a more limited range of movement; but the animals have more power of sustaining speed than the cats. Cheek-teeth are more numerous and less specialized for a flesh diet. In the typical forms (wolves, hunting dogs) prey is brought down by a combined attack assisted by speed and cunning. Hearing is scarcely less acute than in the cats, there being again an enlarged middle ear though its structure is not identical in the two cases.

In the bear group the range of variation is so great that many systematic regard the group as artificial. Thus while the true bears and the members of the weasel family possess in common certain anatomical features whose significance is not clear, they differ very widely in habits and mode of life. The bears are thought to have had a common origin with the dogs, the two having evolved in different directions. Bears are large, slow-moving, clumsy animals, dull of hearing and, as their cheek teeth show, not fitted for a purely flesh diet. The fore-limbs are powerful and armed with five strong non-retractile claws. Several species do on occasion attack large Ungulates, but most take a considerable amount of vegetable food. Apart from the polar bear, they frequently wooded and hilly country and are good climbers; bears are not social. Being thus without the very specialized weapons of the cats and the speed and power of combination of the dogs, the land bears have followed a line of their own and utilize the varied food resource of the woodlands. Several hibernate after growing fat on the autumn harvest of the woods, the tendency being more marked in the females, who carry their unborn young throughout the winter season. The habit of hibernation is remarkable considering the size of the body.

The civets are small cat-like Carnivores with longer bodies, shorter legs and less specialized teeth and claws than the cats proper. All are confined to the Old World and mainly to the lower latitudes there. Their small size and relative weakness mean that they must prey chiefly on small mammals, birds or even (in the case of the mongoose) reptiles. Now vast numbers of birds migrate to high northern latitudes to nest and rear their young, while the cosmopolitan Rodents are abundant in high latitudes generally. Thus a large potential food supply for carnivorous mammals is present, provided these can either climb trees or pursue the Rodents into their burrows and along their runs among herbage. The weasel group, though it includes such relatively large forms as the badger and such specialized ones as the aquatic, fish-eating otter, consists typically of small, slender bodied, very blood-thirsty mammals whose ferocity and agility is the counterpart of the Rodents' fecundity. These weasel-like forms are widely distributed but reach their maximum development in the northern hemisphere and in its temperate regions.

ENVIRONMENTAL ADAPTATIONS

Just as plants develop and show specialized adaptations to environmental, and more particularly to climatic, conditions so, too, do animals. Certain species of animals show distinct preferences for particular habitats; for instance, some prefer to live in the soil, others prefer waterside or marshy environments, while yet others have a predilection for life in the trees.

Creatures that live in the soil are known as Terriolae; examples of terricolous fauna are earthworms, various kinds of insects, rodents and moles. Burrowing animals are generally nocturnal in their habits and resort to hibernation during the lean, cold season. Life in the earth has led to many terricoloud creatures developing specific adaptations, e.g. strong, clawed forepaws for digging, spatulate hind paws for throwing up earth, sharp, pointed heads, strong, forward-projecting teeth, and short or rudimentary tails. Life underground dispenses with the need for sight, and thus the eyes of terricolous creatures degenerate and some are almost blind.

Many creatures are attracted to moist environments and they are known as Anuicolae. Some, such as the beaver and the otter, have even adopted a semi-aquatic mode of life. Many birds and mammals have been attracted to waterside environments as a result of the abundance of food, in the form of larvae, insects, worms, fish, etc., available in streams and lakeside localities. Semi-aquatic mammals, such as the beaver and otter, develop little, streamlined bodies, webbed feet and thick fur. The hippopotamus offers a unique example of an ungulate which has become adapted to a semi-aquatic life; it loves to wallow in warm water and mud. In this case the main adaptations occur in the head, where the ears, eyes and nostrils are found in the upper portion of the skull. The wafer buffalo has a similar love of water.

Animals of arboreal habits, i.e. those which live largely in trees, are known as Arboriclae. Such creatures have developed modifications which enable them to climb, jump and move readily. Monkeys, for instance, show a variety of adaptations, e.g. long forearms, opposable thumbs, long toes and prehensile tails, which fit them for life in the trees. Yet other creatures, such as the flying lemur and the flying squirrel, have developed membranes between the limbs and the body which enable them to glide from branch to branch. Most of the Arboricolae live on a vegetarian diet of leaves, fruits and nuts.

1. Form and Colour

A fascinating aspect of animal life relates to form and colour in animals; form and colour embraces such things as disguise and camouflage, mimicry and luminescence. All these are either in the nature of adaptations to environmental conditions or security mechanisms against attack. When danger threatens, many creatures remain quite still, hoping that their shape and colouring will prevent them from being seen; others try to scare away their enemies by adopting terrifying attitudes and simulating aggression. Defensive behaviour of every kind on the part of the animal is assisted by form and colour.

So-called "protective" colouring is a common characteristic among animals: this helps them to harmonise with their surroundings and escape detection. For example, many creatures living in snowy environments are white or change their summer colouring to winter white with the arrival of the snow, e.g. the ptarmigan and arctic hare, while denizens of the desert are tawny or pale grey to blend with the buff-coloured landscape. Counter-shading, i.e. where the back of an animal is darker than the under part, is a simple form of concealment common to nearly all the vertebrates. Counter-shading has the effect of canceling out the effects of light and shade and enables the animal to fade into its surroundings. Some animals have strongly patterned bodies, e.g. stgrips and irregular patches of contrasting colours; at close quarters these markings stand out clearly but at a distance they blur and provide an effective camouflage. Think, for instance, of the stripes of the zebra against the tall grasses of the savanna or of the black-and-white Malayan tapir which haunts boulder-strewn stream courses or of the leopard whose large dark spots enable it to lurk in the dappled light which filters through the jungle growth. Among the lower animals there are some which are capable of making rapid colour changes, e.g. lizards and frogs.

Many fish show quite remarkable colour patterns. Some of the flat-fishes which live mainly on the sea bed exhibit a rare ability to change their colour and body patterns in a matter of seconds, for instance the turbot. Many tropical fish living in colourful surroundings are themselves brightly coloured or markedly striped. Some small fish have large spots on their bodies which look like large eyes; this is to enable them, when half hidden, to masquerade as rnuch larger creatures.

The body shapes of some animals form a source of protection. Their bodies are shaped or decorated to enable them to blend with their surroundings; when the creatures are still they are virtually indistinguishable as separate objects. Many lizards are very difficult to distinguish against the bark of a tree, and the gecko has a fringe along its sides and tail which helps it to merge with the tree bark. The sea-dragon, a kind of sea-horse, has long outgrowths of skin which closely resemble the fronds of the seaweed in which it lives Protective shapes are especially common among the insects many butterflies have leaf-shaped wings so that when the^ light on a twig they look like a leaf. The stick insects with their thin and nodular bodies have a truly astonishing resemblance to twigs.

Some animals posses striking colorations to call attention to themselves: these may be thought of as "warning" colours advertising the fact that the creatures are unpalatable, dangerous or to be avoided. Wasps, snakes, some toads and the brightly spotted ladybird beetle are some of the animals displaying warning colours. In other words warning colour serves as an alarm signal. Many animals, e.g. rabbits and antelopes, raise their tails to show a white patch when disturbed and frightened. Similarly, the springbok, when alarmed, jumps into the air to display long white back hairs which are normally hidden; these form an alarm signal warning the herd of imminent danger.

Among the many kinds of adaptations is mimicry. Mimicry in animals takes such fraudulent forms as warning colours, frightening attitudes and imitation. Many small, defenseless creatures adopt mimicry to bluff their enemies; for example, certain species of syrphid flies (hoverflies) imitate the colour patterns of wasps, certain edible butterflies mimic those having an obnoxious taste, while one kind of harmless snake mimics, in its colouring and body pattern, the deadly coral snake.

2. Luminescence in Animals

Associated with form and colour in animals is tuminescence, the production of light by organisms. Luminescence is widely spread among animals, occuring in more than half of the zoological phyla. Fish, which have developed luminescence to a remarkable degree, are, however, the only group among the vertebrates possessing luminous characteristics.

3. J.A.C. Nicol Writes

"Although luminescence appears to be most abundant among marine animals, it is likely that these are equalled in number by species of terrestrial fireflies that abound in tropical regions. It is in the three latter groups that luminous organs attain the greatest complexity" (J.A.C. Nicol 1977).

On land, luminescence occurs in some nocturnal creatures, e.g. fireflies, and among some animals which live in dark places, e.g. fungus-gnats. Fireflies, glow-worms and some centipedes are the chief land animals having luminous characteristics. Although there are considerable numbers of luminous animals living in the surface waters of the ocean, luminescence is more especially a feature associated with creatures living in the dimly lit or deeper parts of the ocean. According to Beebe, 'something like two-thirds of all the species of fish living below 55° metres are luminescent", and, fish apart, there are large numbers of demersal jellyfishes, copepods, prawns and squids that are a luminous.

According to Nicol light-production in animals occurs in three different ways: "It takes place within cells- intracellular luminescence; or the light is produced by luminous symbiotic bacteria within the animal." Commonly an animal exhibits only a single kind of luminescence, but there are certain species, e.g. prawns, which possess both intra-and extra-luminescence. Intracellular luminescence takes various forms: some creatures have luminous internal glands; others have luminous circulatory systems; some possess plaques of luminescent cells, as in the case of scale-worms. Extra cellular luminescence or the ejection of luminous secretions occurs in many animals, for example in certain types of fish, prawns, squids, molluscs and worms. When symbiotic bacteria are responsible for luminescence they are housed in special light organs. Some creatures have light organs such as luminous points which can be made to glow, as in the case of angler fish or some sea lilies.

Animals, then, produce light in a variety of ways i.e. luminescence and it's purpose may appear to fulfill many roles: to attract prey, to recognize enemies, as a mating signal, for gregarious purposes.

ANIMAL MIGRATION

1. Introduction

In general, living organisms of all kinds reproduce themselves with quite astonishing rapidity and since nature has provided them with means of dispersal they tend to enlarge their areas of occupation unless some inhibiting factor of a physical or biological character controls their expansion and it is quite remarkable that how quickly organisms decolonize areas. A classic example is provided by the catastrophic votoanic eruption on the island of Krakkatoa-in Indonesia which occurred in 1883. So great was the explosion that much of the island was quite literally blown away while the volcanic debris which rained down upon the remaining fragments covered them with a thick blanket of ash which effectively extinguished all the plant and animal life with the possible exception of a species of earthworm. Yet life reestablished itself on the blighted island remarkably quickly: within three years, alagae, some species of ferns and more than a dozen flowering plants were to be found; within six, some of the smaller animals (spiders, beetles, butterflies and a species of lizard) had found their way there; after twenty-five years 263 animal species were recognized, and after fifty years around 600 species which included a crocodile and a python. Since the nearest land to Krakatoa not destroyed by the eruption is 11-1/2 miles (18.5 km) distant the new inhabitants must have arrived by air or water or by other means of "fortuitous dispersal."

The areal extent of plant and animal distribution is by no means unlimited, however, for there are a number of inhibiting factors:

1. The dispersal capacity of different organisms is very unequal,
2. Dispersal does not happen with equal success in all directions,
3. The constitution of the organisms may limit their movement,
4. Physical conditions may impose strict barriers to movement, and
5. The organic environment may set definite limits to dispersal.

These factors check the free and unlimited distributor of plants and animals.

From what has just been said it will be appreciated that the distribution of any animal species is fundamentally determined mainly by (i) the means and methods of dispersal available to it, and (ii) the physical and biotic obstacles preventing its dispersal. Because of the differences in the means of dispersal of different animal groups, physica obstacles affect the different groups in different ways : for instance, though some land animals can swim, usually they are limited in their spread by stretches of water; while conversely, water creatures are restricted by land barriers again, land animals may have their movements; restricted by high mountains, while flying animals may be able to surmount topographic barriers with ease-birds, in fact, are the animals least affected by barriers of any kind. Inhospitable climatic conditions, due to such conditions as cold, heat or lack of moisture, the absence of suitable supplies of food the presence of predatory enemies or even the presence of more successful competitors, may prove to be obstacles to the movement of any particular groups of animals.

The present disposition of land and sea is not the same as it was 1, 20, 50 or 100 million years ago. There is good reason to believe that land connections once existed between some areas which now lie separated from each other, as, for example, between Siberia and Alaska, between North Africa and southern Europe, and between south-east, Asia and Australia. Oscillations of land and sea have altered the shapes and patterns of the continental areas, and, as a result of suet-changes, the ranges of related animals, at one time continuous, may be separated while, on the other hand, areas characterized by faunas which are only distantly allied may become joined together.

Thus, it is the aspect which deals the means of dispersal and barriers to distribution of marine animal life, fresh-water animals and terrestrial creatures respectively.

2. Marine Animal Life

Though broken up by the continental areas, the oceans form a continuous sheet of water. Though certain areas of the world ocean are given particular names, for instance, there are no sharply defined limits of the South Atlantic, South Indian and South Pacific Oceans has led geographers to lump the southern extensions of these oceans together to form what is often called the Southern Ocean. Marginal seas share many of the characteristics of their neighboring oceans, but the so-called continental seas, e.g. the Mediterranean, Red, Black and Baltic Seas, are more strictly delimited and possess highly distinctive water conditions. Nevertheless, the greater part of the ocean surface is more or less readily accessible. In a theoretical sense, therefore, there are no barriers to swimming creatures; in practice, however, we find that there are barriers to dispersal associated with temperature and salinity conditions, and depth and pressure conditions. Non-swimming marine animals are even much more strictly confined in their movements.

In spite of the water links between all the oceans we find the continental land masses do serve as barriers and restrict the occurrence of marine animals. The Atlantic is separated from the Pacific not only by the continuous land mass of the Americas but also by the cold waters in the Drake Passage between Tierra del Fuego and Graham Land; hence the faunas of the two oceans exhibit striking differences. In contrast, the marine fauna of the Pacific and Indian Oceans shows striking similarities, largely because the two oceans are interconnected in the tropical zone, i.e. by the Indonesian seas. Consequently, there is a notable measure of uniformity in the marine life from the coast of East

Africa through the Indian Ocean into the western part of the Pacific. Excluding some of the marginal and continental seas, the salinity of ocean water does not very much and seldom sufficiently to inhibit the spread of marine creatures; perhaps the most significant interference is where large continental rivers debouch into the ocean and bring in vast volumes of fresh water which sensibly reduce the salinity ; for example; littoral forms of marine life may have their spread checked by the fresher water as happens in the case of the sea urchins living along the coast of Patagonia which are not found north of the Rio de la Plata estuary.

Finally, we may note that some marine forms have had their distribution ranges increased by attaching themselves to moving objects, such as pieces of driftwood, or to other marine animals. For example, barnacles are found on ships' hulls, while sucking fishes may attach themselves to whales, sharks, etc., and so may be transported over long distances.

3. Fresh-water Life

Fresh-water creatures are found in bodies of water on the land surface, as in pools, marshes, lakes and streams. All land-based water bodies are more or less isolated, the chief exception being the rivers, which, apart from streams of interior drainage, flow into the sea. Fresh-water animals which are able to enter the sea and are capable of living in salt as well as fresh water, will naturally have a wider range than those which can exist only in fresh water. Migration from river to river is thus precluded by the barrier of sea-water except in the case of certain tolerant creatures, e.g. salmon, eels, sturgeon. Thus we find that Africa and South America possess almost completely different genera of fresh-water fishes and only those like Arius, which are anadromous, are shared in common. Rivers in the same continent, even neghbouring rivers (especially if they happen to flow into different seas or oceans), may have very different faunas. The headwaters of the Rhine and the Danube are separated by only a few miles and yet these two European rivers have differentiating fish fauna. For example, stick backs and eels are not present in the Danube as they are in the Rhine, while the Danube has many species of eastern fishes which are absent in the Rhine; moreover, while both rivers share salmon and sturgeon.

Waterfalls, cascades and rapids may, and often do, form barriers to movement. Strong swimmers, like salmon, are often able to negotiate obstacles of this kind, although, of course, there are limits; for example, salmon have never been able to pass the Falls of the Rhine and so have always been absent from Lake Constance. In inland waters passive dispersal is often effected by fish, which are used as vehicles of transport by other animals.

More common is the passive distribution of fresh-water animals by birds and flying insects. Eggs and larvae may become attached to the feathers, feet, etc., of swimming or wading birds and so be easily carried over long distances. Tiny creatures may be carried by insects and Allee and Schmidt cite several examples.[3] Some fresh-water animals are even known to have been snatched up and carried distances by tornadoes! "Such means of passive transportation are of little consequence to marine animals, with their continuous habitat," (Allee and Schmidt)

4. Terrestrial Animals

In the case of land animals barriers to movement and dispersal are especially important. Since the Earth's land surface is disposed in four major units-the Old World land mass, the Americas, Australia and Antarctica-together with a large number of islands of varying size which lie detached from the main land areas, the ocean is the primary obstacle to the free dispersion of terrestrial creatures. Any salt-water barrier, no matter how narrow, presents an effective obstacle to non-swimming animals, and Wallace's Line, which follows a water channel, provides a fundamental divide between the animal life of Australia and South-east Asia; in much the same way the Mozambique Channel is responsible for the marked differences in the animal life of Africa and Madagascar. River are less successful as barriers since they are seldom wide enough to prevent some animals from swimming across, at low water they may be fordable, floating tree-trunks and branches may serve as vehicles of transportation, while in times of flood rivers may change their courses, thereby transferring areas of land, and thus their fauna, too have some possibility, from one bank to the other.

Mountain ranges often function as effective barriers. If they are of any height mountains induce climatic changes, e.g. reduction in temperature increased precipitation (or, conversely, a decrease in precipitation on lee slopes), and a lowering of the atmospheric pressure, and such changed conditions may well halt animal movement. It is perhaps these associated climatic changes rather than such purely physical conditions as ruggedness of terrain or steepness of slopes that form the greatest obstacles to movement. The effectiveness of mountains as barriers is illustrated by differences in the animal life to the north and south of the Himalayas and to the east and west of the American Cordillera. On the other hand, the lack of any mountainous divide in Africa south of the Sahara helps to explain the measure of uniformity which characterizes the animal life of that area. The alignment of mountain ranges is also of considerable consequence. If, for example, mountains are latitudinal they run parallel with the zonal belts of climate and may be responsible for intensifying the zonal climatic characteristics and in this way emphasize the difficulties of any north-south crossing, as in the case of the Tertiary fold-mountain belt of Asia. Conversely, if the ranges are longitudinal they may be responsible for extending temperate climatic conditions into tropical areas and, accordingly, for allowing temperate animal forms to penetrate into the tropics as has happened in the America; here the cordilleran system has provided a great north-south avenue of movement and, for example, has made it possible for the puma to spread from Alaska to Patagonia. Of all animal forms, flying forms are least affected by mountain barriers, although it is possible to cite cases of birds being confined by mountain ranges.

Deserts, which are closely associated with moisture deficiency and consequently with lack of vegetation also, form sharply demarcated barrier zones. The Sahara forms the great faunal divide in Africa just as it has functioned as a great human divide. But the limitations set by deserts, as in the case of mountains, are more the outcome of lack of water and scarcity of vegetation than of the actual conditions of the terrain, i.e. sand, stones, etc. Most animals are unable to survive long periods without water and this is usually the critical factor preventing animals from living in, or even crossing, arid deserts; such forms as are found are typically highly specialized possessing the capacity of water retention.

Many animals live off, and in, particular kinds of vegetation and so vegetation may be a limiting factor. For instance, the giant panda of China is a denizen of the forest and subsists upon bamboo shoots; hence it is to be found only where these conditions obtain, and in much the same way the Australian koala bear lives in those parts of the continent where there are eucalyptus leaves to eat. George quotes the interesting case of the European crested tit, which nests only in coniferous trees; its occurrence in Scotland is therefore limited to those highland areas which are under coniferous forest.

Yet another factor in the spread and limitation of animals is the interaction between the animals themselves. A good and well-known example is the influence of the trypanosome-carrying tsetse fly which strictly limits the range of domestic ungulates in Africa. Animals compete with one another in many ways, e.g. for food or territory, and a newcomer into an area may upset the natural balance. If it is a carnivorous creature it may gradually climate other indigenous animals much as the predatory fox is doing in Australia. On the other hand, a newcomer may have very similar requirements in respect of food, shelter and reproduction to an indigenous animal, and this may lead to the latter being squeezed out of existence, a process known as replacement; this seems to have occurred in Australia where the rabbit busted the rabbit bandicoots or bilbies, while the retreat of the British red squirrel before the advance of the American grey squirrel would seem to be another example of replacement.

Theoretically there should be no limitations to the spread of birds since through their ability to fly they are able to surmount almost all physical barriers, but in fact we find that their ranges are often limited. It remains true, however, that flying animals are the ones that are least restricted in their dispersal by physical conditions. Flying animals include bats and insects as well as birds. Apart from the amphibious hippopotamus, the polar bear and the reinder, few land mammals readily take to water and swim well or for long distances; thus stretches of sea-water set limits to their movements and form zones of separation. Amphibia, of course, can swim but they are intolerant of sea-water; hence they have not usually spread across salt-water barriers. Since they are also adapted to damp habitats they are susceptible to drying out and cannot normally live under dry conditions for very long. Reptiles do not suffer the physiological limitations of amphibia, and some reptiles, such as crocodiles and snakes, are known to have swum protracted distances in the sea.

IMPORTANCE OF MIGRATION IN DISTRIBUTION

A fundamental fact of zoogeography is that the fauna of the Earth's surface is not randomly distributed but has a definite world-wide pattern. In connection with this distributional pattern Darlington poses three main questions: (i) what is the main pattern of animal distribution, (ii) how has this pattern been formed and (iii) the pattern been formed? In the fore coming chapter we described the zoogeographical regions which the zoogeographer has delimited and the distribution of some animal species; in the first part of this chapter we have noted the principal barriers to animal movements and the checks to migration. Hence, we are now able to turn our attention to these basic zoogeographical problems put forward by Darlington, that follows, however, is little more than a digest of Darlington's own ideas regarding the dispersion and distribution of animal life.

Let us now try to summaries the arguments relating to the evolution and movement of animals and to the character of the present zoogeographic pattern

1. Dominant groups appear to have evolved successively in the largest and most favourable areas of the Earth, i.e. in the tropical parts of the Old World land mass,
2. The main pattern of dispersal of vertebrates is from larger

to smaller areas and from the more favourable to the less favourable areas which results in successive replacements,

3. Directional movement has occurred along three main routes: (i) into temperate South Africa, (ii) from tropical Asia into Australia and (iii) from the Old World tropics through Eurasia to North America and thence to South America,
4. Factors limiting dispersal, such as physical barriers and geographical isolation, have enabled relic faunas to persist, as in Australia and South America which would doubtlessly have succumbed before advancing successive dominant groups,
5. As new dominant groups emerge and spread, they tend to overwhelm and displace older groups: such replacement commonly, though by no means always proceeds from the primary dispersal centres outwards; hence, there is a continual outward shifting of distribution patterns,
6. The theory of continental drift, though in some cases offering easy and convenient explanations for some problems of animal distribution, is not necessary in the light of the foregoing factors.

ANIMAL MIGRATION

1. Migration in Birds

Flight is the major means of animal movement and provides an efficient way for traveling between distant places Adaptation for flight is highly developed in many animal species including about 9,000 species of birds, about 750,000 species of insects, and about 700 species of bats. Clearly flight has been a successful evolutionary development; the majority of the Earth's animals move by flying. Gliding has evolved among several groups of animals including flying squirrels, flying fish, and flying lizards. However, true flight means self-powered, sustained motion through the air. The evolution of bird flight has long captured the human imagination.

There are two schools of thought regarding the origin of bird flight. One, the arboreal theory, proposed that birds gradually evolved flight through the transition of a tree-living animal from gliding to powered flight. The arboreal theory has been the most appealing explanation of the development of flight. The second idea, the cursorial theory, proposes that flight developed by a running bipedal animal as a result of the evolution of proto-wings that produced thrust and thus greater speed. From an engineering, aerodynamic, and ecological point of view, investigation demonstrates that the cursorial theory holds more promise in explaining the evolution of flight than does the arboreal theory.

The re-valuation of the origin of bird flight was provoked by an essay in which the competitive advantage of small, running insectivorous dinosaurs having net-like appendages as an adaptation for capturing insects was described (Ostrom 1979). The predatory advantage of winged, running, insectivorous dinosaurs interested a multidisciplinary group of researchers who pursued the idea (Caple etal. 1983). The arguments supporting the cursorial origin to flight (i.e. specialized structures to iinprove running) began with empirical information of the winged skeleton of the early bird Archaeopteryx.

The aerodynamic approach has also found critical problems with the arboreal origin of flight. For example, the most difficult flight maneuver for a bird is that of landing on a branch. This maneuver is extremely intricate and has a small margin of error that can only be overcome by exerting large lift forces. In order to move from one tree to another, birds would have had to initiate landing maneuvers at an early stage of development. Yet, according to arboreal theory, lift forces were presumably developed after the gliding stage, and not the other way round. Even more challenging is the fact that the aerodynamic properties required for powered flight are in opposition to many properties that are necessary for gliding. These critical aerodynamic arguments suggest that it would be improbable for birds to have evolved from a gliding stage to a powered flight stage as is predicted by the arboreal theory (Caple et al. 1983). Although the debate continues, the cursorial theory has been shown to be a plausible explanation for the evolution of bird flight.

The capability of birds to migrate long distances is related to their efficiency of flight. The only other form of locomotion that allows even greater range of travel is swimming.

It is appropriate to open this section with some additional comments about navigation, orientation, and homing skills of birds. The skills of birds to navigate under a variety of conditions has been studied and remains, as a reviewer suggests, "one of the most enduring mysteries in biology" (Able 1980). Examples abound of the skills of birds: planetarium studies show that birds such as indigo buntings (Passerina cyanea) and many other species are able to use stars to orient themselves (Ernlen 1975, Able 1980); magnetic orientation appears to be available to many species of birds, as it is to bees as a backup to solar orientation (Walcott & Green 1974, Walcott et al. 1979, Wiltschko et al. 1981). Bobolinks (Dolichonyx oryziuorus) have the longest migration of any bird of the New World and appear to rely more on their internal compass than they do on stellar guidance for orientation (Beason & Nichols 1984). Finally, the oilbird, Steatornis caripensis, is a cave-inhabiting bird of the Neotropics; emulating bats, oil birds have developed the use of echolocation to navigate within the cave environment when they roost and nest (Konishi & Knudsen 1979). Studies have also been conducted on the ability of various species o hummingbirds to learn spatial locations, an adaptation the improves their effectiveness in obtaining food resources (Colt etal.1982).

Migration provides many benefits to birds. By regularly flying to unoccupied habitats that have a seasonal fluctuation of favourable climate, birds are able to rear their young b) exploiting food resources that would be otherwise unavailable. By moving back into a warmer environment during periods of the year that are severe in the breeding areas, birds, warm-blooded as they are, save enormous amounts (about 33%) of their metabolic energy. It has beer estimated that the average migrant demands only about 60% of the food resources from the African ecological system o what is required while breeding in the Pale arctic ecological system (Moreau 1972).

On a global scale migration provides extraordinary

opportunities for birds to exploit the Earth's normal range o resources, especially in places that have seasonal variability of weather. The major bird migration systems of the Earth. The most intensively studies example of long-distance bird migration are between Eurasia and Africa. Less well understood are the migration patterns between eastern Asia and Southest Asia. Only recently have some of the Nearctic-Neotropical patterns of migration beer understood. This differences in understanding is due tc historical ties which were established between Europe and Africa as part of the colonial era of the nineteenth century Hunters, colonial officials, and various European settlers recognized seasonal arrivals of familiar birds form their European homelands.

2. Palerctic-african Bird Migrations

The Paler tic-African bird migration system has two major components. Western European birds winter mainly in West Africa, and birds from Central Asia (and a small number of species from East Asia) migrate mainly to East Africa. The birds a number of flyways into Africa. The various routes which the birds follow present formidable difficulties because of the expanses of unfavourable habitat between Eurasia and Africa.

Table 10.1 shows the number of breeding and wintering species in various parts of the New World. Of the total number of species that breed in the Nearctic, 44% have representatives that winter in Central and South America. In the wintering areas the number of migrants has been compared with the number of resident species. Overall, around 50% of the species inhabiting wintering sites are migrants (Terborgh 1980).

As in the Palearctic-African bird migration system, the birds often Nearctic-Neotropical system became concentrated into a small area during winter, Migratory birds tend to inhabit patches of uncut forests, secondary growth, upland areas, and edge habitats (Morse 1980) for in charge in terms of bird habitat, clearing 1 ha of forest in Mexico.

Table 10.1

Number of Nearctic Breeding Species and Number of Species Wintering in various Regions

Nearctic Breeding Species	*Number of Species Wintering in* Nearctic	Nearctic and Neotropics	Neotropics	Elsewhere
565	286	151	98	30
%	50.6	26.7	17.3	5.3

An alternative approach to examination of the Nearctic-Neotropical migration system has been to consider the likely origin, whether Pale arctic or Neotropical, of the individual bird species. Of the birds that are believed to have entered North America via the Bering Strait, about 57% migrate to southern locations of North America and only 1% migrate to South America. In contrast, only 5% of the birds that were identified as having Neotropical ancestry winter in North America and 36% winter in South America (Williams 1958)

The ratio between number of species of migrants and residents decreases rapidly with decreasing latitude in South America. However, it must be pointed out that eastern Ecuador, Peru, and Bolivia host the most bird species perp area of any place on the Earth: well over 400 species per 1C km^2 have been recorded in tracts of the tropical rainforest. The highest density is in eastern Equador where 480 species per 10 km^2 have been recorded. Nearly 40% of all the bird species known to exist on the Earth live in the Neotropics (Keast1980).

The Nearctic high-latitude summer breeding locations provide some opportunity to study bird populations in habitats that have not yet been severely disrupted by human activities Alaska has some extremely rich nesting and breeding areas that support between 200 and 400 million birds of more than 300 species. Because of the fact that the western lowlands of Alaska are near the extreme margin of North America and Asia, the breeding grounds are a crossroads for birds from several continents. Also, large numbers (about 12 million birds) of waterfowl migrate from Alaska to winter in a number of places. About half of the waterfowl fly south along the Pacific flyway. About 35% of the waterfowl migrate along the east side of the Rockies and the Mississippi to winter in the Gulf Coast. Ten percent fly to the Atlantic coast and winter in places such as the Chesapeake Bay. The remaining 5% o1 the waterfowls winter in scattered location in Asia, Mexico, South America, Antarctica, and the Pacific islands.

As in Africa several species of Nearctic birds are known to migrate across the equator. Notable are Swainson's Hawk (Buteo swainsom) which breeds in western North America and resides in the pampas during the Northern winter (Smith 1980), as well as various shorebirds (Myers 1980).

In contrast to Africa, where most flight paths are across large expanses of unfavorable terrain that require long fights, Neotropical migratory routes are relatively free of enormous stretches of barren land although they do encouter large stretches of water. The influence that the physical differences of the major flyways have on Old and New World bird migration is opposite from what one might expect. In the Nearctic-Neotropical migrations, birds often migrate southward in a single long flight. Various waves of migration are protracted over a number of weeks. Many western species migrate either along the Pacific coast or follow a cource along the middle elevations of the mountain ranges that span between North and South America; the Mississippi valley is another important flyway.

3. Insect Migration

In addition to the foraging behavior of bees as described earlier, insect species of many other groups also undertake long-range migrations. Their migrations are as much an integral part of their life history as the migrations of other groups of animals (Johnson 1969, Dingle 1978). Some insects migrate distances which rival birds. The monarch butterfly (Danaus plexippus) of North America provides a well-studied example of long-distance movement by insects (Urquart 1960, Orr1970).

The eggs of the monarch are laid on the underside of the leaves of the milkweed plant (Ascepias) and other related members of the milkweed family. The larva feeds and molts a number of times until it is about 5 cm long. In a period of a few days to several weeks, depending on conditions, the adult butterfly emerges from the chrysalis. About three broods hatch during the mid-latitude summer. The members of the first two broods live for about 4 to 8 weeks and then, after laying eggs, die.

The members of the last brood of summer behave very differently. They begin together in large groups and migrate in mass southward. The monarchs fly along three major flyways, the East Coast, the Mississippi Valley and the West Coast. The participants of the fall migration undertake a first, time journey to a distant location which neither they nor their parents have ever taken. The monarchs fly a true direction and migrate at times when the wind is in the appropriate direction (Able 1980). Isolated winter routs have been discovered in forest patches in Mexico that are used by monarches at the end of the flight (Brower 1977, Urquhart & Urquhart 1978). Banded monarchs have been recorded that have completed a journey from Ontario, Canada to southern Mexico, a distance of over 3,000 km (Urauhart 1960). During migration and wintering, monarchs are the object of predation by several species of birds that have learned to selectively dismember and reject the cardiac poisons. Although many monarchs fail to survive the round-trip journey, a large number do return to reproduce and continue the population.

4. Fish Migration

The movement of eels (Anguilla) was earlier described as it related to the interaction between terrestrial runoff and the sea. Eels spend most of their lives in fresh water. For purposes of breeding they move down to the sea. They breed in deep water of the ocean and then the elvers (young eels) return in large numbers to the rivers and move far inland where they grow and mature. This pattern of movement is katadromous behavior. Varies species of eels are found in both hemispheres on both sides of the Atlantic and in the western Pacific from China to Australia and the coasts of New Zealand and Africa. They are absent from the shallow waters off the Malayan peninsula.

In more tropical waters fish generally migrate in a katadromous pattern. The southern trouts of jolytails (Glaxias) also follow this pattern.

In mid to high latitudes, fish generally engage in a pattern of migration in which the young move down stream to the ocean to feed and mature, and then return up stream as adults to spawn. This pattern of movement is referred to as anadromous migration. As a family, Salmonidae, including trout and Atlantic and pacific varieties of salmon, are particularly well adapted to cold, nutrient-poor, fresh waters of glaciated areas. The anadromous migratory pattern appears to be an evolutionary adaptation in temperate latitudes by the fish to exploit the much richer food sources available in the ocean (Dingle 1980, Gross et al. 1988).

The Atlantic salmon (Salrno salar) has a life history that begins in the late autumn and early winter when adults return to their native place to spawn. The length of time that the young fish spend at each stage depends mainly on the temperature of the waters. The colder water requires longer periods of time for the alevins to become fry and subsequently, part. Thus, the smolt may take from 1 to 7 years to develop. At the smolt stage, the salmon migrate down stream during spring to the open sea. The smolt remain at sea from 1 to 4 years. When they return to the rivers to migrate up stream, the name salmon is applied to the fish. The salmon do not feed as they migrate up stream, and as they ascend the steepest slopes in the cooler headwaters of the stream, they may have lost as much as 25% of their body weight. After spawning, the adults are called kelt. The survival rate of kelt depends on the length of the stream and water temperature. About 20% to 36% of the kelt survive to travel down stream and then may return to the sea to feed and eventually to spawn again. The number of repeat spawners varies from as low as 3% to as high as 34%, depending on the doncition of the river where the fish were born.

The American shad (Alosa) is a native fish of the Atlantic coast of North America. It has adopted a breeding cycle that is apparently timed by the stream and ocean waters.

As water temperature increases during spring, the shad begin to migrate up stream to spawn. Shad prefer water temperatures of about 54-68% F (12-20° C). Thus, during January and February, shad begin to move up stream in the St. Johns River of Florida. Peak movement occurs at 55-60° F (13-16° C). As the seasonal warming takes place fish begin entering various rivers progressively further north. At Last after crossing some steps in November and December and as seawater temperatures decrease further south, they move southward, eventually reaching the water off the coast of Florida to begin the cycle again. Shad are ectothermic and their energy demands are determined by water temperature. Like salmon, shad do not eat during their freshwater journey to the spawning sites. Generally, the shad of the rivers south of the Chesapeake Bay are only able to spawn once. These shad are subjected to high enough water temperatures that their high metabolic rates use up stored food, and they starve to death before they are able to return to the sea. North of the Chesapeake Bay, an increasing proportion of shad become repeat spawners (Leggett and Whitney 1972, Leggett 1973).

To retain the homing abilities, fish have an extremely sensitive olfactory organ. Research studies deals about the idea that fish use odors as a means of homing in on a particular place. Little is known about the source ans makeup of the odors that are used by the fish for it to return to a specific site, nor is it understood how fish use odors for orientation. It has been suggested that fish create an "olfactory map" which is imprinted during initial movement and subsequently recalled in reverse order to return to the starting point. Many organisms, especially among the reptiles and amphibians, apparently use old factory senses as a principal means for locating and guiding them back to their home habitat (Able 1980, Jones 1981).

6. Migration Among Mammals

Mammals are exceptional because extensive migration occurs among a large number of species using all forms of locomotion: swimming, flying, and walking. This attests to the capacity of the mammals to adapt to all of the major habitats of the Earth.

Examination of mammalian migratory movements will be described according to modes of locomotion among different groups of animals for instances.

(1) Marine Migrations of Whales

The blue whole (Balaenoptera muscules) is a mammal that order Cetacea which includes shales, dolphis, and porpoises. Within the recent past, blue whales attained a length of 30 m and weighed about 136,000 kg. A medium sized blue whale was made up of about 45 metric tons of muscle, 7,600 I of blood that weighed about 7 t, 0.9 t of lung tissue, 54 t of skin, blubber, bones and viscerea. The heart alone weights 590 kg and has a volume of about 1 m3. The heart is so large that a child could easily crawl through its aorta and a trout could swim through most of the major blood vessels. A baby blue whale weighs 1,800 kg at birth, and nurses over 4,500 I of milk per day Whale milk is exceedingly rich and contains about 200 g cream per liter compared to cows' milk which has only 40 g cream per liter. The newborn whale gains about 225 kg per day. An organism this large must play a significant role in the biogeochemical cycles of the marine environment. When feeding in the polar seas, whales probably consume about 35-40 g of food per kg body weight per day (Lockyer & Brown 1981). In the case of a single medium-sized blue whale, about 4,760 - 5,440 kg of krill are consumed each day during the 4-6 months that it spends in the polar waters.

There are over 100 species of whales (McVay 1966). They evolved from a terrestrial mammal that returned to the marine environment about 70 Ma ago. As a group, whales are highly specialized to an aquatic existence. They are streamlined and were once mistaken for fish. Although they breathe air, they can stay under water for long periods of lime. The lungs of one of the large whales can hold 28,000-40,000 I of air. Since air is 21% oxygen, the amount of oxygen being carried is between 5,800 and 8,400 I which lasts up to 45 minutes during a dive. Whales generally surface every 20 to 30 minutes. Whales also have hearing that is adapted for under water. Sound travels much more rapidly in water than it does in air. Higher pitched frequencies are an adaptation taking advantage of the denser seawater medium. However, many whales also produce remarkably low frequency sounds that may travel over distances of hundreds of kilometers (Payne & Webb 1971). The sounds of humpback whales *(Megaptera novaengliae)* have been intensively studied; they produce a wide range of frequencies that are strung together in long passages and phrases and repeated over and over. These audio passage undergo annual changes and are understood as a form of complex communication of song.

Two groups of whales are recognized: Mysticeti, the baleen whales, and Odontoceti, the toothed whales. The migratory patterns of the large whales are known as a result of whaling logs kept during their slaughter. As alternative method of tracking whale movement is by the oxygen-18 variations (similar to that used for recording the temperature of the Earth) of the whales' epizoic barnacles (Killingley 1980). Baleen species inhabiting both hemispheres include the blue, finback (Balaenoptera physalus), minke (B. acutorastrata), and humpback whale. The gray whale *(Eschrichtius gibbosus)* mainly populates the northeast Pacific where it twice suffered near-extinction and now thrives under the protective watch of conservatioin minded citizens. The migrations of these species are similar, although they differ in detail. The bowhead whale (Balaena mysticetus) is exclusively Arctic and does not migrate outside of the polar seas. The sprem whale *(Physeter catodon)* is a tooted whale and represents the migratory pattern that occurs in that group.

Distances are not a problem to whales. Energetics of locomotion through water are very favourable, and whales have developed the capability to exploit the full resource base of three-quarters of the Earth's surface, from the tropical to the polar sea. Baleen whales feed mainly on a swarming planktonic crustacean, *Euphausia,* commonly called krill, that thrives in the cold polar waters. However, during six months of the year, darkness reduces the krill availability and the whales migrate to subtropical and tropical waters. During the feeding period, the whales gain an enormous amount of weight. Calculations for gray whales show that they lose about 29% of their body weight between the breeding (southward) and feeding (northward) migrations and that during their period of feeding, they gain about 40% of their lean body weight (Lockyer & Brown 1981). The food reserve gained and stored during the feeding period apparently becomes the major source of energy while the whales are in tropical waters.

There are two groups of baleen whales, one group which inhabits the Arctic sometime during the months of May through October and another group which inhabits the Antarctic seas sometimes from November through April, In general, at any one time, depending on season, one group of whales is feeding in polar water while the other group of whales is breeding and calving in the tropical and subtropical waters of the Earth.

(2) Bat Migration

As a group, with about 700 species, there are more types of bats than any other kind of mammal. About 600 species are insectivorous and actively pursue their prey using echolocation (Simmons et al. 1979). Echolocation is highly developed in bats and was first demonstrated in the late 1930's (Griffin & Galambos 1941, Busnel & Fish 1980). Equipped with this skill, bats are natural inhabitants of caves and specialists at movement in the dark. They occupy a different niche than do birds because of their generally nocturnal and cave-dwelling habit, and most species are tropical.

For several reasons bats are not as well adapted as birds for long-distance migration (Dingle 1980). Instead of the massive petoralis muscles of birds, bats have many more muscles which make possible the highly maneuverable manner of flight that is necessary for catching flying insects. The bat has wings which are effective for producing high lift at low speeds but the same wings create excessive drag for efficient high-speed travel. Because of inefficient high-speed flight capability, bats are unable to store enough fat to fly long distances.

There are, however, a few species that fly relatively long distances. Myotis lucifugus hibernates in caves in western Massachusetts, Connecticut, and Vermont, and migrates during summer to localities over 300 km away to feed. In Europe, Nyctalus noctula which were banded in Holland, have been recovered as far away as Bordeaux, 900 km away. In the U.S.S.R. the pipistrelle *(Pipis3frellus pipistrellus)* has been banded and recovered at locations 1,160 km away. The swiftest bats fly the longest distance. Perhaps the swiftest bat is the hoary bat *(Lasiurus cinereus)* which summers in the northern coniferous forests and winters from central California south; it is found as far north as Alaska in summer and in southwestern North America during winter-a distance of at least 2,500 km.

(3) Migration of Large Terrestrial Mammals

Two groups of ungulates provide the major examples of long-distance migration among large terrestrial animals. In the far north, studies have been conducted on the cervids (true deer), especially elk (Cervus canadensis) and barren grounds caribou, also known as reindeer, (Rangifertarandus) (Murie 1935, 1951, Lent 1966). The migratory routes tend, during spring, to be toward lower elevation and the taiga where food is available during the winter months. The second example, which will be described in fuller detail here, is from the tropical wet-dry grasslands and savanna of Africa. A far more diverse fauna occurs within the Tropics than in the high latitudes. One migratory system that has been studied is that of the zebra (Equus burchelli), wildebeest (Connochaetes taurinus), and Thomson's gazelle (Gazella thomson) of the Serengeti-Mara region of East Africa (Pearsall 1957, Grzimek & Grzimek 1960). An understanding of the ecological relationships that are involved in the grazing and migration system of the Serengeti stars with a consideration of the soils and vegetation that are the basis of the system for these mammals.

■■■

11

Zoogeographical Regions of the World

INTRODUCTION

The outline of the major faunal regions has changed little since Wallace's 1876 map. De Lattin (1967), lilies (1974), Udvardy (1969), Neill (1969); Kendeigh (1961), George (1962), Darlington (1957), and de Laubenfels (1970) among recent publications, still follow the guidelines of 100 years ago with slight changes in name or emphasis within transitional zones and sub-regions.

Division of the world into these large-scale communities does not represent a static geographic list. Species extinction and species generation proceeds continually, and the mobility of many groups of animals, particularly associated with the deliberate and accident effects of man, override all boundaries. It is still helpful however, to group those animals which characterize the major world regions, because such areas are the theatres of evolution reflecting past and present-day barriers and resulting in unique congregations of species. The overall picture is one of long-standing affinities between the faunas of the Palaearctic and Nearctic (recognized in the combined name of Holoarctic), together with a close resemblance between the Holoarctic, the Ethiopian and the Oriental areas (referred to collectively as Arctogea). The Neotropical and Australian areas are usually considered to be sufficiently distinctive to be referred to respectively as Neogea and Notogea (with the possible exception of the Middle American and East Indian transition zones).

Within the continental regions, various sub-regions have been recognized. These are discussed here in outline only, and may be considered from two approaches. One is essentially geographic recognizing progressively smaller-scale divisions and based in part upon climatic, topographic and vegetational differences and in part upon the pattern of animal evolution in each environment. For example Wallace divided each of his main regions into three or four subdivisions. Equally the transitional areas (for example middle America, the East Indies or the Arctic) and the offshore continental islands such as Madagascar, Tasmania and many others including the British Isles are usually distinguished from the major source areas. Attempts to subdivide based upon the physical environment can be traced back to the nineteenth century, for example Alien's (1871) climate groups extended by Merriam (1898) in his life zone concept, which in turn led to the controversial topic of biotic provinces (.e.g. Dice, 1943), find modern expression in Holdridge's more detailed (1967) classification. The second is a more ecological approach recognizing environmental and biotic interactions. This is exemplified by Darlington's (1957) analysis of the vertebrates based on five major processes which result in the limitation, zonation, radiation, differentiation and concentration patterns that are recognized today. On the basis of these criteria, a progressive subdivision of the world faunal regions has been attempted. A species population or a localized community can be seen to occupy a relatively small area, whereas the distribution of a genus or family of animals or alternatively the larger community in which they live, is likely to occupy an area of continental proportions.

On our planet there are several life forms in which the living plants and animals have their more importance and in this regard upto now it has at least made clear that it is impossible to discuss the present range even of the chief groups. It is estimated-to take but two familiar classes-that there are nearly 10,000 living species of birds and nearly 3,000 of mammals, the vast majority of the latter falling into the Rodent order.

Even the specialist might well quail at the thought of discussing the distribution of all the living Rodents, much more that of the mammals as a whole. Clearly then our study of taxonomic distribution must have well-defined limits, set by a definite aim and that aim is clear. For the student of geography it is of much interest that the different parts of the earth's surface are characterized by different assemblages of plants and animals and that, within limits, it is possible to give a reasoned explanation of that fact. The material selected can only be representative, and because of their geologically late origin and their relative familiarity the mammals among the land animals form the most important group.

1. The Zoogeographical Realms of the World

If animal regions cannot be correlated with climatic and vegetation regions, the question naturally arises: what exactly is a zoogeographical region? Simply it may be defined as a portion of the Earth's surface having an assemblage of fauna, more particularly mammalian fauna, which possess characterizing features distinguishing it from other areas. Miss W.G. George describes the zoogeographical region more particularly as follows:

"When the distribution of all animals are added together, the dissimilarities in individual ranges mark out the world into distinct regions. These regions are differentiated from one another by the different mixtures of animals which they contain, as well as by the fact that they may also contain a family which is uniquely found there. For instance one region is characterized by the co-existence of tapirs and members of the camel family even though neither family is itself confined to the region. No other region has this particular combination. In addition this same region has within its confines several families of vertebrates that are found nowhere else in the world."

Thus it may be said that, in broad terms, a zoogeographical region is an area having a particular assemblage of animals which includes species which are unique to that area.

Although, as will be seen shortly, the zoogeographical regions correspond very roughly with the continents, in fact they either surpass the traditional boundaries of the continents or are confined to areas of more limited extent than the continents. The explanation of these regional limits presupposes changes both in climatic conditions and in the distribution of land and water in the past. The faunal differences of the various zoogeographical regions result from the presence, both in the past and at present, of barriers to animal movement. These barriers have been of two main types: zonal climates which have led to the regional differentiation and limitation of most animal species, and physical barriers, such as mountains and stretches of water, which have confined and isolated some fauna regionally.

Geographic discontinuities, occurrences of the same or related animals in more or less widely separated places, are very common within the main pattern of distribution of vertebrates. Special cases of discontinuity have been overemphasized and misunderstood by some zoogeographers, especially by bridge builders and movers of continents. Here, the present matter treats the discontinuities in a more general way and to try to put them in perspective.

Animals can become discontinuously distributed in three ways: by jumping gaps, as when land animals reach oceanic islands across water; by changes of land, a when parts of faunas are cut off on continental islands by flooding of connecting land (or when continents drift apart, if they drift); and by withdrawals (i.e., partial extinctions) which divide originally continuous distributions.

Single cases are relatively unimportant. For example, the discontinuous distribution of leiopelmid frogs, in northwestern North America and New Zealand, is a unique case and is unimportant as a pattern of discontinuity, although the occurrence of Leiopelma on new Zealand is important for other reasons. However, discontinuities form a number of common patterns.

There are broad discontinuities in the north temperate zone. Many groups of animals occur in temperate Eurasia and temperate. North America but not in connecting arctic areas.

There are many special patterns within this main one. For example, many genera and species pairs of plants and animals occur in eastern Asia and eastern North America but not between. They include tulip trees, magnolias, sassafrases, with hazels, skunk cabbages, and many other plants (Fernald 1929, Li 1952); and paddlefishes, cryptobranchid salamanders, alligators, certain small skinks, and Opheodrys snakes. Some other north temperate patterns are suggested by salamanders. Still other northern patterns have been described better by botanists (e.g., Fernald 1929) than by zoologists. The explanation of most of the discontinuities in the north-temperate zone is evidently withdrawal from connecting areas.

There are still broader discontinuities in the tropics. Many groups of animals occur in the Old World tropics and in tropical America but not in connecting north-temperate regions. And many occur in tropical Africa and tropical Asia but not in connecting regions of temperate Eurasia. Some of the cases of discontinuity between the Old and New World tropics are shown by fossils to be the result of dispersal through the north followed by extinction there, and this is probably the most likely explanation of all the cases at least among existing vertebrates, except those that may reasonably have crossed the sea. Most of the cases of discontinuity between Africa and tropical Asia are certainly the result of dispersal through and then withdrawal from Eurasia above the tropics; Madagascar has obviously not been on the dispersal route of existing African-Asiatic vertebrates, except again a few that may have crossed the sea. Special patterns of discontinuity exist within this main pattern within the tropics. Some groups of animals (e.g., microhline frogs, aniliid and some colubrid snakes, a genus of eagles and one of woodpeckers, and tapirs) occur only or mainly in tropical Asia and tropical America (not in Africa). Others (e.g., several group of fishes, pipid frogs, pelomedusid turtles, amphisbaenid lizards, leptotyphlopid worm snakes, and a few birds) occur only or mainly in Africa and tropical America (not in tropical Asia). Still others (at least Podocnemis turtles and iguanid lizards) occur only in Madagascar and America (not in Africa-but there is an iguanid on Fiji). Some groups (e.g., pheasants, chevrotains) are divided between West Africa and tropical Asia; others (e.g., some fishes, reptiles, and birds), between southern India and the eastern Orient; others (e.g., some snakes), between Indochina and the Greater Sunda Islands., These patterns, and others like them, have evidently been formed mainly by withdrawals from connecting areas.

South of the tropics discontinuities are broader still, in distance over existing land. Leptodactylid frogs, chelyid turtles, and marsupials occur only or mostly in South America and Australia. However, although these animals extend into the south-temperate zone, they are all more tropical than south-temperate in total distribution, and they do not occur on New Zealand. Fossils and other evidence suggest that the frogs and marsupials have dispersed through the main part of the world; the chelyids may have reached Australia directly through the sea.

Some groups of salt-tolerant fishes (e.g., galaxiids) and terrestrial invertebrates, and also certain plants, have zonal "Antarctic" distributions: they are common to the cool southern extremities of South America and Australia, and many of them occur on New Zealand, and some arc represented on the southern tip of Africa too. No terrestrial or strictly fresh-water vertebrates have such distributions.

BASIS OF CLASSIFICATION OF SYSTEMS-ZOOGEOGRAPHY REGIONS

On the basis of the work and studies done by *man)* biogeographers, one can visualize the division of the work into faunal regions to describe the regional vertebrate faunas and their inter relationships. This is to be done first within the limits of the continents and closely associated continental islands. Previously we have already dealt with the outlying islands and island faunas in relation to the existing continents.

The distinction between continents and islands is arbitrary. Australia is an island continent, and parts of its fauna show the effects of isolation more than, for example, the fauna of Madagascar does; South America was an island continent not long ago, and its fauna still shows many effects of isolation. However, it is customary and convenient to treat as continents Eurasia, Africa, North and South America and Australia. They, with the islands that have recently been connected to them, form one nearly continuous system of land, very irregular in shape, unsymmetrically placed on the round earth, and irregular interrupted by mountains, deserts, and narrow water gaps. This is the land now to be divided into regions according to the distribution of animals on it.

Faunal regions are often misunderstood and undeservedly abused nowadays. There is, to begin with, a feeling among some zoogeograhers that existing distribution is unimportant, or at least that present "static" patterns and faunal regions are not worth much consideration in themselves but only in relation to the past, and than it is only the past-the evolution and movement of animals-that really matters in zoogeography. It is only in the present that one can see to much extent that how animals really are distributed and how their distributions are related to space, climate, barriers, other inorganic factors, plant cover, and each other. Knowledge of the present is therefore necessary to understand the past. It is of course also true that knowledge of the past is necessary to understood the present. The present and past are equally important in zoogeography. Neither can be understood without the other. Nevertheless it is logically permissible and in fact necessary sometimes to consider animal distribution exclusively in the present, as if it were static, and to bring in past evolutions and movements later.

The world is full of different ones. That certain barriers rather than others have been found to separate major faunas and faunal regions is not an arbitrary decision but a very significant fact gradually discovered by zoogeographers. As to the philosophical difference between faunas and regions, faunal regions are areas occupied now by faunas. There is a philosophical difference, but if the faunas are real, the regions are real too, and not mythological. The great difficulty with faunal regions is not philosophical but practical. It arises from the complexity of animal distribution. Scarcely any two groups of animals are distributed in exactly the same way, and different major groups (for example different classes of vertebrates) are in some cases very differently distributed. It is hard to reduce this diversity to a simple system.

It should be understood that the system of faunal regions represents an average pattern, not a common one. It is the best average of all the very different distributions of different animals that zoogeographers have been able to devise. It is not and is not intended to be a common pattern which many different groups of animals fit exactly. Wallace knew this, so he exaggerated the sharpness of boundaries of some of the regions, but he understood the underlying diversity of distribution of different animals.

The nature of faunal regions can perhaps be clarified by analogy. Suppose a carpet was woven of many different sets of differently colored threads, representing different groups of animals, with the color differences proportional to relationships. Suppose the carpet was woven very irregularly, thick in some places and thin in others, with different threads and not following a common pattern. Plants and animals do form such a carpet over the world. It is thick in some places and thin in others, and different sorts of plants and animals are variously scattered or concentrated in different places in it. The regional faunas, which determine the faunal regions, tend to be great concentrations of animals in favourable places (corresponding to the thick places of the rug) and main faunas are often separated by unfavourable areas where animals are few (the rug thin).

The system of faunal regions, then, represents the average, gross pattern of distribution of many different animals with more or less different distributions. There is such an average pattern of animal distribution. It is real and very significant. It shows in the broadest way how animal distribution is fitted to the world and how climate and barriers affect it most deeply.

The system of faunal regions is a standard pattern, a sort of meter stick, by which the distributions of different animals can be measured, described, and compared, theil special features determined, and important things about the animals and their histories revealed. The standard pattern is useful for this purpose even if few groups of animals fit ii exactly. There is no more reason to discard the standard pattern of animal distribution because few things in nature are exactly a meter long. Deviations from the standard are excepted and informative. If, for example, a particular group of animals reaches the Australia Region but shows less that standard differentiation there, this suggests recent dispersal and power of crossing water gaps. Or if, in a broader way, c group of animals tends to be unusually well represented in the climate-limited regions but more than usually differentiated or absent in the barrier-limited ones (as many fresh-water fishes are), this suggests fundamental things about the animal's relation to climate and salt-water barriers. To be useful as a standard, the system of faunal regions must be generally accepted. It must not be changed except for good reason and by general agreement. The specialist should accept the standard, find how his animals differ from it, and try to find what the differences mean, Wallace knew this too. Perhaps we should repeat that, although the standard system of regions should be arbitrarily accepted most of the time, the system is (unlike the meter) inherently not arbitrary but real. The standard system of faunal regions is the truest simple diagram of animal distribution that zoogeographers have been able to devise.

Faunal regions have other, less important uses. They help zoologists in different parts of the world set natural limits to regional studies. And the names of the regions are useful terms. For example, "Oriental Region" is simpler, more exact, and therefore more useful than "tropical Asia and certain closely associated continental islands."

It should be plain from what has been said in the earlier pages that regional faunas are not homogeneous assemblages of animals uniformly distributed within common limits. Each regional fauna is more or less concentrated in favourable place, varies in composition in different places, and enters into complex transitions with adjacent faunas. Nevertheless, in spite of the differences, the animals in different parts of one faunal region are on the whole more related to those of other parts of the same region than to those of other regions.

One can hope that all this is enough to make it clear what faunal regions and regional faunas are, and to persuade skeptics that the system of faunal regions is real and useful. If any doubt remain, the best reference we can give for further persuasion is Wallace (1876). Critics of faunal regions may be surprised to find how well Wallace understood what he was doing and how little their criticisms apply to him in future.

Six main faunal regions are now generally accepted. They were first purposed by Sclater for birds in a paper read before the Linnean Society in 1857and published in 1858. Sclater's regions were confirmed by Wallace (1876) for vertebrates in general and for some invertebrates. Reasons for adopting these particular regions are given in detail by Wallace. Other regions have been proposed, but Sclater's regions seem best to combine reality and usefulness. They ' are listed in Table 11.1. Sclater's regions and his names for them still stand with minor changes of boundaries and some simplification of spelling, except that the name "Oriental Region", proposed by Wallace, has replaced Sclater's "Indian Region."

Table 11.1

Sclater's Schema of Avium Distributions Geographcae, on System of Fauna! Regions Based on the Distribution of Birds. Sclater's names and essential definitions (excepting some islands are given.

Crectio Palaeogeana

1. **Palaearetic Region:** temperate Eurasia and the northern corner of Africa, north of the Atlas Mountains
2. **Aethiopian or Western Palaeotropical Region:** Africa except the northern corner, and southern Arabia.
3. **Indian or Middle Palaeotropical Region:** Tropical Asia and closely associated continental islands.
4. **Australian or Eastern Palaeotropical Region:** New Guinea, Australia, and Tasmania

Creatio Neogeana

5. **Nearctic or North American Region:** North Americas south to central Mexico, and including Greenland.
6. **Neotropical or South American Region:** South and Central America and southern Mexico.

Table 11.2

The Accepted System of Continental Faunal Regions Realm Megagea (Arclogea): The main part of the world.
1. **Ethiopian Region**: Africa (except the northern corner), with part of southern Arabia.
2. **Oriental Region**: Tropical Asia, with associated continental islands.
3. **Palearctic Region**: Eurasia above the tropics, with the northern corner of Africa.
4. **Nearctic Region**: North America, excepting the tropical part of Mexico.
Realm Neogea
5. **Neotropical Region**: South and Central America with the tropical part of Mexico.
Realm Notogea
6. **Austrtalian Region**: Australia, with New Guinea, etc.

Although the separate regions are Sclater's they have been arranged and rearranged in different ways by later authors. Sclater grouped the Old World regions against the New World ones in what he called (he was looking for confers of creation) "Creatio Palaeoge,ana" and "Creatio Neogeana," but this arrangement is not the most natural one. Huxley (1868) grouped together the four regions that cover Africa, Eurasia, and North America as "Arctogaea", and he grouped together South America and Australia as "Notogaea." This was partly good and partly not. The faunas of South America and Australia are very different from those of the main part of the world, but they are also very different from each other. Wallace (1876) apparently was more interested in the individual regions than in grouping them; he combined Sclater's and Huxley's systems in one table. Finally Blanford (1890) suggested a grouping which better expresses the real interrelationships of the six regional faunas. He made three main divisions of the world: Arctogaea (the main part of the world, with four subdivisions), the "South-American Region", and the Australian Region. It remained for an anoymous author (1893) to propose that the South American and Australian divisions be called Neogaea and Notogaea, and for Lydekker (1896) to propose that the three divisions be called relams. One change of name is still desirable. "Arctogaea" is an unfortunate, misleading name for the greal area which includes the main part of the Old World tropics and the north-temperate zone, with just an arctic fringe. We propose to call it Megagea, or the great part of the world. Thus amended, the generally accepted system of faunal regions (of the continents) is as given in Table 11.2. One additional term is in common use. Heilprin (1887) combined the two northern regions, the Pale arctic and Nearctic, into a Holarctic Region. They are not combined here, but they may be called the Holarctic Regions, and animals which occur in both are often called Holarctic.

This is, of course, a very incomplete history of ideas about faunal regions. For further details see Wallace (1876), Blanford (1890), Lydekker (1911), Gadow (1913), Serivenor et al. (1943), Sehmidt (1954), and others. The history of faunal regions is only one part of the history of zoogeography, which is treated in a little more detail in the introduction.

The system of faunal regions shows the relative distinctness of the different regions probably as well as any simple system can, but the regions can be grouped in another way to emphasize their natures (Table 11.3-11.4). The two northern regions (Palearctic and Nearctic) are separated from the tropics not by impassable barriers but primarily by zonal climate, because of which their faunas are differentiated and limited. They are in other words climate-limited regions. The Neotropical and Australian Regions owe their special natures to past and present salt-water barriers, which have isolated and in some ways limited their faunas. They are barrier-limited regions. The two remaining regions, the main regions of the Old World tropics (Ethiopian and Oriental), are less limited by climate and barriers. They are not unlimited; no regions are, but they are the least limited, most central ones, and the other regions form an unsymmetrical radial pattern of increased limitation around them. This is the main, average pattern of present distribution of animals, and something like it-radiation from the main Old World tropics-is also the apparent main pattern of animal dispersal.

Table 11.3

The Distribution of Animal Families in Relation to the Major Zoogeographical Regions of the Earth

Common Names	*Families*	*Palearctic*	*Nearctic*	*Nieotropical*	*Ethiopian*	*Oriental*	*Australian*
Rabbits	Leporidae	+	+	+	+	+	+
Mice	Muridae & Cricetidae	+	+	+	+	+	+
Dogs	Canidae	+	+	+	+	+	+
Liata	Onelon Chipetera (17 families)	–	–	–	–	–	–
Shrews	Soricidae	+	+	+	+	+	
Squirrels	Sciuridae	+	+	+	+		
Stoat, badger, skunk, etc.	Mustellidae	+	+	+	+	+	
Cats	Felidae	+	+	+	+	+	
Bears	Ursidae	+	+	+		+	
Deer	Cervidae	+	+	+		+	
Cattle, antelope, sheep and goats	Bovidae	+	+	+	+	+	
Hedgehogs	Erinaceidae	+			+	+	
porcupines	Hystricidae	+			+	+	
civets	Viverridae	+			+	+	
hyenas	Hyaenidae	+			+	+	
pigs	Suidae	+			+	+	
pandas and racoons	Procyonidae	+	+	+			

dormice	Gliridae	+			+
jerboas	Dipodidae	+			+
hyraxes	Procaviidae	+			+
horses	Equidae	+			+
molwa	TAIpidae	+	+		
beavers	Castoridae	+	+		
jumping mice	Zapodidae	+	+		
camles & llamas	Camelidae	+			
mole rat	Spalacidae	+			
selevinia	Seleviniidae	+			
hedgesparrows	Prunellidae	+			
pocket rophers	Geomyidae		+		
pocket mice an kangaroo rats	Heteromyidae		+		
mountain beaver	Aplodontidae		+		
Pronghorns	Antilocapridae		+		
turkey	Meleagrididae		+		
gila monsters	Helodermatidae		+		
garpikes	Amiidae		+		
bowfins	Lepisosteidae		+		
tapirs	Tapiridae			+	+
anteaters	Myrmecophagidae			+	
sloths	Brady podiae			+	
armadillos	Dasypodidae		0	+	

mouseOlike marsupials	Caenolestidae			+			
opossums	Didelphidae		0	+			
New World monkeys	Cebidae			+			
marmosets & tarmarins	Call'rthricidae			+			
tree porcupines	Erethizontidae		0	+			
capybaıas	Hydrochaeridae			+			
guinea pigs	Caviidae			+			
agoutis	Dasyproctiae			+			
pacas	Capromyidae			+			
coypus	Capromyidae			+			
chinchillas	Chinchilliae			+			
rheas	Rheldae			+			
toucans	Ramphastidae			+			
curassows	Cracidae			+			
cock-of-the-rock	Cotingidae			+			
hummingbirds	Trochilidae		+	+			
alligators	Alligatiridae						
American alligator			+	+			
Chinese alligator		+					
caiman				+			
crocodiles	Crocodylidae				+	+	+
electric eels	Gymnotidae			+			
pottos	Lorisidae			+			
galagos				+			

slender iorris		+	
Old World monkeys,	Cercopithecidae	+	
macacques, drills,		+	
baboons			
appes	Pongidae	+	
gorillas & chimpanzees			+
qibbous & oranquatans	Nanulae	-	-
elephants	Elephantidae		
African elephant		+	
Indian elephant			+
rhinoceroses	Rhinocerotidae	+	
giraffes & okapis	giraffidae	+	
hippopotamuses	Hippopotamidae	+	
aardvark	Orycteropidae	+	
otter shrews	Potamogalidae	+	
elephant shrews	Macroscelidae	+	
golden moles	Chrysochloridae	+	
African flying squirrels	Anomaluridae	+	
ostriches	Struthionidae	+	
secretary birds	Sagittarlidae	+	
touracos	Musophagidae	+	
spiny lizards	Cordy lidae	+	
chameleons	Chamaeleonidae	+	0
colugo	Cynocephalidae		+

treeshrews	Tupalidae					+	
tarsiers	Tarslidae					+	
spiny dormice	Platacanthamyidae					+	
pheasants, partridges,	Phasianidae	+	+	+	+	+	
quail & peacocks		+	+	+	+	+	
gavials	Gavialidae					+	
big-headed turtle	Platysternidae					+	
marsupial 'mice', 'anteaters', Tasmanian wolf	Dasyuridae					+	
marsupial mole	Notoryctidae						+
bandiccot	Peramediadae						+
flying phalangers and opossums	Phalangeridae						+
kangaroos & wallabies	Macropodidae						+
wombats	Phascolonidae						+
spiny anteaters	tachyglossidae						+
duck-billed platypuses	Ornithorynchidae						+
cockatoos	subfamily kakatoeinae						+
lories	subfamily Lorlinae						+
pygmy parrots	subfamily micropsittanae						+
cassowarriers	Casuarlidae						+
emu	Promalidae						+
honeysuckers	Meliphagidae						+

lyrebirds	Menuridae						+
birds of paradise	Paradiseidae						+
snake-necked turtles	Chelidae			+		+	+
newts	Tailed amphibians	+	+	0		0	
European salamander		+					
giant Asian salamander		+					
American salamander				+			
common toad	Tailless amphibians	+	+	+	+	+	
hylid tree frogs		+	+	+		+	
polypedatid tree frogs		+			+	+	
South American lungfish	Lepidosiren			+			
African lungfish	Protopterus				+		
Australian lungfish	Neocerotadus						+

0 = One genus only

Table 11.4

Arrangement of the Faunal Regions to Emphasize Their Natures

Climate Limited Regions	
1.	Palearctic Region
2.	Nearctic Region
Main regions of the Old World Tropics	
3.	Oriental Region
4.	Ethoipian Region
Barrier Limited Regions	
5.	Neotropical Region
6.	Australian Region

In treating each one, we shall first tell what continents or parts of continents compose it and what the general nature of its climate and plant cover is, then summarize the composition and relationships of its vertebrate fauna, then discuss its boundaries briefly, and then indicate the main pattern of distribution of the fauna within the region. Where the land is more or less continuous, exact boundaries are hard to define and are not very important; transitions, their nature and extent, are more important; and the faunas themselves, their natures and interrelationships, are most important of all.

It is impossible to describe the regional faunas adequately in a few pages. Wallace (1876) devoted nearly 500 pages to them, to "a review of the chief forms of anima life in the several regions and sub-regions". He called this "zoological geography" in contrast to "geographical zoology", which is the distribution of animals by taxonomic groups rather than by regions. Wallace's old account of the regional faunas is still the best three is, although out of date in detail. A new, good, detailed and accurate regional or faunal zoogeography is much needed. It would help to relieve the tendency to provincialism of naturalists everywhere.

To analyze the regional faunas statistically in a few pages is also impossible. An adequate statistical treatment would have to deal not only with families but also with genera and perhaps with species. It would have to describe not only the composition and relationships of each fauna but also transitions between faunas. It might have to do all this for different parts of faunas separately, e.g., the forest part, savanna part, desert part, freshwater part, etc. And there are again many other complications and many chances of error.

One of the particular errors to be avoided both in describing the regional faunas and in treating them statistically is mixing the present with the past. In describing the relationships and transitions of existing faunas, animals should be classified strictly according to their present distributions, not according to their past derivations. Peccaries, for example, now mainly-in South and Central America extending into southern North America, are at present a Neotropical element in the edge of the Nearctic fauna, even though they reached South America from North America not long ago. Faunas can be analyzed in terms of past derivations, too, but this should be done separately.

Further in this context, during the course of descriptive account in the forthcoming pages of this chapter, the following abbreviations are used to indicate the principal (not necessarily the entire) occurrences of different groups of animals outside a given regional fauna.

excl.: exclusive; indicates groups confined to the region in question

World: the world or most of it, including at least parts of all continental faunal regions

Wide: much of world but not all of it

trop.: the tropics, including at least part of all tropical faunal regions

O.W.: Old World

Warm O.W.: warmer parts of the Old World

trop. O.W.: tropical parts of the Old World

Amer.: the Americas: the New World

Warm Amer.: warmer parts of the Americas

trop. Amer.: tropical America

Afr.: Ethiopian Africa

O.: Oriental Region (some groups so designated extend into temperate Asia)

Hol.: Holarctic Regions

Pal.: Palearctic Region

N.A.: Nearctic North America

S.A.: South American (some groups so designated extend into Central America, etc.)

ZOOGEOGRAPHICAL REGIONS

1. The Ethiopian Region

The Ethiopian Region is Africa, less its northern corner, plus (if one wishes) part of southern Arabia. Madagascar is often included, but here it is considered separately. In the following summaries, the presence or absence of groups in Madagascar is not mentioned except in a few special cases.

The Ethiopian Region is mainly tropical. There is a large blow of rain forest in equatorial West Africa and many small patches of rain forest elsewhere, notably on isolated mountains in East Africa. Much of the rest of Africa is covered by dry or seasonal thorn Scrub or grassland, grading into desert northward and south-westward. The southern tip of Africa is warm-temperate (reaching a latitude equivalent to that of South Carolina), with complexly mixed vegetations.

Ethiopian fresh-water fishes are diverse: archaic bichirs (excl.) and lepidosirenid lungfishes (S.A.); several families of Isospondyli (most excl.); many Ostariophysi, including many catfishes (some families excl., others O.), manycharacins (S.A.), and some cyprinids (extending from Asia) a few spiny-rayed families (most O.); and salt-tolerant cyprinodont (warm, wide) and cichlids (S.A., South India).

Ethiopian amphibians are caecilians (O. and S.A.) primitive pipid frogs (S.A.); and higher frogs, especially bufonids and ranids (trop. O.W., except Bufo and Rana wide and rhacophorids (O.), and fewer or more localizec phrynomerids (excl.), brevicipitids (warm world), and (in South Africa) a genus of doubtful leptodactylids (S.A. and A.).

Ethiopian reptiles are pelomedusid turtles (S.A.) trionychids (O. and N. A.), and testudinine land tortoise; (warm world except A.), and (in north-western Africa) an emydine (extending from Europe); crocodiles (trop.); many geckos (trop.), a few agamids (O. W.), chameleons (also Madagascar, etc.), many skmks (world), a few feyliniids (excl.), gerrhosaurids (Madagascar), lacertids (Eurasia) amphisbaenids (warm Amer., etc.), Varanus (warm O. W.) and cordylids (excel.); and Typholops (trop.) and Leptotyphlops (warm Amer., etc.), pythons (warm O. W.), e sand boa (genus also Pal.), many colubrids (world), one or more dasypeltids (O.), elapids (warm world), and typical viperids (Eurasia).

Ethiopian birds are too numerous to list in detail. They include many representative of widely distributed families such as hawks (including conspicuous Old World vultures) owls, herons, storks, cuckoos, goatsuckers, kingfishers larks, swallows, shrikes, thrushes, finches, and many others: of Old World or chiefly Old World families such as bustards, rollers, bee eaters; of Old World fly-catchers and warblers, motacillids, weaverbirds, starlings, orioles, drongos, etc.; of tropical or Old World tropical families such as trogons (few), hornbills, barbets, most honey guides, pittas (few), bulbuls, and most sunbirds; moderate numbers of parrots and pigeons; and a few exclusively Ethipoian families named below. Of course this list is incomplete. Of 67 families o1 birds represented on land and fresh water in the Ethiopian Region, 53 occur over all or much of the world, of much o1 the Old World, or the warmer parts of it; 3 (honey guides, broadbills, and bulbuls) are shared only or mainly with the Oriental Region; 5 (the Crab Plover, sand grouse, hoopoes, a doubtful bombycillid, and a doubtful honey eater) have special or doubtful relationships; and only 6 are exclusively Ethiopian. Of the 6 families that are exclusively Ethiopian or nearly so, 3 consist of single species (the Ostrich, Secretary Bird, and hammerhead), and the others are the touracos (19 species), mouse birds (6 species), and helmet shrikes (13 species-and there is a doubtful member of the family in Borneo). The following additional subfamilies are exclusively Ethiopian or nearly so: guinea fowls (7 species), tree hoopers (6 species), bush shrikes

(42 species), buffalo weavers (3 species), widow birds (9 species), and tickbirds (2 species). This geographical classification of families is somewhat arbitrary, but is serves to show the diversity of Ethiopian birds and the small number of exclusively Ethiopian families and subfamilies, which total only 110 species. The relationships of Ethiopian birds are shown better by genera than by families. Many genera are endemic; many occur also in the Oriental Region or have relatives there; some extend into temperate Eurasia, but many of these are migratory; and few have other relationships.

The Ethiopian Region is notable for its big game, but some of the less conspicuous mammals are more important zoogeographically. Ethiopian mammals are the Otter Shrew (excl. fam.), golden moles (excl.), hedgehogs (Eurasia), elephant shrews (almost excl.), and shrews (wide); lemur-like lorisids (O.), Old World monkeys (O.), 2 great apes (O.); scaly anteaters (O.); eanids (wide), mustclids (wide), viverrids (O. etc.), hyaenas (near part of Asia), and eats (wide); the Aardvark (excl. order); an elephant (O.); pige (Eurasia); 2 hippopotamuses (excl.); a tragulid (O.); 2 giraffids (excl.); many bovids (Eurasia and a few N.A.); rabbits (wide); many rodents: squirrels (wide), anomalurids (excl.), the Spring Haas (excl. fam.), a few crieetids (wide), bamboo rats (O.), many murids (O.W., but some subfamilies are excl. Afr.), dormice (Pal.), jerboas in the Sahara etc. (Pal.), Old World porcupines (0. etc.), and 4 additional families of probable or possible hystricomorphs (fams. excl. but some apparently related S.A.); and fruit bats (warm O.W.) and S. families of insectivorous bats: rhinopomatids (northeastern Africa and southern Asia), emballonurids (trop.), nycterids (O., etc.), megadermatids (warm O.W.), 2 families of horseshoe bats (warm O.W.), vespertilionids (world), and molossids (warm world). This mammal fauna is a diverse mixture of more or less widely distributed families shared with the Oriental Region, and exclusive families, and a few families with other relationships. The Oriental relationships are relatively stronger than shown, foi many Ethiopian genera and even some species of mammals occur also in the Oriental Region or have close relatives there.

The fresh-water fishes of the Ethiopian Region are a very distinctive assemblage, with some clear but distant relationships toward South America, some closer ones toward the Orient, and important exclusive groups. Ethiopian amphibians and reptiles are less distinctive, with again some South American relationships (pipid frogs, pelomedusid turtles, amphisbaenid lizards, leptotypholopid worm snakes), more Oriental ones (more than the list of families shows, for many Ethiopian genera occur also in the Orient or have close relatives there), and some exclusive groups. Ethiopian birds are still less distinctive, strongly Oriental in their main relationships, with relatively few exclusive groups. And Ethiopian mammals are a mixed assemblage, rather strongly Oriental in their main relationships, but with a number of exclusive groups.

The Ethiopian vertebrate faunas as a whole (so far as so complex a thing can be treated as a unit) is most like the Oriental one. The two are roughly similar in size, roughly similar in composition (least so in fishes), and they share many families, very many genera, and some species. Parts of the Ethiopian fauna have also close relationships with the Pale arctic, formed principally by northward extensions of tropical groups, including many migratory birds and certain families, genera, and species of other vertebrates. Some Ethiopian vertebrates are, much more distantly, related to South American ones; they include several important groups of fishes, certain amphibians and reptiles, but very few birds and mammals. There are hardly any direct relationships between Ethiopian and Australian vertebrates. The Ethiopian fauna also has important endemic groups, especially of fishes and mammals, which have no living relatives outside Africa.

The boundaries of the Ethiopian Region are the ocean, except in the north. Most Ethiopian vertebrates occur only south of the Sahara, or extend north only along the Nile. A very small northern corner of Africa, consisting of the northern parts of Morocco and Algeria north of the Atlas Mountains, has a depauperate fauna which is European in most of its relationships. In between, the great deserts of northern Africa have a very limited, specialized fauna with mixed relationships, part

Ethiopian and part Eurasian. Under these circumstances it is not important whether the northern boundary of the Ethiopian Region is set at the Atlas Mountains (where Sclater put it) or across the middle of the Sahara at the northern boundary of the tropics (where Wallace and most later zoogeographers put it), or whether the Sahara is considered a transition area. Southwestern Arabia, across the southern Red Sea from Africa, has a vertebrate fauna which is in some ways Ethiopian, but depauperate. This part of Arabia can be included in the Ethiopian Region or it can be considered part of a complex transition area.

Within the Ethiopian Region, the fauna is richest and most diverse in the more favourable tropical areas. There is a strong, general reduction of the fauna northward into the Sahara and a less strong reduction and some differentiation southward into South Africa. There is also some differentiation southward into South Africa. There is also some differentiation of a West African west-forest fauna and an East African open-forest and steppe fauna, although the two overlap and mix complexly. These general differences led Wallace to divide the continental Ethiopian Region into three sub regions, corresponding to West Africa, East Africa and South Africa. Further details of distribution within the Ethiopian Region vary with different groups of animals and are too complex to discuss here in details.

2. The Oriental Region

The Oriental Region is essentially tropical Asia and closely associated continental islands, including Ceylon, Sumatra, Java, Borneo, Formosa, and (if one wishes) the Philippines.

The Oriental Region is mainly tropical but extends a few degrees north of the tropics, especially in northern India. In the eastern part of the region, from the northeastern corner of India, Burma, Indochina, etc., to the Greater Sunda Islands, there is much rain forest, although it is interrupted in places by more open, drier country. High mountains, with rich and diverse plant cover, extend northward from Burma etc. to south-western China and the eastern Himalayas. Westward, the main part of peninsular India is relatively dry and open, but there is an isolated, wet, low-mountainous, forested strip along the south-west coast, and there is an interrupted ranges of low mountains (the Satpuras) across India from northeast) to southwest which has apparently been a route of dispersal of wet-country animals in the past (Hora 1953). The Himalayas too become drier and less hospitable westward.

Oriental fresh-water fishes include no archaic groups; one ostcoglossid (trop.) and a genus of notopterids (Afr.); many catfishes (some fams. Afr: and/or extending into Pal, other excel.) and an over whelming diversity of cypriniforms, including cyprinids (Pal., N.A., Afr.), cobitids (Pal. etc.), and homalopterids (excl.); a few nandids (Afr., S.A.) and pristolephids (excl.); anabantids (most, but one genus extends to Afr.), channids (Afr.), and the only luciocephalid (excl.); and a few secondary-division cyprinodonts (warm, wide) and, in peninsular India and Ceylon, a genus of cichlidi (related Afr., Madagascar).

Oriental amphibians are caecilians (Afr., S.A.); a few salamanders in northern Indochina etc. (extending from Pal.); a few localized discoglossids (Pat.); pelobatids (Hoi.); buffonids (wide); many ranids (wide) and rhacophorids (Afr. etc.); Hyla in northern Indochina etc. (extending from Pal.); and brevicipitids (warm world).

Oriental reptiles are many emydine turtles (Pal. and Amer.), the only platysternine (excl.), trionychids (Afr., N.A.), and testudinine land tortoises (warm world except A.); crocodiles (trop.) and gavials (excl.); many geckos (warm world) and agamids (O.W.), a chameleon in southern India and Ceylon (related toward Mediterranean region), many skinks (world), a few dibamids (extending to New Guinea), a few lacertids (Afr., Pal.), Varanus (warm O.W.), localized anguids (Pal., Amer.), and Lanthanotus in Borneo (excl.); and many snakes: Typhlops (warm world) and Leptotyphlops (marginal, Afr. etc.); the localized family Uropeltidae (excl.): a few aniliids (trop. Amer.); the one xenopeltid (excl.); phythons (warm O.W.); sand boas (marginal, Pal. etc.); many colubrids [Dipsadinae (trop. Amer.), Xenoderminae (S.A.), Colubrinae (world), and aquatic Acrochordinae (A.) and Homalopsinae (A)]; a dasypeltid (Afr.); elapids (warm world); sea snakes (Indo-Pacific); and true vipers (Afr. and Pal.) and pit vipers (Pal. and Amer.).

Oriental birds include almost all the widely distributed, Old World, tropica, and Old World tropical families that occur in the Ethiopian Region, but in somewhat different proportions. The Orient has fewer representatives of some groups (e.g., of shrikes, hoopoes, honey guides, sunbirds, and finches), and more of others (e.g., of woodpeckers, pittas, babblers, and corvids). The Orient also has many pheasants (only one in Africa), many pigeons, but (like Africa) only a moderate number of parrots. Of 66 families of birds represented on land and fresh water in the Oriental Region, 53 are more or less widely distributed elsewhere; 3 are shared only or mainly with Africa; 4 have special or doubtful geographical relationships: 5 are shared only or chiefly with the Australiàn Region (megapodes, frogmouths, wood swallows, flowerpeckers, and honey eaters-but the lasts does not extend into the Orient beyond bail); and only one is exclusive. The exclusively Oriental family is the Irenidae, the fairy bluebirds and leafbirds, with 4 genera, 14 species. This partly arbitrary geographical classification shows the general nature of the Oriental birds fauna. It is most like the Ethiopian one, diverse, with even fewer exclusive groups, but with some Australian relationships too. The genera of Oriental birds include many endemic ones, many shared with or related toward Africa, many shared with Pale arctic Eurasia (many of these are migratory), some shared with Australia, and very few with other relationships.

Oriental mammals are spiny and hairy hedgehogs (the former Afr. and Pal., the latter excl.), shrews (wide), moles (local, extending from Pal.); flying lemurs (excl.); tree shrews (excl.), lorisids (Afr.), tarsiers (excl.), Old World monkeys (Afr.), and apes (Afr.); scaly a'nteaters (Afr.); canids (wide), bears (Pal. And Amer.), mustelids (wide), vive rids (Afr. etc.), one hyaena (Afr.), and cats; an elephant (Afr.); a tapir (trop. Amer.); 2 rhinoceroses (Afr.); wild pigs (Afr., Pal.); chevrotains (Afr.); deer (Pal. and Amer.); bovids (Afr., Pal., a few N.A.); rabbits (wide); many rodents: squirrels (wide) and flying squirrels (Pal. and N.A.), a few cricetids (wide), bamboo rats (Afr.), many murids (O.W.), spinsy dormice (excl.), and Old World porcupines (Afr.); and fruit bats and 8 families of insectivorous bats (same as Afr.). This Oriental mammal fauna is a mixture of more or less widely distributed families, families and genera shared with the Ethiopian Region, exclusive families, a few groups of murid rodents and many genera and species of bats shared with the Australian Region, and a very few groups with other relationships.

The fresh-water fishes of the Oriental Region are a rich and dominant assemblage, notable for lack of archaic groups and for dominance of cypriniforms. Oriental amphibians and reptiles are partly like and partly unlike the Ethiopian ones:

some notable differences are that Orient lacks pipids and has pelobatid frogs: lacks pelomedusids and has emydine turtles; has gavials; lacks or has only a few chameleons, gerrhosaurids, and has unopeltids, ilysiids, additional subfamilies of colubrids, and pit vipers; in general, Africa has a greater diversity of lizards, the Orient of snakes. Oriental birds are strongly Ethiopian in their main relationships, with many Palearctic and some Australian relationships too, with few important exclusive groups. And Oriental mammals are rather strongly Ethiopian in general but include some groups with other relationships and some important exclusive groups.

The Oriental vertebrate fauna as a whole is most like the Ethiopian one, as indicated there under, in spite of the differences listed above. Parts of the Oriental fauna too have Pale arctic relationships, especially through eastern Asia. A few Oriental vertebrates, chiefly certain reptiles, birds, and bats, are related to Australian ones. And a very few (exceptional frogs, snakes, and birds, as well as tapirs) have tropical American relatives. The Oriental fauna has few important endemic groups of vertebrates confined to it, fewer than any other tropical regional fauna. Either the Orient has been a center from which vertebrates have tended to spread into other regions, or it has been a main crossroads in dispersal, or both. (In fact, the Orient seems to have been a center of dispersal for some vertebrates, e.g., cyprinid fishes, and a crossroads for others, e.g., birds.)

The boundaries of the Oriental Region are not sharply defined, for the Oriental fauna enters into complex transitions in several directions. The dry country of north-western India and beyond is "debatable land" (Wallace), with an impoverished fauna in which transitions occur both from east to west and from south to north (see under fresh-water fishes, pp. 65-66). Where regional boundaries are drawn here is perhaps not very important. A little farther east the Himalayas form a natural boundary several degrees north of the tropics. This mountain barrier is not the main cause of differentiation of the Oriental and Pale arctic regional faunas-the main cause is evidently the zonal climatic difference-but the mountains and the dry country west and north of them do form a barrier which permits parts of the Oriental fauna to extend some what north of the tropics without much mixture of northern elements. Still farther east, in the mountains of Burma, south-western China, etc., and along the coast of China, there is a very broad, complex transition, and the boundary of the Oriental Region is hard to fix; it is usually drawn across southern China not far above the Tropic of Cancer, where many tropical groups of animals reach northern limits. Southward and eastward, Ceylon and Formosa (which have somewhat depanperate continental faunas) as well as Sumatra, Java, and Borneo (which have almost full-scale Oriental faunas) are included in the Oriental Region, and the Philippines may be included, although their fauna actually forms a fringing pattern of strong, progressive subtraction with increasing distance from Borneo. Beyond Java and Borneo, the Oriental fauna forms a broad, complex transition with the Australian fauna.

Within the Oriental Region, the fauna shows both east-west and north-south differentiation. It is richest and most varied in the wetter eastern part of the region (from South China etc. to Java and Borneo), where, for example, most Oriental pelobatid frogs, emydine turtles, and pheasants occur, and less rich and somewhat different westward, in India. And there is partial differentiation in the east of a northern sub fauna (in South China, Indochina, Burma, Siam, etc.) and a southern one (in the Malaya Peninsula, Sumatra, Java, Borneo, etc.), and in the west of a northern sub fauna (in the main, drier part of India) and a southern one (in south India and Ceylon), the latter with some isolated Malayan and even a few Madagascan elements. Wallace divided the Oriental Region into for sub regions along these lines, naming them; Indochinese, Indo Malayan, Indian, and Ceylonese, sub regions are not formally recognized here, but the expressions "Indochinese Sub region" and "Malayan Sub region" (Wallace's "Indo-Mayalan") are sometimes useful.

3. The Palearetic Region

The Pale arctic Region is essentially Eurasia above the tropics, plus a small northern corner of Africa.

The Pale arctic is north-temperate with an arctic fringe. In the wetter parts of eastern Asia, including parts of temperate China and Japan, is fine, mostly deciduous forest. Much of the interior of Asia is arid and open, and the arid area extends through south-western Asia to North Africa. The arid zone grades into grassy steppes especially along its northern edge. In Europe there is again much deciduous or mixed forest, but it is less rich, with many fewer species of trees, than the forest of eastern Asia. Across northern Asia and Europe is a tremendous stretch of coniferous forest, and above it tundra.

Pale arctic fresh-water fishes are a paddlefish in China (N.A.), 2 suckers in eastern Asia (N.A.), many eyprinids (O., Afr., N.A.), cobitids (O. etc.), a few localized catfishes (fams. O.), an umbrid in the Danube etc. (N.A.), Dallia in eastern Siberia (Alaska), the Pike (N.A.), some percids (N.A.), and a very few anabantids, channids, and a mastacembelid in eastern Asia (extending from O.); and a few secondary-division cyprinodonts southward (wide, warm). The Cyprinidae is the only family of this list that is numerous and dominant throughout the Pale arctic Region, but shortage of other strictly fresh-water fishes is partly made up by peripheral ones, especially salmonids (N.A.) northward.

Pale arctic amphibians are salamanders (N.A. etc.), discoglossids (localized in O.), pelobatids (N.A., O.), Bufc (wide), Hyla (wide), many Rana (wide), and a few Rhacophorus and brevicipitids in eastern Asia (extending from O.).

Reptiles that are more or less widely represented in the Palearctic Region are emydine turtles (O., N.A., etc.), skinks (wide), lacertids (Afr., O.), anguids (Amer., local in O.), many colubrids (wide), true vipers (Afr., O.), and in Asia pit vipers (O., Amer). Additional reptiles which occur in parts of the southern edge of the Palearctic Region or eastern Asia are Testudo (warm, wide), Trionyx in eastern Asia (Afr., O., N.A.), an alligator in China (N.A.), geckos (warm world), agamids (warm O.W.), a chameleon (Afr. etc.), amphisbaenids (Afr., warm Amer.), Varanus (warm O.W.), Shinisaurus in China (excl. fam.), Typhlops (warm world), Leptotyphlops (Afr., warm Amer.), and sand boas (Afr., etc.).

Palearctic birds include representatives of 53 families on land and fresh water, not many fewer than occur in Africa or the Oriental Region, but some of them are only marginal or local in the Pale arctic. Only about 37 of the families are more or less widely distributed in the Palearctic, and some of them are mostly migratory there. They include grebes and loons, hawks, herons, stroks, ducks etc., quails and grouse, cuckoos, rails, plovers etc., pigeons, owls, goatsuckers, kingfishers, swifts, woodpeckers, larks, swallows, thrushes and Old World flycatchers and warblers, motacilids, tits etc., finches, weaver finches, starlings, and jays and crows. Most of the families that are widely distributed in the Palearctic are widely distributed elsewhere too, over much of the world or much of the Old World, but loons and creepers (as well as auks, which are sea birds) are Holarctic, and grouse and waxwings are additional Holarctic subfamilies, and hedge sparrows (1 genus, 12 species) are exclusively Palearctic. Besides the 37 families that are widely distributed at least in summer, 10 additional families (pelicans, ibises, flamingos, button quails, thick-knees, swallow plovers, sand grouse, rollers, bee eaters, and hoopoes) are only marginal (in the warm southern edge) or local in the Palearctic, and 5 more Old World tropical families (bulbuls, cuckoo shrikes, sunbirds, white-eyes, and drongos) are represented in the Palearctic only or chiefly by migratory forms which extend northward in eastern Asia. The final family is represented by two American wood wablers which extend their breeding ranges into eastern Siberia. This geographical classification of families is partly arbitrary (there is no sharp distinction between the families that are "widely distributed" and "marginal" in the

Palearctic), but it shows well enough that Palearctic birds are less diverse than but otherwise not much different from Ethiopian and Oriental ones. The relationships of Palearctic birds are shown better by genera than by families: many genera including many that are migratory in the north are shared with the Old World tropics; many genera and even many northern species are shared with North America; and some genera are exclusive to the Palearctic.

The principal Palearctic mammals are hedgehogs (Afr., O.), shrews (wide, but the doubtful subfam. Soricinae is Kol.), and moles (N.A.); canids (wide), bears (O., Amer.), pandas (excl. subfam. localized in southwest China, but fam. also Amer.), mustelids (wide), and felids (wide); horses etc. (Afr.), pigs (Afr., O.), a localized camel (S.A.), deer (O., Amer.), and bovids (Afr., O., N.A.); pikas (N.A.) and rabbits (wide); squirrels (wide) and flyihg squirrels (O., N.A.), a beaver (N.A.), a fair number of cricetids (wide), localized mole rats (almost excl.), many murids (O.W.), dormice (subfam. excl., but fam. also Afr.), a localized seleviniid (excl.), jumping mic (N.A.), and uerboas (northern Afr.); and bats, mostly vespertilionids (world), Besides these, the following additional families reach small marginal areas in the Palearctic: elephant shrews in North Africa (Afr.), scaly anteaters in eastern China (0., Afr.), Old World monkeys in North Africa and parts of China and Japan (Afr., 0.), vive rids (Afr., 0.), a hyaena and hyrax in parts of southwestern Asia (extending from Afr.), ctenodactylid rodents in North Africa, and fruit bats and several families of insectivorous bats (from tropics). The genera of Palearctic mammals are partly endemic, partly shared with the Old World (especially Oriental) tropics, and partly shared with North America. The North American relationships become very strong in the north.

In summary, Palearctic fresh-water fishes are cyprinids (extending from the Orient); a few, mostly localized species of other primary-division families (many with North American relationships); and peripheral fishes (many in the north, with North American relationships). Palearctic amphibians are salamanders (N.A.); frogs of 3 widely distributed dominant genera (Rana, Bufo, Hyla); and more or less localized representatives of 4 other families of frogs with Oriental tropics. Palearctic birds are of less-than-tropical diversity; most are related (at the generic or specific level) toward the Old World (especially Oriental) tropics or North America.

The Palearctic vertebrate fauna as a whole is much less rich than the Ethiopian and Oriental ones. It is, in terms of existing relationships, a transitional fauna, a complex mixture of Old World tropical and North American groups, the former most numerous southward, the latter northward, with few important endemic groups of its own.

The Palearctic Region is bounded on the south by the Ethiopian and Oriental Regions, and on the north by the limit of land. Westward it includes the British Isles and conventionally, Iceland, although the latter has a fragmentary fauna; and eastward it includes Japan and is bounded by Bering Strait.

Within the Palearctic Region the fauna is richest in the warmer areas, where they are wet enough, and diminishes northward, until, in most of the arctic, vertebrates are reduced to fresh-water fishes, mostly peripheral; one frog (Rana); no reptiles, a few land and more fresh-water birds, mostly migratory; and a few mammals, as few as 8 species in the highest continental arctic. The fauna is reduced and specialized in dry and mountainous places too. These is also some differentiation from east to west, more in the south than in the north: (the richest part of the south than in the north: and is the richest part of the Palearctic) and includes many Oriental elements; that of the Mediterranean Region is rather rich too, but with more Ethiopian elements. Wallace divided the Palearctic into four sub regions: Siberian, European, Manchurian, and Mediterranean; but the first two are not very distinct, and the others are not worth formal recognition, although "Mediterranean" is a useful descriptive term for some distributions.

4. The Nearctic Region

The Nearctic Region is North America above the tropics.

The Nearctic too is north-temperate with an arctic fringe. The original cover of much of eastern North America in the mid-latitudes is deciduous or mixed forest. Westward, in the middle part of the continent, are extensive grasslands, and, farther west, a complex of more or less arid country from which rise mountains with strips of mixed or coniferous forest. Northward, as in Eurasia, there is first a great stretch of coniferous forest and then tundra.

Nearctic primary-division fishes are one or 2 paddlefishes (China); the Bowfin (excl. order); a few mooneyes (excl.); suckers (E. Asia), many small cyprinids (O., Pal., Afr.), ameiurid catfishes (almost excl.); a few umbrids (eastern Europe), Dallia in Alaska (E. Siberia), and Esox (Pal.); a few trout perches and aphredoderids (both excl.); basses etc. (excl. fam.); and many percids (Pal., one subfam. excl. N. A.). Nearctic secondary-division fishes are gar pikes (also Central America) .and Cyprinodontes (warm, wide). Besides these, a primary-division characin and a secondary-division cichlid reach the Rio Grande (extending from S.A.), and there are many peripheral fishes, especially northern salmonids (Pal.).

Nearctic amphibians are salamanders (Pal., etc.); a localized leiopelmid (New Zealand); pelobatids (subfam. also Europe); Bufo (wide), Hyla etc.(wide), and Rama (wide); and a few leptodactylids and brevicipitids (extending from S.A.).

Nearctic reptiles are snapping and musk turtles (extending to parts S.A.), emydines (Eurasia and trop. Amer.), an endemic genus of land tortoises in south (subfam. warm, wide), and Trionyx (Afr., O., E. Asia); an alligator in the southeast (China) and a crocodile in southern Florida (warm world);

geckos in the south-west (warm world), many iguanids (trop. Amer. etc.), Heloderma (excl. fam.), xantusiids in south-west (Central Amer. etc.), skinks (wide), teiids (trop. Amer.), amphisbaenids in the south (S.A. etc., Afr.), anguids (trop. Amer., few Pal. and O.), and anniellids in southwest (excl.);

and Leptotyphlops (trop. Amer., Afr.), a few small boines in west (subfam. also in parts Afr., asia, etc.), many colubrids (world), coral snakes (trop. Amer, fam. warm world), and pit vipers (temp. and trop. Asia, trop. Amer.).

Nearctic birds include land and fresh-water representatives

of about 49 families. About 39 of them are more or less widely distributed in the Nearctic or the warmer parts of it at least in summer. They are grebes, loons, pelicans (local), hawks (3 fams.) and New World vultures (trop. Amer.), herons, ducks etc., quails and grouse, turkeys (nearly excl.), cuckoos, cranes, rails, plovers and sandpipers, gulls, pigeons, owls (2 families), goatsuckers, kingfishers, swifts, humming-birds (trop. Amer.), woodpeckers, tyrant flycatchers (trop. Amer.), larks (one sp.), swallows, thrushes and mockingbirds (subfam. trop. Amer.) and wrens (subfam. mostly trop. Amer.) etc., motacillids (pipits), shrikes, waxwings, creepers, nuthatches, titmice and chickadees, vireos (trop. Amer.), wood warblers and tanagers and cardinal grosbeaks (fam. trop. Amer.), finches, icterids (trop. Amer.), and crows and jays. This list shows a mixture of many widely distributed families, some dominant New World ones ("trop. Amer."), a few Holarctic ones, and only one (turkeys) exclusive or nearly so. Representatives of the following 10 additional families enter the southern edge of the Nearctic Region from the tropics, reaching to or nearly to the southern edge of the United States: ibises, a stork, a flamingo, a cracid, the Limpkin, a jacana, parrots, a trogon, a motmot (only to northern Mexico), and a cotinga. Of genera of Nearctic birds, some (including many migratory ones) are shared with Central and South America, some (especially northward), with the Palearctic Region, and some are endemic.

Nearctic mamals are an opossum (extending from S. A.)'^ Shrews (wide, subfam, also Pal.) and moles (Pal,); an armadillo in Texas etc. (extending from S.A.); canids (wide), bears (Eurasia, S. A.), raccoons etc. (trop. Amer., related pandas in Asia), mustelids (wide), and cats (wide); peccaries in south (extending from S. A.), deer (Eurasia, trop, Amer.), the Pronghorn in the west (excl.), and a few bovids (Pal., O Afr.); pikas in the west (Pal.) and rabbits (wide); the Sewellel in the west (excl. fam.), squirrels (wide) and flying squirrels (Eurasia etc.), pocket gophers and pocket mice mostly in the west (extending to Central and northern South Amer. respectively), a beaver (Pal.), many cricetids (wide), jumping mice (Pal.), and a porcupine (trop. Amer.); and vespertilionids (wide) and south-ward a few leaf-nosed bats (trop. Amer.), long-legged bats (trop. Amer), and molossids (warm world). This fauna is obviously a mixture of families shared with the Palearctic Region (and other parts of the Old World) and families shared with the American tropics, with few important exclusive groups. Nearctic genera of mammals show this same mixture, but with relatively more relationships toward the Palearctic, especially in the north, and with numerous endemic genera in some groups, especially rodents.

In summary, Nearctic fresh-water fishes are numerous and distinctive; most of the families are exclusive or are shared with the Palearctic. Dominant Nearctic amphibians belong to the same groups as Palearctic ones (salamanders, Rana, Bufo, and Hyla), and Nearctic pelobatids are related to Palearctic ones, but a few Nearctic frogs have South American or New Zealand relationships. Nearctic reptiles are a mixture of Palearctic (or Old World) and tropical American groups (the latter especially lizards), with few important exclusive groups. Nearctic birds are a mixture of Palearctic (Old World) and tropical American groups, the former more numerous northward, the latter southward, although many that winter in tropical America breed far northward. Nearctic mammals too are a mixture of (relatively more) Palearctic or Old World groups and (relatively fewer) tropical American ones, with few important exclusive groups.

The Nearctic vertebrate fauna as a whole, like the Palearctic one, is much less rich than the tropical regional faunas and is mainly transitional, a mixture of Palearctic and tropical American groups, the former more numerous northward, the latter southward, with few important groups of its own except of fresh-water fishes.

Northward, the Nearctic Region Includes Newfoundland, the Arctic Archipelago, and Greenland-Greenland mammals are all American, although some of the birds are European. Southward, the Nearctic fauna forms a complex transition with the Neotropical one as described later in this chapter; the boundary is usually set in southern Mexico, where the cooler Mexican highlands meet the tropical lowlands and where many tropical vertebrates reach northern limits.

Within the Nearctic Region, vertebrates are most numerous in the most favorable southern areas (which differ for the different classes), and the fauna diminishes progressively (but irregularly) northward until it is reduced to a small arctic fauna much like the Palearctic one. There is also east-west differentiation, stronger in some groups than in others: e.g., most fresh-water fishes and turtles are concentrated east of the Rocky Mountains; salamanders are more numerous in the east than in the west but form an isolated western sub fauna there are relatively more snakes in the east and more lizards in the west; and some families of mammals are represented only or chiefly in the west (the Pronghorn, pikas, the Sewellel, pocket gophers, and pocket mice); but birds as a whole, dominant mammals other than rodents, and some families and genera of other classes show much less east-west differentiation. Walace divided the Nearctic Region into four sub-regions: a northern one extending across the continent and below it an eastern, a west-central (Rocky Mountain etc.) and Pacific coast ("Californian") one. These sub-regions obviously correspond to more or less different climatic and vegetation areas, and their faunas are to some degree different; Merriam (1892 etc.) divided North America into a more complex system of "life zones" based on temperature. These zones are useful in some ways, but they have been overemphasized. They are not well-defined with their faunal sub regions.

5. The Neotropical Region

The Neotropical Region is South and Central America and the tropical lowlands of Mexico with Trinidad and, if one wishes, the West Indies proper, but the West Indian fauna is limited and is in some ways transitional, and forms a complex fringing pattern rather than part of a continental one.

This region is mostly tropical, but southern South America extends into the south-temperate zone, reaching a latitude equivalent to that of Labrador or England, with temperatures between the two. There is a huge tract of rain forest in the Amazon Valley and separate, smaller tracts elsewhere in South and Central America, as well as tracts of drier forest. There are also extensive areas of savanna and grassland in the tropics, as well as grassland south of them in Argentina, and there are also desert and sub-desert areas, especially in western South America but widely scattered elsewhere. Vegetation is in fact very complexly distributed in South America and perhaps still more so in Central America, where many sorts of wet forest, dry forest, savanna, sub-desert, and mountain vegetations exist in comparatively small areas. The Andes support a succession of altitudinal forests and grasslands in northern South America, in southern Chile and the western part of Tierra del fuego, there is a special, wet, cool-temperate forest named for the southern beech, Nothofagus, which forms forests also in New Zealand and southern Australia and Tasmania.

Neotropical fresh-water fishes are very numerous but belong to few basic groups. They are dominated by certain Ostariophysi: characins (Afr.), gymnotid eels (excl.), and eat fishes (excl. fams.). There are also a lungfish (fam. also Afr.), 2 osteoglossids (discontinuously trop.), 2 nandids (Afr. 0.), a number of secondary-division Cyprinodontes (warm, wide) and cichilds (Afr:), and some peripheral fishes; and suckers, ameiurid eat fishes, and secondary-division gar pikes extend to parts of Central America (from N.A.).

Neotropical amphibians are caecilians (Afr., 0.), plethodontid salamanders (most N.A.), pipid frogs (Afr.), Rhinophrynus in southern Mexico etc. (excl. fam.), many leptodactylids (A. etc.), Bufo (wide), many atelopodids (few in trop. O.W.), many hylids (Hoi., A.), a few Rana (wide), and brevicipitids (subfam. also 0. and extends into N.A.).

Neotropical reptiles are a dermatemydid in northern Central America etc. (excl. fam.), a Chelydra in Central America etc. (N.A.), staurotypines in northern Central America (excl.) and Kinosternon (N.A.), a few emydines (related N.A. and 0.), Testudo (warm O.W.), and pelomedusid (Afr.) and chelyid (A.) side-necked turtles; crocodiles (trop.) and caimans (excl.); geckos (warm world), many iguanids (N.A., etc.), xantusiids in Central America etc. (also southern N.A.), a few skinks (world), an elytropsid in southern Mexico (excl. fam.), many teiids (N.A.), amphisbaenids (Afr. etc.), anguids (N.A., Eurasia, etc.), Xenosaurus in southern Mexico etc. (excl. fam.); and Typhlops (trop. etc.), Leptotyphlops (Afr., southern N.A.), many colubrids (world), coral snakes (N.A., fam. warm world), and pit vipers (N.A., Asia).

The Neotropical bird fauna is very rich and very distinct. Of 67 bird families represented on land or fresh water in the region, about half are. widely distributed elsewhere; a few have special or doubtful relationships; and nearly half are exclusive or are at least confined to the New World.

Neotropical mammals are opossums (nearly exclusive, but one extends to N.A.) and caenolestid marsupials (excl.); a few shrews in Central America etc. (extending from N.A.); monkeys (2 excl. fams.); anteaters (excl.), sloths (excl.), and armadillos (nearly excl., one extending to southern N.A.); mustelids (wide), a bear (N.A., Eurasia), procynids (N.AJ, mustelids (wide), and cats (wide); tapirs (O.), peccaries (extending to N.A.), camels (Pal.), and deer (N.A., Eurasia); rabbits (wide); squirrels (wide), pocket gophers and pocket mice in Central America etc. (both extending from N.A.), many cricetids (N.A., parts of O.W.), New World porcupines (N.A.), and 10 additional families (all excl.) of hystricomorph rodents; and 9 families of insectivorous bats: emballonurids (trop. etc.), noctilionids (excl.), many phyllostomatids (extending to southern N.A.), true vampire bats (excl.), natalids (nearly excl.), furipterids (excl.), disk winged bats (excl.), vespertilionids (world), and molossids (warm world).

In summary, Neotropical fresh-water fishes are very numerous and highly endemic (most families exclusive) but with general African relationships. Neotropical amphibians and reptiles are mixed: some groups of them are primarily tropical and subtropical (e.g., caecilians, Testudo, crocodiles, Typhlops); some, African in their relationships (e.g., pipid frogs, pelomedusid turtles, amphisbaenid lizards, Leptotyphlops); some, Oriental (a subfam. of brevicipitid frogs, a genus of cmydine turtles, and aniliid and some groups of colubrid snakes); some, Australia (leptodactylid and hylid frogs and chelyid turtles); and some, North American (plethodontid salamanders, iguanid and teiid lizards, and many genera of other families). Neotropical birds are very numerous, and very many of them belong to exclusive families, though others are wide-ranging. Neotrpical mammals are a mixture of very distinct exclusive families and families shared with other parts of the world, usually including North America.

In short, the whole existing Neotrpical vertebrate fauna is a mixture of surviving parts of an old, endemic, Tertiary fauna of which the geographical relationships are now diverse (presumably determined by extinctions and survivals more than by directions of dispersal) and a new fauna received via North America. The old fauna includes all the strictly fresh-water fishes (except a few recent arrivals in northern Central America), probably a majority of the reptiles in South America but relatively fewer of those in Central America, very many birds (but the old and new groups are not so clearly distinguishable among birds), and about half the mammals.

The northern boundary of the Neotropical Region is the southern boundary of the Nearctic (above).

The main pattern of distribution of vertebrates within the Neotropical Region is one of richness in the main tropical part of South America; subtraction, mixture with additional North America elements, and some differentiation in Central America; subtraction and some (but in most cases not much) differentiation outward, it southern South America; and less important differentiation of rain forest, grassland, desert, and mountain faunas. Wallace distinguished "Brazilian" (main South American), "Mexican" (Central American), and "Chilean" (south-temperate) subregions, which, of course, are not formally recognized here.

6. The Australian Region

The Australian Region is Australia and New Guinea, with Tasmania and certain smaller islands which have (depauperate) continental faunas.

The Australian Region is partly tropical and partly south-temperate New Guinea is wholly within the tropics. Much of the island is covered with rain forest, but there are also areas of grassland as well as a series of altitudinal vegetations on the mountains, and on the south coast are areas of open eucalyptus woods like those of Australia. Northern Australia too is tropical, with diverse vegetations which include, in northern Queensland, a series of isolated patches of fine rain forest called "scrub" locally. Farther south, in the temperate zone, eastern and south-eastern Australia is fairly well watered, with much open eucalyptus woods and some wetter, denser forest on the mountains. Most of the interior of Australia is arid. South-western Australia is moderately wet but is cut off by deserts from the southwest. Tasmania is cool-temperate, equivalent in latitude to New York or Boston (but not so cold in winter), and is partly wet and forested.

Australian fresh-water fishes are a ceratodontid lungfish (excl. fam.) and an osteoglossid (O. etc.), both restricted in distribution, and various peripheral fishes.

Australian amphibians are only frogs: leptodactylids (S.A. etc.), hylids (S.A. etc.), a few ranids (wide), and brevicipitids (warm world, but subfams are nearly exct.).

Australian reptiles are Carettochelys (excl. fam.) and a trionychild (species also O.) in New Guinea, and Chelyid turtles (S.A.); crocodiles (trop.); many geckos (warm world), agamids (warm O.W.), many skinks (world), a Dibamus in New Guinea (O.) Varanus (warm O.W.), and pygopodids (excl.); and Typhons etc., (warm O.W.), some colubrids in New Guinea and parts of Australia (world), and many elapids (warm world).

The birds of Australian Region include representatives of about 58 families on land and fresh water. Of these, 44 families are more or less widely distributed elsewhere, over the world, or the tropics, or all or much of the Old World. Two small families (frog mouths and wood swallows) are divided between the Australian and Oriental Regions. The 12 remaining families are exclusive to the Australian Region or occur primarily there: cassowaries (6 species), emus (2), megapodes (to edge 0.) (10), owlet frogmouths (also some islands) (8), lyrebirds (2), scrubbirds (2), flowerpeckers (into 0.) (54), honey eaters (also many islands and doubtfully S. Afr.) (159), bell magpies (11), magpie larks (4, bowerbirds (17), and birds of paradise (43).

These families total 318 species, including the few extra-Australian ones. The Australian Region also has more than its share of pigeons and parrots, including important exclusive groups, and many "Australian warblers" (Malurinae) (also Polynesia etc.) (85 species). The proportion of Australian birds in exclusive or nearly exclusive families is larger than in any other continental faunal region except the Neotropical.

The native land mammals of the Australian Region are only a few monotremes (excl.subclass), many marsupials (6 excl. fams.), rather diverse rodents of the family Muridae (O.W.), and fruit bats (warm O.W.) and 6 families of insectivorous bats (all occurring elsewhere).

In summary, the vertebrate fauna of the Australian Region consists of only one or 2 fishes of strictly fresh-water groups, one of them a striking relict, plus peripheral fishes; 4 families of frogs, none strikingly primitive, and none exclusive, although 2 subfamilies of brevicipitids are nearly so; a moderate variety of reptiles, none strikingly primitive and few in exclusive families; a fair variety of birds, a fair proportion in exclusive families; and a very limited mammal fauna, with strikingly primitive and exclusive elements.

To bring in the past again for just a moment, the Australian vertebrate fauna is made up of a few very old endemic groups which have survived or radiated in Australia for a very long time, plus an accumulation of additional groups of salt-tolerant (but perhaps no strictly fresh-water) fishes and of frogs, reptiles, birds, rodents, and bats. The most extreme endemics are the lungfish, monotremes, and peculiar super families of marsupials. Australia has no comparable relict or endemic groups of amphibians, reptiles, or birds; if some of these animals have been in Australia as long as marsupials have, they have not radiated to the same extent. Some of the older Australian vertebrates (some frogs, turtles, and the marsupials) now fine their living relatives principally in (tropical) South America; in most cases this is apparently a result of withdrawal or extinction in the main part of the world. Strictly fresh-water fishes, terrestrial reptiles, and birds seem to show no particular relationships between Australia and South America, and the Australian vertebrate fauna as a whole has little direct relationship with the African fauna. Many of the more recent Australian vertebrates (ranid frogs and many reptiles, birds, rodents, and bats) still have relatives in tropical Asia.

The north-western boundary of the Australian Region is discussed under "Wallacea," below. Whether or not various islands to the east of Australia and New Guinea are included in the Australian Region is a matter of preference rather than of fact.

Within the Australian Region, the faunas of Australia and New Guinea are somewhat differentiated. Among other differences, Australia along has the lungfish; Australia has more leptodactylid frogs and New Guinea more brevicipitid frogs; Australia has most pygopodid lizards, New Guinea, relatively more colubrid snakes; Australia has emus, New Guinea, most birds of paradise, Australia has the Platypus and more (and more specialized) marsupials, and new Guinea has relatively more rodents. But these details are not very important. The vertebrate faunas of Australia and New guinea are much alike as wholes (see comparison of the mammals, and of the birds); they share many groups, even many genera and species; and there is extensive to the areas of open eucalyptus woods in southern New Guinea, and various New Guinean animals extend to the areas of rain forest in north-eastern Australia. Within Australia, there is some further faunal differentiation from north to south, and between the wetter eastern zone, that great central and western arid area, and the moderately wet southwestern corner of the continent.

TRANSITION BETWEEN REGIONAL FAUNAS

Wherever regional faunas meet or are separated only by partial barriers, there is transition: overlapping of faunal elements, with progressive subtraction, in both directions.

Faunal transition is a very complex thing. Two adjacent regional faunas usually consist of some families, genera, and species which are shared, some which occur mostly in one region but extend into parts of the other (these are the strictly transitional elements), and some which occur in one region but not the other; but this is just the beginning of the complexity. A family shared by two regions many contain transitional in one direction may condition genera or species transitional in one direction may contain genera or species transitional in the other direction; different transitional groups extend for different distances; and situations are usually complicated in other ways and by special or doubtful cases.

The tropical Ethiopian and tropical Oriental vertebrate faunas have many that occur in one region. but not the other, but few that are strictly transitional. A few African families, genera, and species do extend (in some cases discontinuously) through south-western Asia to the near part of the Oriental Region (e.g., chameleons, some birds, a hyaena, and the Lion); a few Oriental groups extend to the near part of AFrica (e.g., cobitid fishes); and there is additional, but still very limited, transition in south-western Asia as described especially for fishes and birds. This transition faunas. It is at the level of genera and species as well as families. The zone of transition is rather wide but lies mainly in arid country between more than within the limits of main faunas. And the direction of transition is doubtful; it is doubtful whether there is more extension of African vertebrates toward the Orient or of Oriental ones toward Africa. There is also a mixture of (many) African and (fewer)Oriental vertebrates in Madagascar which makes a transition of a sort, but the African groups in Madagascar rarely extend to the Orient that way (salt-tolerant cichild fishes are an exception), and the Oriental groups that reach Madagascar rarely extend to Africa.

The tropical Ethiopian and temperate Palearctic regional faunas share may groups of vertebrates, although there are many others (chiefly on the Ethiopian side) that are not shared. Actual transition, however, is limited, although some does occur in the Sahara and the Mediterranean area. Most of it is due to extension of Ethiopian (tropical) families, genera, and species into the southern edge of the Palearctic: e.g., cyprinodintid fishes; Testudo, geekos, chameleons, amphisbaenids, etc.; birds", of which various Ethiopian (tropical) groups extend for different distances into southern Europe as residents or migrants; and elephant shrews and macaques (in Palearctic North Africa), a porcupine, a hyaena, viverrids, a hyrax, and bats. Extension of Palearctic groups into the edge of the Ethiopian Region occurs in comparatively few cases: e.g., an emydid turtle probably extends into part of western tropical Africa, and Microtus (voles) extends to a small part of non-Palearctic or transitional North Africa. This transition between the Ethiopian and Palearctic vertebrate faunas involves rather small fractions of the main faunas. It is at the level of genera and species as well as families. The zone of transition is only moderately wide, and much of it is in arid country between the limits of the main faunas. And the direction of transition is mostly northward: many more Ethiopian (tropical) vertebrates extend into the edge of the Palearctic Region than vice versa.

Transition between the tropical Oriental and temperate Palearctic faunas is extensive in eastern Asia in all classes of vertebrates. A number of families, genera, and species of Oriental fresh-water fishes extend into temperate China and several reach the Amur. Several Oriental families and genera of frogs extend into temperate China, and the brevicipitid Kaloula reaches Manchuria, and Rhacophorus, northern Honshu in Japan; and, in the other direction, a few Palearctic salamanders and Hyla extend for comparatively short distances southward, into the edge of the Oriental Region. Many Oriental groups of reptiles extend for various distances into temperate Asia. So do many Oriental birds, both resident and migratory ones. And of mammals, many Oriental families and lesser groups extend for various distances into temperate Asia; and a few Palearctic ones extend into the Oriental tropics: e.g., the Serow (representing a Palearctic tribe of bovids) extends to Sumatra; a mole (representing a Holarctic family), to the Malay Peninsula; and the Wolf (a Holarctic species), to part of tropical India. A substantial part specially of the Oriental vertebrate fauna (but still only a part of it) is involved in this transition. The transition is at the level of genera and species as well as families. The transitory occurs in a broad zone of favourable country within the limits of the main faunas concerned. And the direction of transition is mainly northward; many more Oriental vertebrates extend into the Palearctic than vice versa.

That the transitions of both the Ethiopian and Oriental vertebrate faunas with the Palearctic fauna are formed mainly by northward extensions of tropical groups reflects the general reduction of vertebrate life north of the tropics and the fact that in many ways the Palearctic fauna is little more than a depauperate fringe of the tropical faunas.

Transition between the temperate Palearctic and temperate Nearctic faunas is extensive through the north in all classes of vertebrates. The northern parts of both fauna are alike in many ways, with even many species is common. This transition involves considerable parts of both faunas i.e. Palearctic and Nearetic. Most of it is at the level of genera and species rather than families. It occurs in a broad zone, much of which lies in rather unfavourable, cold country. And the direction of the transition is doubtful: it is doubtful whether (in terms of existing distribution) there is more extension of Palearctic groups into the Nearctic than vice versa.

In a broader way, the Palearctic and nearctic faunas an themselves in many ways transitional between the faunas o the Old and New World tropics.

1. Central American-mexican Transition Area

The vertebrate faunas of the Nearctic and Neotropica Regions are very different in many ways, but they also share many families and genera and some species, and there is transition especially in Mexico and Central America, and to some extent in a still wider area.

Among fresh-water fishes, some Nearctic primary-division families do not .even reach the Rio Grande centrarchids and percids reach the Tropic of Cancer ir Mexico; cyprinids reach the Rio Balsas in southern Mexico and suckers and ameiurid eat fishes reach Guatema o1 Neotropical primary-division families, some do not even reach Central America; others do not extend beyond Panama; the northern most gymnotid eel reaches Guatemala; the northern most South American fresh-water catfish,

Rio Panuco on the east coast of Mexico; and the northernmost characin, the Rio Grande. Among strictly fresh-water fishes, then, transition involves only very small fractions of the Nearctic and Neotropical faunas; the fraction represent different families; and overlapping occurs only from the Rio Grande to Guate-Nearctic gar pikes extend south to Lake Nicearagua; Neotropical cichlids, north to the Rio Grande; and Cyprinodontes extend so far into North America that they might be considered as shared rather than transitional.

Among amphibians, transition involves larger parts of the two faunas and a much wider area, but transition is still mostly at the family level. Of Nearctic families, some (especially some families of salamanders) extend south only to Texas or the northern corners of Mexico; ambystomid salamanders and pelobatid frogs cross the Tropic of Cancer on the plateau of Mexico but do not reach the tropical lowland; and plethodontid salamanders and ranids (Rana) extend through Central America into northern South America. Buronids (Bufo) are so widely distributed in South as well as North America that (in terms of present distribution) they are shared rather than transitional. Of Neotropical families, pipid frogs do not reach Central America; atelopodid frogs extend at least to Nicaragua (and Cuba); caecilians, to southern Mexico; leptodactylids, to Texas and southern Arizona; and brevicipitids, to southern Iowa, Indiana, and Maryland. Hylids and Hyla are so widely distributed in North America that it is probably best to consider them shared. This pattern of transition of amphibian faunas at the family level is complicated by transitional genera in some families and by the occurrence of localized genera and even a localized family of frogs (Rhinophrynidae) in parts of Central America and Mexico.

Among reptiles, transition is still more complex in a wide area. It tends to involve relatively more genera as well as families. Of turtles, Nearctic snapping turtles and Kinosternon extend through Central America into parts of South America; but South American turtle families (pelomedusids and chelyids) are, as now distributed, a shared family with both northern and southern transitional genera: from the north, Terrapene extends south to southern Mexico, and Pseudemys, through Central and much of South America (perhaps it should be reckoned a shared rather than transitional genus); and from the south, Testudo extends north to Panama, and Geoemyda, through Central America to parts of Mexico, of crocodilians, the Nearctic alligator does not extend south of the Rio Grande; but Neotropical caimans and a crocodile extend north to parts of Mexico and (the crocodile) southern Florida. Of lizards, the principal families in America are mostly tropical, extending for different distances north ward, but the pattern of distribution of genera is very complex; some genera are mainly Nearctic and extend into Central America etc. as northern transitional elements, and others extend northward from South America. Of snakes, the northern transitional elements in Mexico and Central America are mostly genera of colubrids and pit vipers. Of Neotropical snakes, Typhlops reaches Southern Mexico; Leptotyphlops, southern-western United States; and many South American genera of colubrids extend for varying distances into Central and southern North America. A surprising number of North American reptiles extend into Central America without reaching South America. And the transition is complicated by the presence of a number of localized, endemic or relict genera and even families of reptiles in Mexico and Central America.

Among Birds, transition of Nearctic and Neotropical faunas is very extensive and complex, involving many genera and species as well as families and covering not only Central America and Mexico but also much of North and South America. Some (but comparatively few) Nearctic groups extend into the Neotropics as breeding birds: e.g., turkeys, to guatemala; kinglets, creepers, titmice, evening grosbeaks, crossbills, and crows, to parts of Central but not South America ; the Horned Lark, to northern South America; etc.; but the most conspicuous Nearctic elements in the transition are the many genera and species which (regardless of their geographical origin) now breed in the Nearctic but winter in the edge of the Neotropical Region. In the other direction, many (but far from all) families of the rich South American bird fauna extend through Central America; many important groups (e.g. tinamous, puffirds, jacamars, toucans, the superfamily Furnarioidea, manakins, honey creepers, and many smaller limit in southern Mexico; and many other Neotropical groups extend for different distances into temperate North America: e.g., motmots reach northern Mexico; cracids, jacanas, parrots, trogons, and cotingas reach southern Texas and/or Arizona; ibises and limpkins reach south-eastern United States; New World vultures extend farther north, and hummingbirds, still farther, until it becomes a question what groups are to be considered transitional and what shared, in terms of present distribution. This pattern of transition of families is reinforced and made far more complex by numbers of transitional genera and species.

Among mammals too, there is extensive and complex transition of the existing Nearctic and Neotropical faunas, formed by overlapping of families, genera, and species. The main part of the transition occurs in southern Mexico and Central America, but some Nearctic elements extend for varying distances into South America, and some (but fewer) Neotropical ones extend into parts of temperate North America.

This has been no more than a superficial sketch of the transition of the Nearctic and Neotropical vertebrate faunas. This transition has never been adequately treated in detail by zoogeographers. It has received nothing like the attention given to Wallace's Line and Wallacea, although it is probably equally important.

Transition of Nearctic and Neotropical faunas occurs in Mexico and Central America in all classes of vertebrates, but it is different in the different classes. It is simplest (involves fewest elements), is at the highest level (involves mostly different families), and is confined to the narrowest area in the classes that disperse most slowly. Among strictly freshwater fishes, the transition is formed by few elements; the Nearctic and Neotropical components all belong to different families; and the area of overlap extends only from the Rio Grande to Guatemala. At the other extreme, the transition of Nearctic and Neotropical birds is formed by a great number of elements; most of them are only genera and species, although some different families are involved too; and the area of overlap includes much of North and South America. The complexity, level, and width of the transition in other classes of vertebrates are between these two extremes. All this is as would be expected: transition is proportional to the powers of dispersal of the different animals concerned.

Transition of the temperate North American and tropical South American vertebrate faunas has just been summarized as a complex overlapping in a broad zone, in terms of present distributions, but the transition can be looked at in other ways. An actual boundary, still in terms of present distributions, or either overlapping in a broad zone or crossings of the boundary may be considered in terms of past movements rather than present distributions.

The fauna of Central America is much more Neotropical than Nearctic in all classes of vertebrates, except perhaps in reptiles. This is, presumably, because Central America is tropical. Many of the Neotropical groups extend to the tropical lowlands of Mexico but no farther; it is principally these groups that determine the commonly accepted boundary between the Neotropical and Nearctic Regions, in southern Mexico about at the line between the tropics and the north-temperate zone. On the other hand, the fauna of the tableland of Mexico is mainly Nearctic, and some Neacctic groups reach southern limits in southern Mexico near the northern boundary of the Neotropical groups.

Few strictly fresh-water fishes extend across the boundary line in either direction, and none of them goes far. Of amphibians, a few groups extend across the boundary in reach direction, and for roughly equal distances in each direction, but the number of Nearctic groups extending to. Central but not South America is unexpectedly large. Of birds, there is more northward than southward extension of non-migratory groups, but the difference is partly made up by migrants that breed in the north and winter southward into the edge of the tropics, the boundary into the Neotropics, but few Neotropical ones (except bats) extend far northward.

That different classes of vertebrates seem to differ in direction of transition across the boundary of the Nearctic and Neotropical faunas suggests differences in relative dominance. Fresh-water fishes and amphibians extend across the regional boundary about as much southward as northward, which suggests that the Nearetic and Neotropical faunas of these animals are about equally dominant. Mammals (other than bats) extend more southward than northward; the Nearctic mammal fauna is evidently dominant, perhaps because so many "Nearctic" mammals really represent dominant Megagean groups, while parts of the South American fauna have been isolated through the Tertiary. Of reptiles, too, more probably extend southward (at least to Central America) than northward; this again is probably partly because some "Nearctic" reptiles really represent dominant Megagean groups. Of birds, however, more extend northward than southward; the Neotropical bird fauna seems to be relatively dominant, perhaps because it is a very large fauna and has been less isolated (because birds can fly) than the rest of the vertebrate fauna of South America. It seems, than, that the Nearctic and Neotropical faunas are about equally dominant in their fishes and amphibians; the Nearctic may be dominant in at least some reptiles as well as mammals; and the Neotropical is dominant in birds.

WALLACE'S LINE, WEBER'S LINE, AND WALLACEA

The faunas of the Oriental and Australian Regions are extraordinarily different. What happens where they meet in the Indo-Australian Archipelago has long fascinated zoogeographers. In fact "Wallace's Line," the supposed boundary between the Oriental and Australian faunas, was the focus of generations of zoogeographers after Wallace.

As first drawn by Wallace (1860), the line drawn between Bali and Lombok, between Borneo and Celebes, and between the Philippines and the Sangi and Taland Islands (and the Moluccas) The difference between the faunas of Bli and Lombok, which are separated by a (deep) strait only about 15 miles wide, was especially emphasized. Later authors debated the position of the line, especially the northern part of it. Huxley, for example, who named Wallace's Line, thought it should split the Philippines, putting Palawan in the Orient and the rest of the Philippines in the Australian Region. Still later even the existence of the line was debated-whether there was any definite boundary between the Oriental and Australian faunas. Mayr (1944) outlines the history of the debate and it is not discussed here in details.

Of strictly fresh-water fishes, there is a great fauna in the Orient, and the main part of it reaches Sumatra, Java, and Borneo, but that is the limit of most of it. Of the many strictly fresh-water groups on Borneo, none reaches Celebes except two or three species probably carried by man. Or Java, there is some decrease of the Oriental fish fauna from west to east, and no strictly fresh-water fishes except a few small eyprinids reach the Lesser Sundas, except again certain species probably carried by man. Bali does not have any significant fraction of the Javan fish fauna.

The only strictly fresh-water fishes apparently native on Bali are two or three small cyprinids of the genera Puntius and Rasbora, and both gnera occur also on lombok, and Rasbora extends to Sumbawa too. Secondary-division cyprinodonts and their derivatives do reach Celebes, and the probably salt-tolerant eyprinodont genus Aplochcilus extends also to Lombok and Timor. At the other end of the archipelago, the Australian Region is almost completely without primary-division fishes, and the one or two that are there (the lungfish and osteoglossid) are localized. However, certain small Australian fishes of the atherinid subfamily Melanotaeniinae are supposed to be zoogeographicaly significant. They are derived from marine or salttolerant ancestors, but they are thought to be confined to fresh water now. They occur from the warmer part of Australia to New Guinea, the Aru Islands, and Waigeo (Beaufort 1926) and so are apparently confined to the limits of the Sahul shelf. However, their distribution and salt tolerance are perhaps not yet fully known.

Of amphibians, caecilians are not known east of Java and Borneo (disregarding the Philippines). Of Oriental frogs, the pelobatid Megophrys and the breviciptid Microhyla extend to

Ball; Bufo, to Celebes and to Bali and Lombok; the brevicipitid Kaloula, to Celebes and along the Lesser Sundas to Flores; Rhacophorus, to Celebes and to Timor; and ranids, including Rana in a broad sense, to New Guinea, the Solomons, etc., and northern Australia. Of frogs of the Australian Region, leptodactylids reach New Guinea and the Aru Islands; the brevidpitid subfamily Asterophryinae extends to the Moluccas; Australian forms of Hyla extend in decreasing numbers to the Moluccas, Timor, and the eastern Lesser sundas, to Sumba; and one genus of sphenophryine brevicipitids (Oreophryne) extends from New Guinea to the Moluccas, Celebes (some Philippines), and the Lesser Sundas from Flores to and including Bali. The distribution of genera and especially of species of frogs are really more complex than this summary suggests. A noteworthy detail is that 10 species of frogs are considered the same in Borneo and Celebes, on opposite sides of Wallace's Line, but some of them may have been carried by man. For example, Parker (1934) thinks Kaloula pulchra may have been introduced into Celebes, although another Oriental species of the same genus (K. baleata) is supposedly native on Celebes.

The distribution of reptiles between the Oriental and Australian Regions is too complex to describe in detail. There are also many Oriental groups of reptiles which do not cross Wallace's Line, and many others which extend for varying distances toward the Australian Region but do not reach it. In short, a considerable part, but only part, of the Oriental reptile fauna extends toward Australia, with progressive subtractions increasing with distance from the Orient, but with many groups actually reaching New Guinea and fewer reaching Australia; but the pattern is complicated by shared groups, by discontinuities in some cases, and by genera localized within the transition area. On the other hand, there is comparatively little extension of reptiles of Australian groups toward the Orient. Only a few Australian snakes (elapids) extend west even to the Moluccas. We cant not analyzed the distribution of genera in the widely distributed lizard families Gekkonidae, Agamidae, and Scincidae, but a leafing through of these families, Roooji (1915) suggests that the Australian- New Guinean elements usually do not extend far westward. The gradual change in percentages of western (Oriental) and eastern (Australian) reptiles along the Lesser Sundas etc. to the Kei and Aru Islands is shown in Table 11.5.

Table 11.5

Percentages of Western (Oriental) and Eastern (Australlian) Reptiles along the Lesser Sundas etc. to the Ket and Aru Islands (Aftter Mertens 1934)

	Western %	*Eastern %*
Bali	93.9	6.1
Lombok	83.0	13.0
Sumbawa	87.2	12.8
Flores	78.1	21.9
Alor	75.0	25.0
Wetar	63.2	34.8
Tanimbar	40.6	39.4
Kei	32.5	67.5
Aru	22.2	77.8

The distribution of birds between the Oriental and Australian Regions is even more complex than that of reptiles. There are many shared groups, many transitional ones (families, genera, and species), and many which occur in one region but not the other and which do not enter into the transition. The transition itself is very complex and covers a very wide area, for some Oriental birds extend to New Guinea or northeastern Australia, and some (but fewer) Australian ones extend into the edge of the Oriental Region, across Wallace's Line to give all the details here. Some of them are given by Mayr (1944). Ornithologists have stressed the difference between the birds of Ball and of Lombok. Statistically, there is a change of only 14.5 per cent of the birds from Oriental to Australian types from Bali to Lombok, and almost three-fourths of the birds of Lombok are still Oriental, but the dominant, conspicuous species are said to be mostly Oriental on Bali, mostly Australian on Lombok. The actual percentages of western and eastern birds along the Lesser Sundas from Bali to the Alor Group are given in Table 11.6.

Table 11.6
Percentages of Western and Eastern Birds on Lesser Sunda Islands (after Mayr 1944)

	Western %	*Eastern %*
Bail	87.0	13.0
Lombok	72.5	27.5
Sumbawa	68.0	32.0
Flores	63.0	37.0
Alor	57.5	42.5

Of mammals, many Oriental families, genera, and species reach Borneo and Java, but only a few extend farther east. The Bornean (Oriental) groups of flightless land mammals (other than murid rodents) that reach Celebes are shrews (Crocidura and Suncus), tarsiers, monkeys (Macaca and the endemic genus Cynopithecus), a porcupine (Hystrix), squirrels, viverrids (4 genera, one of which is endemic), pigs (including the endemic genus Babirussa), deer (Cervus), and cattle (the endemic Anoa); and a small elephant occurred on Celebes in the Pleistocene (Hooijer 1951). Of these mammals on Celebes, the following extend still farther east, to some of the Moluccas; shrews, Cynopithecus monkeys (Batjan only, apparently introduced), 2 civets (Viverra tangalunga and Paradoxurus hermaphroditus), the Babirussa (only to Bum), pigs, and deer; but they are apparently not at all or not much differentiated on the Moluccas, and some or all may have been introduced there. Paradoxurus hermaphroditus is recorded even on the Kei and Aru Islands but is presumably introduced there. Java lacks some Oriental mammals that occur on Borneo. This fact was known to Wallace and is shown by comparison of the lists of mammals of Borneo and Java given by Carter, Hill, and Tate (1945) - these authors also give separate lists of the mammals of many other islands in the Indo-Australian Archipelago, although some of the lists are not quite accurate. Nevertheless, Java still has a good mammal fauna. Many groups of mammals that reach Java do not reach Bali: e.g.; hairy hedgehogs (gymnures), flying lemurs, lorises, gibbons, flying squirrels (4 genera), some other genera of rodents, the Asiatic Wild Dog (Cuon), mustelids (weasels, badgers, and otters), the Leopard, a rhinoceros, chevrotains, and probably wild buffalo. Bali does not share the main part of the Javan mammla fauna (cf. Carter, Hill, and Take's lists), mammals that do extend to Bali but not to Lombok include a tree shrew, 2 monkeys, a scaly anteater, 2 squirrels, the Leopard Cat, and the Tiger. Very few flightless land mammals extend east of Bali along the Lesser Sunda: porcupines (Hystrix) extend to Lombok, Sumbawa, and perhaps Flores; and shrews (Crocidura and Suncus), the Crab-eating Monkey, a civet (Paradoxurus hermaphroditus), pigs, and Cervus deer occur on some or all of the Lesser Sundas to Timor. The list of mammals that reach Timor is nearly the same as the list of Oriental mammals that reach the moluccas. It is a question whether some of them are native in either place; in fact there might be some doubt about all of them. Porcupines are good food ("like pork") and are presumably carried about. At least one of the shrews (Suncus) often lives in houses and "is carried about on native boats like the house mouse" (Carter, Hill, and Tate). Tame monkeys and other animals are often carried about by roaming malays (Wallace), and the Crab-eating Monkey in particular is often carried (Wallace 1869). Some civets are carried and sold for their musk and may even be released on islands after their musk is taken (Wallace 1869). Pigs are staple food. And deer are often tamed and petted, esteemed for their flesh, and probably deliberately introduced when remote islands are settled. Some of these mammals on the Moluccas or Lesser Sundas are supposed to be distinguishable subspecies, but there may be a doubt how distinct they are, and a further doubt whether, even if distinct, they need be native. Some mammalogists apparently share these doubts. Laurie and Hill (1954), for example, list endemic subspecies of pigs from Flores and Timor but consider them "feral descendants of pigs carried from island to island by human agency."

Of Australian mammals, few extend much west of New Guinea. Monotremes (spiny anteaters) reach Salawati Island off the Bird's Head. Of marsupials, the Aru Islands have a1 least the following: 3 dasyurids, a bandicoot, severa phalangerids, a Thylogale wallaby, and possibly a tree kangaroo. The Kei Islands have at least a bandicoot, Phalanger and a small flying phalanger

(Petaurus). Thylogale, and possibly a tree kangaroo. Pseudocheirus phalangers reach Salawati, and Dorcopsis wallabies reach Waigeo etc., off the west end of New Guinea, as do Phalanger, Petaurus; and perhaps some other marsupials.

Murid rodents complicate this simple pattern. In derivation they are Oriental elements in the Australian Region but in present distribution they are shared and include both Oriental and Australian groups. The murid subfamily Hydromyinae is almost completely confied to the Australiar Region, extending west only to the Aru and Kei Islands anc Waigeo (Hydromys, Tate 1951), except that 2 doubtfully related genera are in northern Luzon in the Philippines. Rattus is a shared genus, with both Oriental and Australian species groups. The distribution and relationships of other murids between the Oriental and Australian Regions are too complex and in some cases too doubtful to be discussed here, but it is likely that native murids occur on all the habitable islands of the transition area.

Bats are very numerous in the Indo-Australian Archipelago, and the pattern of their distribution is complex. We can not tried to analyze it in detail It is clear from Tate (1946) that many groups are shared; other occur in one region but not the other; many Oriental genera and species extend for varying distances toward Australia; some (fewer) Australian ones extend toward the Orient; and some genera and species are endemic within the transition area.

Of mammals as a whole, it can be said that most of the main Oriental mammal fauna, excepting murid rodents and bats, stops on Borneo and Java; rather small fractions of it reach Celebes and Bali; and little or none of it reaches the Moluccas or the outer Lesser Sundas. The main Australian mammal fauna stops in New Guinea; rather small fractions of it reach the Aru and Kei Islands etc.; a still smaller fraction reaches some Moluccas; and only Phalanger reaches Celebes and Timor. These Oriental and Australian mammals overlap very little. If the Oriental species on the Moluccas and Timor and introduced, the only natural overlap is on Celebes, where two species of Phalanger occur with a small variety of surely native Oriental mammals. The doubtful details are not very important. The important fact is that, excepting murids and bats, the mammals of the Moluccas and outer Lesser Sundas are very few and, for the most part, not much differentiated and probably recent.

The Oriental and Australian vertebrate faunas are, then, separated by a broad zone of subtraction and transition. The subtraction is a very important part of the pattern. The absence of strictly fresh-water fishes and the very poor representation of terrestrial mammals in the transition zone are as significant as the gradual change from Oriental to Australian animals from west to east in other classes.

The limits of this subtraction-transition zone are rather well defined. The western limit is the line between Borneo and Celebes and between Java and the Lesser Sunda Islands This is virtually Wallace's Line, the line which Wallace thought separated the Oriental and Australian faunas but which in fact separates the nearly full-scale Oriental fauna from a strikingly depauperate fauna and the beginning of obvious transition. The only question here is whether Bali should go with Java or with the other Lesser Sundas, and this is perhaps a matter of preference. We may follow the custom and pul Bali with Java in the Oriental Region, in spite of the fact that the vertebrate fauna of Bali is unbalanced and limited, especially by lack of most fresh-water fishes and of many mammals.

The eastern limit of the subtraction-transition zone lies jut west of Australia and New Guinea but includes certain small, closely associated islands: the Aru (and perhaps the Kei) Islands, and Salawati, Batanta, Waigeo (and perhaps Misol) just west of the Bird's Head of New Guinea. The islands not in parentheses have an almost pure New Guinean fauna, which is depauperate, but perhaps only in proportion to the size and nature of the islands. The Kei Islands and Misol lack some significant groups which some of the other listed islands have, including melanotaeniine fishes and certain mammals.

Between these limits, the vertebrate fauna changes progressively from west to east, from predominantly Oriental to predominaauntly Australian, although it is still not possible to give an exact description of the whole transition. The fauna of Celebes is at least three-fourths Oriental (Mayr 1944), from authors Oriental elements, though reduced, are apparently still in the majority in the (more depauperate) faunas of the Talaud and Sula Islands. But on Buru, Australian (New Guinean) elements are in the majority, and they become overwhelmingly so on Cream and the northern Moluccas. Along the line of the Lesser Sundas, the transtion is more gradual and better documented. Oriental elements comprise something like 90 per cent of the vertebrate fauna of Bali; the proportion falls by steps to something like 60 per cent or 70 per cent on the Alor Group; and Oriental elements are still in the majority on Timor and even on the Tanimbar Islands, or at least on the western ones, although the fauna of these islands is very depauperate in some groups. On the basis of these facts, a line can be drawn which separates the islands with a majority of Oriental animals from those with a majority of Australian ones. This is the line of faunal balance, or Weber's Line. It is discussed in more detail by Mayr (1944), who notes that there is still difficulty in fixing the southern end of it. Mayr notes that Weber's Line is nearer the Australian than the Oriental side of the transition zone, which is another way of saying is more extension of Oriental than of Australian groups into the transition area.

In bounding the Oriental and Australian Regions, zoogeographers may follow either of two reasonable courses. The eastern boundary of the Oriental Region may be drawn at or near Wallace's Line, and the western boundary of the Australian Region may be drawn just west of New Guinea (to include certain-small! islands named above);

the intervening area may then be considered a separate subtraction-transition area, not part of either region. This area has been named "Wallacea" (by Dickerson et al. 1928) and this is an appropriate and useful term in any case. The other course is to draw a common boundary between the Oriental and Australian Regions along Weber's Line or near it. Both these courses have advantages and dis-advantages. But it perhaps appears that the recognition of a subtraction-transition area- "Wallacea", is more likely to make the situation clear in present context, i.e. from zoogeographical point of view.

12

Biomes and Biotic Regions Ecosystems

INTRODUCTION

1. The Biomes

After knowing about the concept of the biome, it may be defined, in broad terms, as a major terrestrial community of plant and animal life. "Regional climates interact with regional biota and substrate," says Odum, "to produce large, easily recognizable community units called biomes." In other words a biome is an area possessing particular climatic conditions and whose limits are largely controlled on land by climate and which is distinguished by the dominance of certain, and usually distinctive, species of plants and animals. The biome is the largest community unit on land which can be conveniently recognized and the various biomes correspond in a close way with the geographer's major vegetation regions, although it should be emphasized that the biome comprises animal as well as plant life. Here, it should be noted, we are concerned only with the land biomes, although and this should not be forgotten, there are also the biomes o the sea and the shore.

Despite the different pathways of plant and anima evolution within the various terrestrial and aquatic environments, the vegetational and faunal patterns over the surface of the earth can be related approximately to present-day climates (Hold ridge et a!., 1967, 1971). These climatic influences within each major biogeographical zone can be summarized in diagrammatic form, following the scheme outlined in Walter and Leith (1967) or Walter et al. (1975).

The lack of correspondence between regional climate and the contemporary distributions of plants, animals and soils stems from several sources. Besides soil formations significant basic role it is also observed that there may be local factors which override the regional climate. At a local scale there are many such factors which result in divergences from the regional pattern and shows strong resemblances between different geographical sectors in each biome. Perhaps these partly result from the influence of a similar environment but in any case are manifest in convergent evolution.

The extent and productivity of these divisions provides a rapid indication of their importance as a resource in the biosphere and an attempt is made in this chapter to describe and interpret the principal features to each biome, to give an idea of the major environmental controls and to consider the impact of man upon their character and development potential.

The distribution of the natural vegetation of the Earth's surface, in its broad outlines, corresponds closely with the biomes of the ecologist. In a particular vegetation formation the life-form of the climatic climax vegetation is uniform; i.e. in the cold coniferous forests the climatic climax vegetation is forest, even though the dominant species of trees may very between one part of the biome and another. There are, however, two points which need emphasizing: first, although a given biome may be of great areal extent and relatively uniform in its climatic climax vegetation (which is the key to its recognition), it also includes the entire complex of serial or developmental stages and edaphic climaxes, and, second, although the biomes are largely complete communities they are not always nor necessarily sharply defined and extensive ecotones may link one biome with another.

The biome, the, is a major biotic zone or life zone, a community unit which comprises animals and plants in association. The biome provides the most convenient unit for the study of ecological relationships.

Table 12.1
Major Subdivisions of the Biosphere based on Climatic Zonation

A.	Tundra	– Arctic	
	Taiga	– Alpine	
B.	Temperate	– Boreal Forest	– North American and Asiatic formations
			– Montane forest
		– Deciduous Forest	– North American and European formations
		– Grasslands	– Soviet steppe and North American prairie
			– Pampa, veld and Australasian grasslands
		– Mediterranean (woodland)	– Northern and Southern Hemisphere
WARM TEMPERATE			
C.	Tropical	– Forest	– Evergreen rainforest
		– Secondary forest	
		– Semi-evergreen and	
		– Semi-deciduous forest	
		– Montane forest	
		– Swamps and marshes	
		– Savanna	– Savanna woodland
			– Woody grasslands
		– Deserts and Arid	– Microphyllous forest and grassland
			– Semi-desert scrub
			– Desert
D	Aquatic	– Marine Fresh water	– River
			– Lakes

Let us now turn our attention to each of the land biomes and attempt to elicit and to show the ecological relationships which exist in each. We shall be concerned primarily with the interrelations and interactions between climate, soil, vegetation and animal, including human, life to much extent.

THE TUNDRA

In the northern hemisphere the tundra biome is circumpolar and almost continuous. In North America it stretches from Alaska to Labrador and in continued in the southern fringe of Greenland. In Eurasia it stretches from northern Scandinavia to the easternmost peninsula of Siberia. A corresponding biome can scarcely be said to exist in the southern hemisphere since in those latitudes where the climatic conditions would give rise to tundra there is the Southern Ocean, however, something approximating to tundra occurs in small areas on Tierra del Fuego, in Graham Land and in some of the sub-Antarctic islands. The tundra of the northern hemisphere is relatively the most continuous rather than southern hemisphere, and in many ways the most sharply defined, of all the biomes.

Although there are areas of mountain and highland in the tundra, its dominant physiographic character is that of a flat of gently undulating plan with frequent lakes and bogs occupying depressions in the surface. The climate of the tundra is determined by the 'annual cycle of solar radiation'. During the long winter the tundra lands are frost-bound for at least more than six months. Places north of the Arctic Circle have several weeks or even months of continual darkness, and this absence of solar energy, together with the loss of heat from the ground and the high pressure which obtains, results in a very cold and relatively dry climate.

Precipitation is low and much of it falls in the form of snow. Climatic conditions in winter are fairly stable, though there may be some buzzards. In the short summer, the long days help to make up for the low angle of the sun but the air temperatures seldom exceed 15.5°C (60° F). Most of the precipitation comes in summer when the weather is often unsettled and widely. The total annual precipitation is light or moderate, often under 10 inches (254 mm).

The soil and the sub-soil are permanently frozen in winter, but in the brief summer the surface thaws out though the sub-soil remains frozen where, as in northern Asia and Canada, great rivers flow pole wards, extensive flooding occurs during the summer thaw.

Clearly, the climatic conditions are not conducive to vegetation growth. From the point of view of plant life the tundra is a land of physiological drought; in other words, plants are starved of moisture because water is in the unassimilable form of ice. During the long winter period of limited light, low temperature and physiological drought, plants must live off this stored food energy. Few species are able to tolerate these exacting conditions and the tundra flora is poor in plant species and totals only a few hundred. Characteristically the tundra vegetation is one of low, herbaceous, perennial plants. The herbaceous character of these perennials also gives a measure of protection, for the plant buds which occur under the soil or near the surface can be protected by the winter snow occur from the wind.

The vegetation of the tundra varies from one locality to another, often within very short distances, grasses and sedges tend to dominate the summer landscape but there are extensive spreads of lichens and mosses. Herbaceous plants such as bilberry, cranberry, yellow cloudberry and saxifrages, grow during the summer. Few trees grow, but here and there where there is shelter, as in a hollow or in the lee of a rock, e.g. stunted dwarf willows, alders and birches are found which grow along the ground rather than upwards and they seldom grow more than a few inches high. Most of the plants show xerophytic characteristics: plant stems are short, while leaves are small, often of leathery texture and sometimes bearing fine hairs or having their edges roiled inwards.

In spite of the rigours of environment, animal life is generally much more plentiful in the tundra than is commonly believed, although the number of species is somewhat limited. There is, however, a great contrast between the almost teeming life of the brief summer season and its sparsity in winter. These factors help to explain the their large numbers in summer; (i) the prolific marine life which supports both land and water creatures, (ii) the pole ward migration of many land animals from the taiga and (iii) migratory birds which flock to the summer tundra.

Seasonal migration is one of the outstanding features of tundra life. Vast numbers of migratory birds, especially waterfowl and shorebirds, throng the tundra in summer, when they lay their eggs and raise their young. They are able to take advantage of the long summer days which permit almost round-the-clock food-gathering. Many animals, but notably the caribou (and its ecological equivalent, the reindeer of Eurasia), migrate from the shelter of the forest into the tundra for the summer season. In a sense, most of the animals, and particularly the herbivores, are migratory since the tundra vegetation has a low productivity such as caribou, reindeer, musk oxen, lemmings and the arctic hare which subsist on lichen, grasses of the tundra, remaining there the whole year round, e.g. the musk-ox, arctic hare, arctic fox, lemming and ptarmigan. The ptarmigan is one of the few resident birds in the tundra and, along with the arctic hare and the arctic fox, it changes its summer colouring to white in winter.

Some of the tundra animals are of special interest. The musk-ox (Obvos moschatus), so called because it sometimes emits a musk-like odour, is an arctic American bovine ruminant which lives largely off lichen. It has a long, brown haired shaggy coat and the male carries wide, flattened horns

The caribou is a variety of reindeer confined to North America; unlike its Eurasian counterpart it has never been domesticated. Formerly, the caribou roamed the barren lands in vast herds, thousands strong, but their numbers have beer greatly depleted. Farely Mowat painted a vivid picture of the caribou and drew attention to the strange and incomprehensible temporary retreat back to the forest edge in August.

Interesting, too, are the lemmings (Lemmus lemmus) small rodents which feed on grasses, lichens and the shoots of dwarf birch. They breed fairly, rapidly and after about three years; when they have multiplied their numbers exceedingly they begin an extraordinary migration to the coast. Armies of these restless creatures, traveling only by night, and followed by a host of predators, make for the sea; those that reach the water plunge in and swim until they are exhausted and die.

The tundra has a prolific inset life: though the species of insects are few, their populations are beyond belief and in the height of the season highly favourable haunts for their propagation. The bogs and marshes provide highly favourable haunts for their propagation. The biting Diptera, such as mosquitoes and black flies, are a particular pest. It is partly because of this rich insect life that migratory birds are attracted to the tundra lands in summer.

Arctic waters are rich in marine life. Here we find an interesting food chain: the wealth of diatoms and other floating microscopic plants provide food for zooplankton, or microscopic animals; the plankton support an abundant crustacean life which provides food for fish; fish, in turn, support marine mammals such as the seal and walrus; and these are preyed upon by the polar bear as that, "Some such as gulls and foxes, migrate to the seashores, where they become commensal with the seal-hunting polar bears."

The tundra biome has proved to be inhospitable and unproductive to man. In North America, a few Eskimo have managed to make out a precarious existence and most of them, no doubt, have tended to depend upon marine ecosystems which, by and large, are more productive than their terrestrial counterparts. In Eurasia, the Lapps and other groups have based their existence upon the domestication of the migratory reindeer (Rangifer tarrandus) which supplies clothing, meat and milk. Man, however, so far, has had little effect upon the tundra lands have few people, but certain stretches of coast and some river banks have permanent settlements where fishermen and hunters and trappers live.

THE TAIGA

In the northern hemisphere the tundra gradually gives way to coniferous forest which extends in a broad belt across North America and Eurasia. This forms the taiga biome. With the boreal coniferous forest we may link the montane coniferous forest. The biome is confined almost exclusively to the northern hemisphere; only in the South Island of New Zealand is there a forest which bears some similarity with it. The lands of the boreal forest have a cold continental type of climate. Summers are short with long days; winters the reverse. Only four to five months have temperatures higher than 6°C (43°F), the temperature below which plant life cannot grow. In summer, days may be warm, occasionally very warm, especially in interior locations, but winters are long and cold with temperatures below freezing. Precipitation is generally scanty to moderate (except in west-coast areas), usually between 12 and 30 inches (304.8-762 mm), and occurs chiefly in summer. In winter the ground is snow-covered. Winter weather is typically cold, crisp and calm with occasional blizzards; summers are usually warm and sunny and pleasant with convectional showers.

The needle-leaved, cone-bearing evergreen is the identifying life form. Millions and millions of tightly packed conifers cover vast areas of Eurasia and North America. These boreal forests form one of the outstanding natural features of the Earth's surface and they are vast and impressive. The dominant species are mostly spruces but they are often associated with pines and firs. On the polar margins of the biome, the trees are small and stunted and more widely spaced, and between them there is a ground layer of tundra-type plants. On the southern margins of the boreal forest, where the climate is often less harsh and wetter, conifers may be mixed with deciduous trees. The trees show adaptations to cold, snow and wind through physiological changes, their compact form, conical shape, needle leaves, downward-bending branches and cones instead of fruit. Severe frost may, and sometimes does, damage trees, and occasionally trees may be seen that have been split and killed by frost action, but mostly the trees tolerate extremely keen frosts and the spruce, for example, can tolerate January temperatures of - 40°C (-40°F). The needle-shaped posses thick cuticles, have a restricted evaporation surface, and, when-winter comes, close their stomata. The conical shape and bending branches enable the trees to shed their burden of snow. In a variety of ways, therefore, the coniferous trees show a wonderful adaptation to the harsh environment in which they grow.

The wet temperate coniferous forests of the northwestern Pacific coast of North America and the montane coniferous forest form, in many ways, separate from terrestrial ecosystem types. The montane coniferous forests are frequently equator ward extensions, along meridional mountain systems, of the northern forests. The climate under which such montane coniferous forests grow, however, is very variable, the conditions ranging from wet, windy and frosty to very warm and relatively dry. At higher elevations the wind-beaten trees become stunted, twisted and flagged and these sub-alpine forests show a resemblance to the dwarfed trees of the timberline at the edge of the tundra. The rain forests of north-western North America are distinguished and dominated by species of giant conifers such as the Douglas fir, redwood, Sitka spruce, western hemlock and arbor-vitae. The mild, very wet conditions clearly assist the conifers to attain their gigantic dimensions.

Sphagnum moss and edges grow around the edges of the ponds and lakes and gradually they fill up with dead and decaying organic matter to form peat bogs or muskegs as they are termed in North America. In these localized, specialized environments the vegetation is different from that growing on the surrounding pod sol soils; e.g. herbaceous plants such as pitcher plants and sundews and moisture-loving conifers such as the black spruce grow in the muskegs of North America.

Typical of the boreal forest is the pod sol soil. The plant litter-needles, cones, twigs- forms a thick layer of vegetable material which breaks down only slowly owing to the poverty of soil fauna and the low temperatures of the short, rather cool summers, to form a strongly acid more type of humus. Strong leaching gives these soils an ash-grey A horizon, but lower down they become iron-stained and brown, and a hardpan may develop which militates against drainage of the soil and which may prevent root penetration of the trees. The process by which organic acids remove the iron compounds from the upper to the lower horizon is termed, as we have already noted, podsolisation, and since podsolisation occurs only under the acid more type of humus the formation of pod sol soil is to a very large extent the, and is consequence of the type of vegetation; Billings comments that "the true podsol and the boreal forest are almost inseparable." Many areas within the biome have peaty soils. Mosses and sedges growing in the moist depressions eventually form peat bogs whose slowly decaying organic matter produces deep layers of peat. The formation of peat has an interesting physiographic side-effect: since it acts as a good insulator, it prevents the summer thaw.

Differences in aspects, forest structure and tree type vary little between the North American and Eurasian formations, although the species differ. Animal life in both formations shows close similarities although there are greater differences between the animals than there are between the plants. Animals, as in the tundra, show a pronounced seasonal periodicity and populations have cyclical oscillations in their numbers. For example, many birds, caribou and foxes migrate according to the season and seek the shelter of the forest in winter, while animals such as the lynx, snowshoe hare and fox show phases of abundance and decline in numbers.

Although the taiga winter is neither so severe nor so prolonged as that of the tundra, it is very cold and snow lies heavier upon the ground. Many creatures escape the problems of winter by hibernating; others, such as bears, though not entirely dormant, sleep for long periods. Birds tend to migrate. Many animals, particularly the deer and fur-bearing creatures, remain active the whole year round. Many of the larger mammals renew their fur early in winter and this affords a measure of protection against the cold. Thus, in general, the wildlife of the taiga meets the conditions of winter in much the same way as does that of the neighbouring tundra. The taiga has a rich and varied wildlife, but this is more particularly apparent in summer. "The surplus of food supplied by the wood, leaves, browse and seeds of the trees, and by the herbaceous plants that live in the deep shade of its forest floor, supports a notable assemblage of animals strictly associated with the plant-defined biome."

Of the larger herbivorous vertebrates, the moose is the most conspicuous. The moose (Alces alces) is the largest of the living species of deer. In Eurasia it is known as the elk. These handsome creatures, having a height of around 6 feet (1-8 m) at the shoulders, are now few in numbers and are now everywhere protected by law. They feed on willows, broadleaved herbs and water plants. In the mating season the males fight with great ferocity, often to the death. In addition to the caribou of the tundra which winters in the forest, there is the forest caribou which lives within the forest all the year round. Both the moose and caribou have long legs which help them to wade about in the snow. Another notable large animal is the bear, an omnivorous eater, of which there are various species; the brown bear is found in both North America and Eurasia but the grizzly and black bears are natives only of North America. The most important predators are the wolf, fox and lynx. There are numerous rodents and lagomorphs. Especially abundant and characteristic, however, are the fur-bearing members of the family *Mustelidae,* of which there are six sub-families. Four of these sub-families occur in the taiga, represented by, respectively, the weasels, bedgers, skumks and otters. Most of these animals depend very largely for their food supplies on water habitats; hence they tend to frequent the bogs and marshes on the banks or rivers and lakes.

As in the tudra, inserts life is prolific in summertime. The swarms of insects attract many birds of migratory character. The marshes, swamps and muskegs form ideal breeding grounds for the swamps of insects which plague the life of man and beast in summer. Some of the insects attack the coniferous trees: they are subject to "outbreaks of bark beetles and defoliating insects (sawflies, budworms, etc.), especially where stands have but hardly one or two dominant species.

The taiga areas have a very low density of population and settlement is essentially sporadic. Along the southern margins of the forest human settlement has long taken place. But even where the climate is suitable for hardy crops, such as rye, potatoes and fodder-grasses, the acid podsols are of limited agricultural value and their infertility severely restricts tillage. In the early days hunting and trapping were almost the only occupations of the forest lands, and for many centuries the animal resources were of most economic consequence. Although for-bearing animals are to be found in other biomes, the boreal forest is the home of the richest fur-bearing fauna in the world. The forests provide extensive habitats offering favourable combinations of climate, vegetation and water features, the last yielding the chief source of food supplies for many of the species.

Creatures such as the badger, beaver, ermine, fox, marten, mink, muskrat, otter, sable, squirrel and wolverine provide the mos1 coveted pelts. Intensive trapping in many of the more accessible areas has led to the depletion of many of the fur-bearing animals, and this fact, together with the high prices fetched by furs, has led to the development of commercial fur-farming. At present the greatest economic value of the coniferous forest lands lies in their timber resources, especially lumber and wool-pulp for which in recent times there has been an almost insatiable demand.

TEMPERATE DECIDUOUS FOREST

The temperate biomes lie in mid-latitudes and are to be found on both the western and the eastern margins of the continental land masses, but those on the western sides occur in the higher mid-latitudes (approximately between 45° and 60°) and those on the eastern in low mid-latitudes (approximately between the tropics and 50°). On the western sides of continents the regions lie in the track of westerly winds and depressions which bring maritime influences and rain at all seasons. Warm ocean drifts move towards these regions, bathing the coasts in warm water and in winter cold as well as maintaining ice-free ports. Winters are quite warm (usually around 4°C (40°F) in coastal areas) and summers cool (around 160C (600F) near to the sea) with only moderate ranges of temperature. Winters are cool enough, with occasional frosts, to halt plant growth and to cause trees to have a deciduous habit. The plentiful but usually gentle rainfall, anything from about 20 inches (508 mm) in the drier rain-shadow areas to over 100 inches (2,540 mm) in exposed situations, is well distributed seasonally. Strong winds plentiful cloud, and frequent fog and mist are characteristic of the winter half of the year. On the eastern sides of the continents, more especially in the northern hemispher, the climatic conditions are more extreme, particularly in the areas in higher latitudes. Winters, as in northern China, can be very cold with keen frosts and snowfalls, sometimes of a heavy character, occurring; on the other hand summers are very warm and humid. Monsoonal influences tend to occur and result in moderate to heavy rainfall, around 40 to 60 inches (1,016 to 1,524 mm).

The mid-latitude deciduous forest biomes are found in both hemispheres but they are much more extensive in the northern. The chief regions in the northern hemisphere are the eastern United States, Western Europe and eastern Asia (Manchuria, Korea, northern and central China and Japan); in the southern hemisphere there is a small area of somewhat similar forest in southern Chile and comparable forests in south-eastern Australia and Tasmania and in New Zealand.

The natural vegetation is deciduous forest, except where altitude or soil conditions promote either coniferous forest or heath and moorland. The trees have an abundant foliage of broad leaves which they shed in autumn, providing an abundance of leaf litter which decomposes to give plentiful humus for the soil. The natural forest, however, is layered, so that in addition to the forest trees the biome possesses shrubs of both a deciduous and evergreen kind, many herbaceous plants and ferns and mosses at ground level. In general terms, the deciduous forest is fairly productive. The temperate rain forests, which may be thought of as a variety within this type (unless the forests are essentially coniferous, as in north-western North America) are much more luxuriant and therefore more productive. Billing divided into three parts, viz. the eastern North American, Western European and East Asian. The European segment was more drastically curtailed than the other two, with the result that today the deciduous forest of Europe is somewhat poorer floristically.[9] These three formations and their differences have already been described The forests of Europe and China were drastically modified by man many centuries ago; in most of western Europe the forest cover was cleared and replaced by meadow am cultivated land and likewise in China with the growth o population and the need for food and fuel and building material, the forest was destroyed and replaced by cropland In North America it was otherwise: the native Indians had no a highly developed culture and neither were their number; great; hence the forests remained more or less intact until the arrival of Europeans. The economy of the Indian tribe; was based upon the forest ecosystem, i.e. the vegetabh products which they gathered and the animal life for which they hunted and fished.

Because of the relatively high productivity of this deciduous forest, there was, originally, a great variety o consumers existing in appreciable numbers. Among the larger mammals there were carnivores and herbivores. Deer bears, oxen, wolves, foxes, pigs, wild cats and smaller creatures were common in Europe; deer, black bears panthers, red foxes, opossums, raccons and grey squirrel; frequented the American forests. Insect life was plentiful and as a consequence, there were many insectivorous birds Europe had many birds of prey such as eagles, hawks am owls, and America had wild turkeys. Many of the birds were migratory, leaving the forest during the lean season. Man animals gathered and stored food for winter use and some o the mammals hibernated. Amphibians and reptiles were once fairly common, the latter hibernating in winter. Streams am lakes were rich in fish. wild-life in eastern Asia, apart from birds and rodents is rather rare nowadays.

The deciduous forest biomes in the southern hemisphere are neither so extensive nor so modified as the regions i the northern hemisphere. The forest in southern Chile consist very largely of beeches belonging to the genus Nothogaus most of which are evergreen except for one or two species

The forests of comparable areas in Australia and New Zealand have a unique plant life and animal life. Australia has few mammals, and no mammals or reptiles existed in the original forest of New Zealand. In these lands marsupial fauna and flightless birds take over the niches filled in the other biomes by placental mammals.

The deciduous forest biomes have been altered by man to a greater extent than any other biomes, e. g. the "Mediterranean" regions. In Eurasia the biomes early became the targets of human settlement and here civilization blossomed and population accrued with the result that the native vegetation and animal life were displaced wholesale and today man-made ecosystems replace natural ecosystems. In most of Western Europe the forest cover has long since been of the mixed type, but because of the cool, moist conditions the region is especially suited to dairying, and it has become the world's premier dairying region. The grey-brown forest soils which develop under deciduous forest, though podsolised, are less acidic and less leached than true podsols and provide reasonably fertile soils. They are used for rotation farming, which keeps them in good condition, the presence of plentiful coal deposits in Western Europe, together with the fact that the Industrial Revolution had its origin there, led to the large-scale development of mining, manufacture and commerce and this, in turn, led to a rapid growth in population and urbanism. A roughly comparable development occurred in the eastern United States. The Chinese area appears to be following suit. But none of the other regions has become developed to anything like the same extent and the southern hemisphere regions are in the early stages of development, with New Zealand, Tasmania and southern Chile still having primarily an agro-forestal economy.

TEMPERATE GRASSLANDS

Mid-latitudes, and typically in mid-continental regions, lie the temperate grassland biomes They cover extensive areas, especially in the northern hemisphere, and they are of great importance from the human point of view. The principal temperate grassland areas in the northern hemisphere are the Great Plains regions of North America, the steppe belt of Eurasia and the Plains o Manchuria; in the southern hemisphere there are also three areas, the pampas of Argentina-Uruguay, the veld of South Africa and the interior plains of the Murray-Darling Basin ii Australia.

The temperate grasslands lie, typically, in mid continental areas between approximately 30° and 50° N. in the northern hemisphere but in rather lower latitudes in the southern hemisphere. In the northern hemisphere the temperate grasslands have strong seasonal temperature contrasts with cold winters (several months are usually below freezing) and hot summers. Winters are much less severe in the southern hemisphere and the range of temperature is greatly reduced; these more tolerable conditions are due to the narrower width of the southern continents in temperate latitudes and to the fact that maritime influences are nowhere completely absent. Characteristically, the temperate grasslands have a low total precipitation, about 15 to 2C inches (381-508 mm). The exception to the general rule is the humid pampa of Argentina, where the rainfall ii appreciably greater and in coastal areas may be as high as 40 inches (1,016 mm). Rain, mainly of the convectional type comes in late spring and early summer; there is occasional light snow in the northern hemisphere.

Topographically, these grasslands are level or gentle rolling plains they are grass covered because of the lone period of winter frost, the low rainfall and the high rate of evaporation in summer which are hostile to tree growth. Firing may have extended the grassland at the expense of woodland the nature of the grass cover varies: in the moister areas tall grasses, sometimes standing over 6 feet (1.8 m) high may occur; in the drier areas the grass is short and sparse and grows in clumps. Generally speaking, these grasslands are lands of vast, unbroken horizons, uniform and monotonous in aspect, particularly in late summer when the ground is baked hard, the grass is withered and tawny in colour, and the air is dusty. In spring they are more attractive, for at that time the grass is green and there are innumerable gaily coloured flowers.

In their original natural state the temperate grasslands supported a rich and varied fauna. Animals were mostly grazers, first-order consumers, but there were always some predators. Large grazing herbivores were conspicuous, as the following table 12.2 shows:

Table 12.2

North America	*Eurasia*	*South Africa*	*Australia*
Bison	Wild horse	Antelope	-
Kangaroo			
Pronghorn	Wild ass	Zebra	
	Saga antelope	Gnu	

The dominant herbivore of the Noth American prairie was for many centuries the bison (Sison bison) incorrectly termed the 'buffalo'. Great herds of the animals evolved as an essential element of the biome, thriving on the rich summer herbage. The bioson therefore had a very wide range. The animals relied on their size, strength and numbers of their herds for protection against attacks of wolves, but were an easy prey for Indian hunting tribes whose culture they supported.

Aggregation into herds was characteristic-witness the vast herds of bison of the North American prairies- and in the open type of habitat which the grasslands provided this life hait provided some measure of protection against natural predators. In most of the grassland areas today the native herbivores have been displaced and replaced by domesticated herbivores such as cattle and sheep.

Most of the larger native animals also had a fleetness of foot which, again, may be looked upon as a protective device. Many of the smaller animals were burrowing creatures, able to find refuge underground, e.g. the ground squirrels, prairie dogs and gophers of North America; these lived largely off the grass seeds that were available. In North America the chief predators were the wolf, fox, coyote and panther : all of these, except for the coyote, have been eliminated by man. Although very much less conspicuous than the mammals, many kinds of insects exist and some of these, such as grass-hoppers, are especially significant because of their numbers. Many insectivorous birds occur, but these tend to be migratory, moving away when, at the end of the summer season, the insect life dies off. Some avifauna are see-eating and others, such as hawks and owls, prey upon small rodents.

1. The North American Prairie

In North America, temperate grassland originally covered much of the interior lowland between the Rocky mountain edge and the Eastern Deciduous Forest, forming natural pririe occupying a plateau; this sloped eastwards from an elevation of about 1670m near the mountains to about 152m in the Central Lowlands. Westwards of this main area grassland occurs in the montane plains and plateaux of Canada and the USA, such as the Central Valley of California.

In the main pririe region the climate is continental with hot summers and cold winters; rainfall is heaviest in summers and varies from 10150mm in the East to less than 400mm in the West. Effective precipitation diminishes to the South as evaporation increases with the higher summer temperatures. The entire region is subject to periodic droughts, particularly in the Great Plains where rainfall is marginal.

The pririe consists of three main types of grassland associations distinguished by the height of the dominant species, manely the tall, the mixed and the short-grass porairie; they form North to South belts and are -the counterpart of the similar zones of the USSR steppes, but locally a mixture of the three types may occur consisting of tall grasses and the shorter grasses in moist lowlands and valleys and the shorter grasses on drier elevated sites. Trees are mainly confined to watercourses.

The general unity of the grassland climax is indicated by the large number of grass genera that are dominant in almost the whole floristic province, accompanied by many species of forbs, which like the grasses afford valuable grazing for animals.

The tall grass prairie lies farthest east of the these belts, between the deciduous forest of the Central Lowland and the mixed grass prairie. This is an area of transition between grassland and forest represented by a mosaic of bluestem grasses (Andropogon-Panicum-Sorghassum spp.) and scattered islands of oak-hickory woodland (Quercus-Carya spp.) the latter often on hillsides. The tall grass species attain a height of 1.5 to 2.4 m. In Canada, tall grasses formerly occupied the Red River region of Manitoba, now a rich farming region; here the grassland was separated from the northern forest by a type of wooded prairie, the Parkland or Grove belt.

The mixed prairie is the most characteristic vegetation of the Great Plains of the USA. From Canada it forms a broad belt from the Dakotas southwards to Texas, westwards of the tall grass prairie. The vegetation is composed of middle height and short grass species but four major mid-grasses are present almost throughout: needle-and-thread (Stipa comnata), sand dropseed (Sporobolus cryptandrus), western wheat-grass (Agrophyron smithii) and Junegrass (Koeleria cristata); all these with a height range of 0.6 to 1.2 m. Short grass species include blue grama

(Bouteloua gracilis) and buffalo grass (Buchloe dactyloides). Overgrazing tends to promote the spread of the shorter grasses; in the Texas prairie these are accompanied by desert shrubs such as mesquite (Prosopis).

The short grass prairie occupies the western limits of the Great Plains, extending westwards from the mixed prairie to the montane forests of the Rocky Mountains. Here the grasses are less than 60 cm tall and compose a grama-buffalo grass (Bouteloua-Buchloe) association, accompanied in some areas by mesquite and succulent xerophytes such as cactus (Opuntia). The short grass prairie coincides with the driest climate (only 400 mm y^{-1} or less rain) but is regarded as a disclimax or disturbance climax, resulting from heavy grazing of the taller grasses.

The prairie zones are all represented in Canda, where the tall grasses of the Red River region were succeeded westwards by the mixed grasses of Manitoba and Alberta and the short grasses in the semi-arid parts of these provinces.

The temperate grassland are not only of great economic importance at the present day but of great interest since they present a sequence of evolutionary development in which the natural ecosystems have been largely replaced by man-made ecosystems. Five phases are distinguishable:

1. Originally these grasslands were regions inhabited by nomads, either nomadic hunters, such as the Plains Indians of North America who followed and killed the bison, or by nomadic pastoralists, such as the Kirghiz of the Asiatic steppe who reared animals.
2. The second phase led to the opening up of these grasslands by European peoples who developed large-scale cattle-ranching and sheep-farming, in the earlier days to provide hides and wool but subsequently to produce meat as well.
3. In the more moist and fertile areas, where rich blak prairie soils or chernozems were found, animal raising was displaced by large-scale grain farming, animal farming being relegated to the drier areas of the grasslands.

4. In due course, partly to maintain soil fertility and partly because of economic considerations, the extensive cultivation of cereals was replaced in some areas by farming of a more mixed type in which a wider variety of crops come to be integrated with animal industry.
5. Industrialization is beginning to invade these areas, which hitherto were essentially concerned with primary activities.

Not all the temperate grassland regions have passed through, nor will necessarily pass through, these stages of development.

2. Soviet Steppes

In eastern Europe and western Siberia, the Russian plain, with it uniformity of relief and geology, exhibits clearly the relationship between climate, vegetation and soils From the cool, humid forested areas in the North towards the warmer and drier South and South-East there is a gradual transition of climatic characteristics reflected in parallel zones of soil and vegetation.

The forest region is separated from the steppe grassland by a transitional belt, the forest-steppe, where tracts of woodland alternate with open steppe. Most of the steppe areas and much of the forested area have now been cleared and cultivated, hence the landscape consists of ploughed fields alternating with woodland. The forest-steppe and steppe together occupy more than 260 million hectares within the USSR, or approximately 12 per cent of the total land area and their very productive soils sustain the greater part of the Union's cereal crop.

The tracts of forest of the forest steppe consist of oaks, limes, elms and maple, in Europe, but in Siberia where climatic conditions are more severe, arboreal vegetation is represented by birch with an admixture of aspen and willow. The intervening open areas were formerly covered with a varie grassy vegetation, with many dicotyledons, and hence called meadow-steppes. In these meadow-steppes the fescues (Festuca) and the feather grasses (Stipa) with Koeleria are among the commonest genera.

The higher precipitation of the forest-steppe (500-600 mm)

compared with the open steppe to the South (400-500 mm), together with the lower evaporation of the forest-steppe, has led to a process of slow advance of trees on to the steppe. Although isolated trees cannot compete with grasses in the competition for moisture, along the edge of a belt of woodland next to open steppe, an accumulation of snow occurs, blown from the open country, giving rise to increased reserves of soil moisture along the forest edge and creating more favourable conditions for tree growth. The forest-steppe is therefore the product of a long-continued historical process of mutual encroachment of grassy and arbofeal vegetation.

Each of these types of vegetation is associated with a distinctive kind of soil. The development of woodland modified the typical chernozem of grassland, because trees deposit a different type of litter and also produce moister soil conditions by reducing wind speed and hence evaporation. The result is the formation of a slightly leached profile represented by such soils as the grey forest soils or by the degraded chernozems. Such podzolized soils in the steppe area are very common beneath the wooded belts situated in topographic depressions on the steppe or in the steppe-sided river valleys.

Conditions in the Siberian forest-steppe resemble those in eastern Europe : the wooded steppe there is, however, a transitional zone between the coniferous arboreal forest and the open steppe, with birch and aspen woods having invaded and consolidated themselves in small, well-moistened depressions. Here, the dry continental climate, level relief, and often the presence of saline groundwater have favoured the development of Stalinization of soils and many saline lakes and swampy depressions occur with a halophytic type of vegetation.

The steppes are one of the most striking topographic features of the USSR. They form a broad, rolling plateau, treeless except for patches or ribbons of woodland, mainly situated along the deep river valleys. In its uncultivated condition, this temperate grassland consisted of drought-resistent grasses mixed with brightly-flowering dicotyledons; the steppe was then most beautiful in spring and early summer when many plants were in flower.

The climate, vegetation and soil type change their character from the North to the South and South-East. As the climate becomes drier and the summer's hotter, there is a gradual transition from grassy steppe with its chestnut soils, which in turn grade into the deserts and semi-deserts of Soviet Central Asia and Mongolia. Each of the plant communities was associated with a particular soil type. In the North is the meadow-steppe, developed upon deep and rich chernozems; this is composed of turf-forming grass species, such as Stipa and fescue species (Festuca) with a abundant flowering herbs, such as Trifolium, a plant of the clover family, and many types of daisy (Composites). Xerophytic shrubby species of Artemisia become common in this part of the steppe. These types of vegetation and soils thus follow each other in the order of vegetation and soils thus follow each other in the order of increasing climatic aridity, illustrated by the annual totals of precipitation which are ca. 500 mm at the northern steppe limit, but only 300-350 mm at its southern edge.

Finally, we may refer to the changes which have taken place in a southern hemisphere grassland, the pampas of Argentina and Uruguay. These natural grasslands, stretching for some 350 to 400 miles (560-640 km) north, west and south of Buenos Aires, form a wide, level, monotonous plain in the centre and west and undulate slightly in the north and south. Virtually the whole region, which covers more than 250,000 square miles (650,000 km^2), lies under 500 feet (150 m). The soil, which is a deep, stone less loam, is extremely fertile and easily worked and even today, after many decades of crop-growing, shows little signs of exhaustion. Climatically the pampas have hot summers and warm winters; frosts and snow are rare; rainfall is fairly plentiful, falling in spring and summer mainly, with a maximum in the latter season, but the amount decreases towards the south and west. In their natural state the pampas were covered with grass and, in the drier parts, scrub, a vegetation known as Monte. In the wetter areas nearer the La Plata estuary prairie grasses 4 feet (1.2 m) high and more, with silver, feathery plumes, were typical. This difference in vegetation suggests a division, and it has become usual to differentiate between the humid pampas and the dry pampas (cf. the tall-grass and short-grass prairies of North America).

When European first arrived in the early sixteenth century the grassy plains were the habitat of the guanaco and rhea (a large running bird), which were hunted by the indigenous Indian inhabitants. Thus the original grassland ecosystem was dominated by different kinds of grasses which formed the basis of a food chain that ran from the guanaco and rhea to the puma and other predators, and man. The native Plains Indians were members of trophic level three (T3) living mainly off the game they caught and vegetable foods they collected. With the colonization of the pampas by Europeans and the introduction of ranching and farming, the old ecosystem was gradually replaced by a new controlled man-made ecosystem. The Indians were both too few in numbers and important against European guns to flight back or even to survive and they gradually perished.

The pampas are noted for their cattle, and yet cattle were unknown until, as the story goes, the famous "seven cows and one bull" were introduced in 1552 by two Portuguese brothers named Goes. More cattle were introduced as time went on, as well as horses, sheep and goats the wild catties herds in past that. So numerous were they that anyone had the legal right to take up to 12,000 head of them! Man, in the beginning, made little attempt to herd the cattle; he merely hunted them, killing wholesale for hides and tallow since these were the only valuable products. During the past hundred years a further change has come over the pampas region; arable farming now competes with pastoral farming, and is equally also. While arable farming has tended to push pastoral farming into the dry pampas, it should be noted that nowhere in the humid pampas is there less than 40 per cent of the area devoted to pasture and that alfalfa, a deep-rooted plant belonging to the clover family and an invaluable forage crop, is very widely grown and is the "pivotal crop" in the pampas economy.[14] Here, then, we have a new man-controlled ecosystem which differs quite markedly from the natural ecosystem of the past.

BROAD-LEAVED EVERGREEN FOREST MEDITERRANEAN BIOME

These biomes, although of very limited extent, are of great human importance. They occur in mid-latitudes on the western margins of the continents, and the climate under which the biomes develop and which is called the "Mediterranean" or western marginal warm temperate type is highly distinctive in its characteristics.

1. Northern Hemisphere Mediterranean Formations

In the lands bordering the Mediterranean Sea, species of oak formed the dominants of the original forests; the-evergreen oak, (Quercus ilex), once wide-spread as climax woodland in lowland situations but now restricted to scattered clumps, favours typical summer-dry climates and a variety of soil types. It is replaced by deciduous oaks in more oceanic conditions or by the economically valuable cork oak (Q. suber) on siliceous soils. In the eastern Mediterranean the Kermes Oak (Q. coccifera) tends to replace it, and the Aleppo Pine (Pinus halepensis) occurs on lime-stones and also on littoral sands. Some authorities have distinguished a climatic climax of olive (Olea) and carob in regions where the evergreen oaks cannot form forests. With increasing altitude the evergreen oak is replaced gradually by deciduous oak, beech and, finally, by coniferous forests and pine.

2. Southern Hemisphere Mediterranean Formations

In the southern hemisphere, plant life in the Mediterranean regions has evolved independently so that each has a highly individual floristic composition. Despite their taxonomic dissimilarity, however, many plants show a similar response to the environment; the maquis or mattoral of Chile resembles the woody fynbos of the Cape region of South Africa and also has a counterpart in the mallee scrub of Australia and the chaparral of California.

The regions are areas of marked seasonal changes, but the changes relate more particularly to precipitation rather than to temperature. The regions are commonly identified as having warm, wet winters and hot, dry summers; this, as a broad, general statement is acceptable, although a careful study of "Mediterranean" regimes shows that it is subject to modification. Winters are typically mild, with no month averaging below 6°C (43°F), although occasional frost and snow may occur in some areas, while summers are hot, with temperatures over 21 °C (70°F), and in interior locations away from the sea they are frequently over 27°C (SOT). A distinguishing feature of 'Mediterranean' region is their high amount of sunshine; even in winter there is little cloud. Rainfall varies between approximately 10 and 30 inches (254-762 mm), though places in exposed situations sometimes receive appreciably more than the latter figure.

Winter and spring rains produce an accumulation of moisture in the soil which plants utilize during their most active growth period in spring, when temperatures are rising. During the summer, the high temperatures and prolonged drought result in water deficiency and a check to plant growth.

The regions are defined in terms of climatic similarity, characterized by a marked seasonal alternation of hot, dry summer with cool, wet winters, the distinct and rather emphatic seasonal changes-springs and autumns are somewhat brief-are due to the position of the regions in latitudes (30-45°) which come under the influence of cyclonic storms in winter, which bring heavy but infrequent rain, and tropical high-pressure systems in summer. Thus they may be said to have cool temperate conditions in winter and hot desert conditions in summer. They are "transitional" in much the same way as the savanna lands are "transitional". They consist of five isolated regions with pronounced similarities of topography, climate and biogeography. The areas are the coastlands surrounding the Mediterranean Sea, the coastlands and Great Valley of California, central Chile, the south-western corner of Cape Province, south-western West Australia and the district around Adelaide in South Australia.

The differing variations of climate found within the limits of these so-called 'Mediterranean' lands, the variety of soils and the accidented relief are the main factors affecting the nature and distribution of the natural vegetation. The natural vegetation is classed as broad-leaved evergreen forest and scrub. Originally, most of these regions must have been quite thickly wooded, except where soils were thin and dry, but long human occupance in the lands surrounding the Mediterranean Sea and well-developed colonization in the other 'Mediterranean' lands of the Earth has resulted in a drastic modification of the original vegetative cover.

The vegetation is thus of a unique type which shows adaptations to the hot, dry summer. Adaptations such as pinnate leaves (small, tough, leathery leaves often covered with hairs or varnish), compact, shrubby growth, thick bark and long, wide-spreading roots are all concerned with preventing excessive transpiration and tapping sub-surface supplies of water. Much of the original forest has been cleared and in many areas replaced by a tangled bushy scrub known as maquis in France, macchia in Italy, mattoral in Spain and chaparral in California. In drier, limestone areas a thinner, degenerate growth, generally termed garrigue, is found. Thus this ecosystem type tends nowadays to be dominated by woody plants with hard, evergreen leaves which form a scrubby vegetation. Beneath and scattered among the sclerophyllous trees and shrubs are herbaceous flowering plants, bulbous and tuberous plants, which store moisture in their root systems, and grasses.

Many plants develop extensive root systems such as that of the almond (Prunus amygdalus) whose deep tap root often penetrates crevices in rock; or the chamise, which has both superficial and deep roots. Another xerophytic adaptation is the ability to increase the osmotic pressure exerted by the root during dry conditions. Yet another group of plants evades the dry summer by adjustment of their life cycle to the climatic regime. Such are therophytes and geophytes. Therophytes pass through their complete growth and flowering stages during the cooler, moister period, each species surviving the summer drought in the soil as seeds or spores. Geophytes are represented by many beautiful bulb and tuber plants which flower in spring and become dormant in summer, such as Hyacinthus, Crocus, Lilium, and Orchis.

However, because of variations in climate, soils and relief, several different types of vegetation may be distinguished within the ecosystem type; these may be classified as follows: (i) broad-leaved evergreen forest, (ii) degenerate woodland and scrub (maquis and garrigue), (iii) deciduous forest, found at higher elevations, (iv) coniferous forest, again found at higher altitudes, (v) steppe grassland, (vi) aquatic grasses and reeds and (vii) alpine vegetation. In the lands surrounding the Mediterranean Sea the vegetational pattern is complicated by the relief and one finds a mosaic of vegetation types.

The characteristics and features of the climate and the physiognomy of the broad-leaved sclerophyllous vegetation are similar in all the 'Mediterranean' regions but, in contrast, the floras in the different regions are distinctive. This is perhaps what one might except considering the regions are so remote from one another. In the southern hemisphere this is especially the case that the Cape region, with 2,600 species within a very small area, has a uniquely distinctive flora. The flora of Australia is equally distinctive if less rich in species. The regions in the northern hemisphere-the Mediterranean and California areas-have more in common and share several genera, although each region posses its own endemic species.

The word 'Mediterranean' regions, follows-lands surrounding the Mediterranean Sea but it is also pertinent to the other "Mediterranean" regions of the world. First, man and his animals have so effectively destroyed the original plant cover that it is difficult to realize that the wide areas of scrub vegetation were once forests of evergreen or deciduous trees. Second, many species of plants, wild and cultivated, which associate with 'Mediterranean' lands and look on as being characteristic "Mediterranean" species (e.g. oranges, lemons, the vine, and even wheat) are not indigenous but importations. In the Mediterranean lands of Europe such shrubs as aloe and cactus were introduced from America, while various forms of eucalyptus have been introduced from Australia. Third, the present landscape bears scant resemblance to the natural aspect, though there are in places relicts of the former natural vegetation, most of the landscape shows the strong imprint of human influence;

for instance, in the lands around the Mediterranean Sea the terraced fields, the horticultural gardens, the orchards and olive groves are all man-made. Usually only on the higher mountain slopes .does there occur any extensive cover of natural vegetation.

Animal life is not particularly abundant in these biomes and is less so now than formerly. The ecosystem is not very productive because of the long dry summers and this has militated against a prolific animal life. Neither was the animal life distinctive; nor it consisted mainly of life-forms from neighbouring biomes and comprised an ecotone where animals from other communities mixed. In Mediterranean Europe there were herbivorous and carnivorous creatures at one time, and rodents and reptiles are still fairly common though much of the native animal life has been eliminated. The rodents and reptiles exhibit some of the adaptations of those living in the nearby desert regions. Estivation, i.e. the practice of going into a state of dormancy, usually occurs during the dry season.

A few wild creatures, such as mountain goats, wolves, gazelles and monkeys, continue to survive, but they are largely relegated to the rocky, mountain, forest or marshy areas. For example, the Las Marismas region of southwestern Spain, a low, flat plain seamed with stream channels, lakes and marshes and fringed on the coast with sand-dunes, is a rich haunt of wildlife, as are, also, parts of the Camargue, the Rhone delta region. On the other hand, domesticated animals are numerous and enter into the economy of the Mediterranean region to a very considerable extent. The ubiquitous goat is the animal par excellence of the Mediterranean world and has probably been more responsible for the damage to the natural vegetation than any other factor. Mention should also be made of two insect pests which have caused much trouble, and still do though to a much smaller extent than formerly: these are mosquitoes and locusts. The Anopheles mosquito, which carries the malaria parasite, breeds in standing, stagnant water, and previously was prevalent in the Mediterranean region. The European part of the Mediterranean region is almost completely free from locust infestation, although in the past Spain, southern France and the Balkans were plagued by the insect pest.

In the other 'Mediterranean' regions of the world wildlife was more abundant before European colonists appeared on the scene. For example, according to Billings, animal life was firly well developed in California until the mid nineteenth century : herbivorous creatures, such as deer, elk tain lion, and numerous birds, such as the giant condor, were common. In south-western Australia animal life was dominated by kangaroos and other marsupials which filled similar ecological niches in the 'Mediterranean' ecosystem.

Among vegetation type, genus Eucalyptus dominated in this landscape.

Eucalyptus are the commonest dominants and are the most characteristic feature of the vegetation, not only in the Mediterranean areas but in the broad peripheral area surrounding the central arid zone, except where they are excluded from certain areas of the eastern rain forests. Eucalyptus are evergreen woody plants, mostly trees and many are evergreen woody plants, mostly trees, and many are very large in the areas of higher rainfall, such as karri (E. divers color), found in the South-west, a forest tree sometimes attaining more than 70 m. Others are much smaller such as the species of the mallee scrub, where the plant produces several stems from a common underground woodys stock. The adult leaves of eucalypts are leathery and tough in texture. The plants are in general xerophytes adapted to drought stresses, and the hard tissue developed in the leaf allows them to withstand severe wilting without lasting damage.

In the lands around the Mediterranean Sea both vegetation and agriculture have been affected quite considerably by the character of the soils. Calcareous soils, lying upon and developed from limestone rocks are typically reddish in colour, are rich in lime but poor in humus, known as terra rossa because of their red colour, these soils are not only frequently impoverished but are often interrupted by bare, limestone outcrops. Hence the vegetation is scanty and patchy and crop growing is handicapped by their thinness and dryness. On coastal plains the soils are usually deep, rich and fertile. In high plateau areas, especially where inland drainage occurs, soils have saline tendencies and halophytes grow. However, the soils of the Mediterranean lands vary considerably, largely because of the marked local differences with respect to geology, relief, rainfall and vegetation.

Man has found the 'Mediterranean' regions especially attractive and wherever occur he has been drawn to them in appreciable numbers. The result of this settlement has been to modify quite drastically these natural environments: the indigenous plant and animal life has been largely removed to make way for cultivation and domesticated animals while the attractiveness of the climate has stimulated urban development and modern tourism. In the lands surrounding the Mediterranean Sea small-scale fruit and grain farming, the production of olive oil and wine together with transhuman animal grazing are the traditional occupations but more recently commercialized intensive fruit farming and market gardening, usually by irrigation, have become important.

DESERTS AND DESERTIFICATION

To the geographer, the term 'desert' is linked with rainfall; deserts are areas of deficient moisture. Generally speaking, they occur in regions with less than 10 inches (254 mm) of rainfall, though they may be found in areas experiencing a precipitation which is higher but very unevenly distributed. Most deserts receive some rain every year-at least the total amount is very small-but there are regions where rain is extremely spasmodic, falling perhaps only once in many years, as happens in the Atacama Desert of northern Chile. In such areas the land appears to be totally barren and lifeless. Biogeographically, the principal, if negative, feature of desert areas is the sparseness of the vegetation cover, Deserts are seldom completely devoid of plant life but it ma^ be very thiny scattered or ephemeral in its nature.

The arid climates of the world extend well outside the lines of the tropics, and comparable features of plant and animal life are found over a wide range of latitudes. In this section the emphasis will be placed upon the hot deserts although many of the principles are relevant to the study of non-tropical arid areas.

The broad climatic and biotic gradient from the margins of the savanna and microphyllous woodland through progressively more arid environments ultimately to desert is well understood, but what may be less clearly appreciated is the considerable variation in biogeography that may occur within a small area. In such areas there is an uneven vegetation pattern and an even greater irregularity in anima distribution.

Deserts form the extreme conditions in the sequence, The term 'desert' has also been used more loosely, however, to comprehend the greater part of the arid world. Dictionary definitions usually stress tile wateriess and barren character of deserts and the fact that they tend to be desolate and uninhabited in any permanent sense. Even this definition needs qualification, since there are very few localities without some form of specialized plant, animal and soil life. An extreme contrast is presented in oases which can have permanent, dense settlement in the midst of large tracts o1 almost sterile land (Cloudsely-Thompson, 1974). The areas of arid land has also been calculated from the vegetation cover. Raheja (1966) based on Shantz (1956), estimated that there are over 6.3 million km^2 of extremely arid (desert; vegetation, 33.4 million km^2 of arid grass-savanna and desert grass-shrub land, and 7 million km^2 of semi-arid vegetation made up of sclerophyllous brush land, thorn forest and short grass.

1. Arid Landscapes

A useful approach to understanding the biogeography of arid areas is to define the types of landscape, physiography the exercises a powerful influence over drainage and strongly affects wind erosion and deposition and these factors are, in turn, major influences on the distribution of plant and animal life. The sharp outlines characteristic of much arid topography provide therefore, a means of distinguishing plant and animal habitats. On this basis Walter (1973) recognized their six types (the synonyms are taken mostly from Saharan terminology):-

1. Rocky and stone deserts (hamada): these are plateau features characterized by sand-abraded surfaces resulting from sweeping winds. Frequently there is a residual, sometimes

cemented and hard-packed layer of stones at the surface, with wind-faceted stones (ventifacts), resulting an even paved appearance ("desert pavement'). Condensation caused by the nocturnal drop in temperature is frequently sufficient to mobilize iron and man-ganese compounds which, together with salts brought to the surface by capillarity, evaporate and leave with dark coloured precipitates over the surface ('desert varnish'). The surface is often underlain by salt deposits and vegetation tends to be restricted to xero-halophytes growing in rock crevices.

2. Gravel deserts (reg or serir) are composed of mixed parent materials sifted by wind and typically coated with desert varnish. Pavements are formed when the gravels are closely packed. The plants are mostly restricted to depressions which trap transported material and have more favourable water resources.
3. Sandy deserts (erg or areg) usually occupy large basins, but they make up a smaller proportion of the total area than is often imagined (around 30 per cent of the Sahara). Many dunes have a characteristic morphology, and may be covered by a superficial precipitate of iron oxide. Where the dunes are stable, the sub-surface sand can store water and this permits colonization by dune grasses and shrubs such as Zizyphus spp. Some perennial shrubs act as 'traps' producing a series of dune mounds.
4. Dry valleys (wadis or oueds): most have originated in previous more pluvial periods, but still direct the flow of storm waters. They tend to be too unstable for plant colonization, although at the sides some halophytes such as tamarisks can gain a foothold, and some non-halophytes may exist where the salt concentration has been lowered by leaching. In more favourable areas, with sub-surface water reserves and less destructive water flow, denser patches of woodland may develop.
5. Pans (playas, sebkas or schotts) are depressions which accumulate fine material and concentrate salts. They may be underlain by less brackish subterranean water reserves. The

delta-like features sometimes found at valley exists are similar. The finer soil textures with low water infiltration capacities restrict plant life to algae and ephemerals, whilst at the same time plants tend to avoid higher salt concentrations.

6. Oases are usually densely vegetated areas with water, normally of low salt concentration, reaching the surface as springs from reserves in artesian basins. There is often a peripheral zone of greater salt concentration little natural vegetation remains today and most oases are inhabited either by sedentary or nomadic peoples.

Taking an ecological viewpoint, one can distinguish different types of desert: in the first place, one can distinguish deserts upon the basis of moisture, drawing a distinction between true deserts and semi-arid regions; and, second, one can separate them on the basis of temperature, recognizing hot deserts and temperate deserts. No matter how they are grouped, however, all deserts have one fundamental common denominator: lack of moisture throughout most of the year. This moisture deficiency is responsible for two distinguishing characteristics of desert vegetation: a particular spatial distribution and distinctive physical adaptations.

Odum emphasis that all desert vegetation has a characteristically 'spaced' distribution pattern; in other words, plants are spasmodically, though often rather regularly, scattered over the land surface with large bare areas between the individual plants. There is a clear relationship, which is quite sharply drawn, he says, between population size and resources in the desert environment. Again, desert plants, whether they belong to the hot or temperate deserts, show very similar life-forms; for example, the characteristic growth form of shrubs is one of numerous branches ramifying from ground level (chamaephytes). Odum illustrates how sagebrush (Artemisia), dominating temperate desert in Idaho, and creosote bush (Larrea), dominating hot desert in Arizona, exhibit the same characteristics, i.e. the chamaephytic growth form and rather regular spacing, odum comments: "With equivalent rainfall, the shrubs of the cool desert would tend to be closer together and the herbaceous cover somewhat better developed because of more favourable precipitation-evaporation relationship." In areas of true desert, as distinct from semi-arid areas, plant life is very limited and is often confined almost exclusively to the banks of streams, the beds of intermittent watercourses and oases, where ribbon-like patterns of vegetation may be seen.

The desert biomes differ from each other floristically, more especially so in the case of the hot deserts. Billings has indicated that the plants in the latter belong to tropical families and genera, while those found in the temperate deserts, with their cold winters, are largely derived from Tertiary mountain flora and from salt marshes. In the hot deserts there has been independent development of the flora but parallel evolution; in other words, although plants may look alike, they are not closely related; for example, the cacti of the American hot deserts closely resemble the euphorbias of the African deserts. In the temperate deserts of the northern hemisphere-those of western North America and Central Asia - the life-forms are very much alike and they share many genera in common.

In the deserts there is too little and too variable rainfall to support more than a few plants, and these are usually specialized types which can withstand drought. We indicated earlier that desert plants either are drought-evading, are drought-tolerant, or store moisture and that they adopt numerous protective devices, such as small, leathery leaves, spines instead of true leaves, wide-spreading root systems, etc.

Because of the lack of vegetation, there .is a corresponding lack of animal life. There is, it should be noted, a considerable diversity of animal life but the numbers of individual creatures are small. Desert animals, like plants, are adapted in various ways to the lack of water. The deserts contain few large herbivores, although there are a number of browsers, e.g. camels, species of antelope and mountain sheep, that are able to subsist upon some of the thorny, tough desert shrubs. Mammals as a group are not particularly well adapted to life in the desert although some species have developed remarkable adaptations. Small rodents tend to be rather common and some of these, such as the kangaroo rat and the pocket mouse, manage to live without drinking water; they produce the water they need in the course of releasing energy from what they eat. Many of these creatures are also nocturnal in habit, remaining in their burrows by day; in this way they escape the heat of daytime. On the other hand, there are some desert rodents, e.g. the wood rats, which cannot live solely on dry food and must have some water which they normally procure from water-storing plants. The camel, which is often looked upon as the typical animal, requires substantial quantities of water but it is able to go for long periods without drinking since it uses the water stored in its body.

Insect life is numerous and most desert insects are 'wax-proofed' against high temperatures. Many small birds are insectivorous, as are some of the lizards. Reptiles, some of them poisonous, are numerous and are to be found even in the most extreme deserts. The dry lands lack large predators and such animals as coyotes and foxes are relatively few in numbers.

The chief hot desert regions are the Sahara and its continuations, the Arabian and Thar Deserts, the Kalahari Desert of South-west Africa, the Great Australian Desert in the western part of that continent, the Atacama Desert of northern Chile which is continued into coastal Peru, and the desert of the Mexico-U.S.A. border.

As in the hot deserts, life is limited by the climatic conditions: not only is there a shortage of moisture but the low temperatures of winter are a limiting factor. Such plant growth as occurs is confined to a brief period between winter cold and summer drought. Sparse tufted grasses and woody shrubs are typical. Population is scanty and comprises either nomadic or sedentary groups. In the past, and still to some extent in the present, in Asia, tribal groups have eked out an existence herding animals and to some extent carrying trade. The sedentary groups are also found commonly and these are distributed were those who congregated around sources of water supply-streams coming down from the adjacent mountains - and created oasis settlements such as the famous Central Asian cities of Baikh, Bukhara, Ferghana, Samarkanc and Tashkent.

The desert ecosystems, when compared with most o' the other ecosystems, have experienced little change, until quite recently, at the hands of man. The only exceptions to this general statement are the oases and the irrigated areas. However, the development of modern irrigation methods and modern mineral exploitation are helping to change the desert environment. Until relatively recent times Turkestan (Soviet Central Asia) was little developed, being largely a pastoral region with a little crop-growing activity. However, great irrigation schemes tike Indira Gandi canal in India and the exploitation of the Karaganda coal deposits have begun to transform the area. Large quantities of cotton are now grown by irrigation and a number of ancient trade-route centres have been turned into important industrial cities. Extensive urban development has taken place in the deserts of the western United States, North America In Patagonia, settlement is thin and extensive sheep rearing With a little cultivation in the sheltered valleys are the main economic activities.

Life in hot desert is hard and hot desert regions are of relatively limited value and use from human environment point of view. Accordingly, they are, in general, very sparsely peopled. Only where there is a major source of water supply, as in Egypt, is population dense. The life style of people of the desert regions fall into three groups.

A. The nomadic camel, sheep and goat herders who wander in search of pasture and frequent the water-holes, people who, in the past, were also often carriers of merchandise and equally as often marauders. But there could have been no nomadic way of life but for these domestic able herbivores which posses devices for survival under drought conditions.

B. The settled people of the oases who grow cereals, vegetables, fruit (notably the date palm in the Old World), and sometimes irrigated cotton and sugar-cane and who also often rear cattle, sheep, goats, camels and asses. Provided water is obtainable, desert soils, though lacking in humus, are normally rich in plant foods, since they have not suffered leaching.

C. The dwellers of the mining settlements who tolerate the harsh climatic conditions for the sake of the mineral wealth, e.g. the gold of Western Australia the diamonds of the Kalahari, the nitrate deposits o northern Chile, and the petroleum of Algeria, Libya Saudi Arabia, Kuwait, south-west Persia and Iraq.

The mid-latitude temperate desert covers a large areas in the heart of the extensive land-mass of Eurasia and considerable areas in the western interior of North America but is represented in the southern hemisphere only by the Patagonian Desert of South America. These regions, which are extensive plains or plateaus, are deserts mainly because of their interior locations remote from the ocean or because they lie, like Patagonia, in a rain-shadow area.

2. Desertification and Land Degradation

More than one-third of the earth's land area is arid and in this area the process of desertification has intensified in recent decades. According to estimates available (UNCOD, 1977) desertification threatens the future of more than 785 million people, or 17.7 per cent of the world's population, who live in these dry lands. Of this number, between 60 and 100 million people are affected directly by decreases in productivity associated with current desertification processes. It is also estimated that between 50,000 and 70,000 square kilometers of useful land are going out of production every year, through desertification. The Sahelian drought of 1968-73 and its tragic effect on the people of that region drew world attention to the chronic problems of human survival and development on the desert margins.

Desertification is a world-wide human and social which is not susceptible to quick solutions, but is already urgent in many areas. It is a self-accelerating process which feeds on itself, and as it advances rehabilitation costs rise exponentially.

Desertification commonly appears as degradation of plant, animal, soil and water resources and general loss of biological productivity in areas under ecological stress. In fragile ecosystems, such as those on desert margins, this degradation can easily become irreversible, and permanently reduce the capacity of the area affect to support human life.

The combating desertification calls for several kinds of action covers areas where desertification is occurring now, and others, which are likely to be affected in the future, including the arid, semi-arid and sub-humid areas:

Desertification can be halted by the year A.D. 2001 and the UNEP's plan of Action was formulated with this goal in mind. Action against desertification cannot, however, yield results unless governments perceive it as an integral part of their established plans for social and economic development. It may be concluded quite confidently that, globally, we now have the basic technology, human resources and finance to solve desertification problems. The key to combative measures is to be found in proper lands use. With the spectacular advances in the technology of remote sensing and the diversification of its uses, remote sensing coupled with ground surveys can be extremely useful for monitoring desertification and related natural resources.

Anti-desertification programmes are necessarily long term. They require a long period of gestation in order to bring them to fruition. Therefore, all countries of the globe, whether or not they are directly threatened by the advance of the deserts, should consider themselevs involved in the fight against desertification. In his recent message to the UNEP's Governing Council (Nairobi, May 16-29, 1984), Dr. Tolba summoned the international community to act now it we are to avoid shortages leading to chaos on a scale hitherto unknown. The extent to which the world's nations cooperate in the implementation of anti-desertification measures, will determine whether or not an impending worldwide crisis can be averted. The immediate goal is to prevent and to arrest the advance of desertification, and where possible, to reclaim affected land for productivity use. The need is recognized for immediate action in applying existing knowledge, not only to stop the physical processes of desertification, but to educate people in minimizing the harm done to the fragile ecosystems of dry lands by existing economic and social activities.

3. Desertification and Desertization

The word "Desertification", first used by the French scientist and explorer Louis Lavauden in 1927 has at least 3 very different meanings at the present time. The first one, as defined at the ad-hoc U.N. conference in Nairobi in 1977, is "a *decrease in the productivity potential of the land under arid, semi-arid and dry sub-humid climates, that may eventually lead to desert-like conditions*". This definition was further broadened at the UN Conference on Environment and Development (Rio de Janeiro, 1992), in order to accommodate the maximum number of countries that could then qualify for external help for their development under the desertification label. One has thus been able to hear and read about desertification in Bangladesh or in Zaire, although the first named is more notorious because of its devastating floodings, while the latter is, with the Amazon Basin, the wettest region on the planet (the green desert?). It thus clearly appears as a semantic abuse. This meaning corresponds with a more conventional, albeit less emotional and mediatic expression: *"Land Degradation"*; and that is what it is all about.

A second meaning of the word "Desertification" is more recent; it emerged from the EEC political administrative and journalistic circles to depict *"Lane Freezing"*, *"Land Abandoment"* by farmers moving to the cities. This meaning incidently, is a semantic error; one should then speak of *"Desertion"*, i.e. people quitting their land.

The third sense is the one Lavauden meant, that is the depletion of vegetation and soils in arid lands, leading to desert-like conditions. This is what, in order to avoid confusion, I label *"Desertization"* a term that connotes some degree of irreversibility of arid land turned manmade desert. There are many examples o1 such irreversibility in the arid lands north and south of the Sahara. Irreversibility, however, should be understood under the time scale which is accessible to us i.e. 25-50 years (25 years corresponds to the first satellite images and 50 years to the first aerial photos of broad, non-military utilizations). Generally speaking arid land degradation results from the misuse and mismanagement by man and/or his livestock of renewable natural resources.

4. Cause of Desertification and Land Degradation Physical Causes

The direct causes of land degradation mainly belong to different kinds of processes that account for some 95% of the havoc: erosion (wind and water) and chemical degradation, either exhaustion of nutrients and/ or trace elements or toxicity from salts such as sodium chloride or others. The latter usually results from the mismanagement of irrigation over irrigation, lack of drainage, utilization of water and/or soils which are inappropriate, water logging and so forth.

Erosion always results from the denudation of soil surface for long periods of time, that makes it sensitive to the degradation forces, strong winds and running water form heavy showers. But the opposite is not necessarily true as farmlands have undergone centuries of farming without many adverse effects. Local edapho-climatic conditions and land management are of paramount importance in the processes of land degradation.

5. Socio-economic Causes

Causes linked to human actions are those which lead to soil denudation for long periods or to their chemical exhaustion in nutrients or their degradation by toxic substances. In other words, the clearing and cropping of land which is not adequate because of climatic aridity or edaphic properties such as sandy soils in arid lands which, when regularly tilled, may undergo wind erosions of 200-300 tons per hectare and per year as measured in Northern Africa and in Inner Mongolia. Cultivation of clay soils on steep slopes is likewise conducive to water erosion of the same order of magnitude as measured in Northern Africa and S.E. Spain.

Such clearing of natural vegetation in arid lands usually results from heavy demographic pressure, in areas with a low standard of living and a low technical konw-how, or at least with a know how which is no longer adjusted to higher populations.

The above is the more true as the conditions are more arid and the demographic pressure higher. The second major cause is overgrazing and overstocking, which in turn, is often tied to the population pressure on the land; but it is not necessarily so; heavy overgrazing may occur in areas with a very low human population density as well, such as in Australia, in Patagonia in the western US rangelands. The third indirect cause of arid land depletion is the over collection of woody plants, particularly for fuel. In other words, a wood harvest that is higher than wood production.

These three causes are responsible for some 80% o1 arid land degradation; some 0.1% of the 250 million hectares of irrigated land in the world are turned partly or totally infertile every year because of faulty irrigation, most of them are located in arid and hyper arid lands.

These conditions, again, are linked with the socio-economic phenomena of low know-how, poverty, underdevelopment as well as various kinds of mismanagement.

6. Extent and Intensity of Arid Land Degradation

The geographic extent and intensity of arid land degradation varies considerably from one region to another, from one continent to another. If the major causes of degradation are every where the same, broadly speaking, their relative importance varies considerably. Generally speaking, clearing and over cultivation is tied to low income and densely populated rural communities of settled farmers, which also goes with over collection of fuel wood: Northern Africa, Near and Middle East, N.W. China, the Sahel, East Africa. Overgrazing occurs in countries such as Australia, United States, Argentina and South Africa, where very large ranches of several thousand or tens of thousands of hectares, with a population density below 1 person/ km^2, may be badly overgrazed or even desertized. Several detailed studies over large areas, using both remote sensing and ground truth techniques found virtually the same figures of 0.6 to 0.7% of arid land depleted every year in the southern Ex-

USSR countries, the north-west of China and northern Africa. This means that if land management remains unchanged these arid lands will be turned into man-made deserts in less than 150 years and, most probably, within the next 50 years or so. Arid lands (100-400 mm of mean annual rainfall) amount to 12% of the overall land surface of the world, inhabited by some 150 million people. Over 1/ 3 and may be up to 1/2 of them are already severely degraded (estimates vary from one expert to another).

7. Sensible Land Use in Arid Regions

The management of ground water is vital to the agricultureal use of the arid lands. In many places in these areas, there are important subterranean water pockets. Overexploitation, together with low rainfall, causes the level of the water to fall and makes its extraction more difficult.

In the Middle East and northern Africa, agriculture is feasible only in the oases and above the subterranean fossil water tables. Techniques such as geallery irrigation (Karez networks) permit agricultural activity in climatically unfavourable areas.

- Zones where the practice of rainwater cultivation causes environmental problems should be provisioned using surpluses obtained in other areas more climatically favourable.
- On the other hand, extensive animal husbandry is an activity which, if practiced with itinerant grazing, permits the exploitation of sub-desert vegetations.
- Animal-husbandry systems should be stratified in order to distribute into different areas the phases of reproduction and fattening. This regionalization of animal husbandry activity would facilitate better integration with arid zones crops.
- A major challenge for the developed countries is to assist in various ways in the improvement of the soil fertility of the countries of the arid regions, which correspond to economically depressed areas, and to contribute to restoring the natural environment affected by desertification.

- Sub-desert soils could be enriched by the addition ol a large part of the surplus of compost obtained from domestic waste or from compost sewage from water-purification plants (suitably treated and analyzed) in industrialized areas.
- In addition, the introduction of microimgatior techniques should be encouraged.
- Cultural differences and ethnic conflicts between countries must be overcome, since this is necessary to foster the technological cooperation needed to prevent the degradation of impoverished arid lands.
- Another factor in desertification is the consumption of firewood. Wood has many uses, and one of the most common is as a fuel.
- It is essential to improve the energy efficiency of cooking ovens, and in general to diversify energy sources. Reforestation programmes must also be encouraged.
- The creation of water points is not always the most suitable of measures. Very often, these palace; concentrate herds and encourage their immobility thereby leading to desertification.
- The discovery of water in arid regions should contribute to the rational management of itinerant animal husbandry.
- In general, one of the principal ecological challenge; is the possible environmental and social impact o the great hydraulic works planned in the arid regions We should not forget that at this moment the possession of water is the basic reason for armed conflicts in several parts of the world. New agricultural techniques enable yields to be increased with very little water, and desert zones to be transformed into gardens.

8. Management Plan

(1) Sunseed Desert Technology

Sun seed Desert Technology is working in the badlands of Southeast Spain, investigating ways of combating desertification that not only address the ecological needs of degraded lands but the economic priorities of rural communities in the developing world. Its emphasis on low-cost, lowtech adoptions of "ideal solutions" provides the role of a link between the world of scientists and the practical realities of-living bound by short term necessities.

In South-east Spain as in .many parts of the world, severe soil erosion has rendered traditional dry land terrace farming unproductive and unsustainable. Sun seed is demonstrating ways of bringing such terraces back into production as part of wider scale land reclamation. Run-off water from eroding gullies is reclaimed in water tanks for irrigation use, to the benefit of short term crop production. By increasing the scale of agro forestry practices from, singly olived trees to line plantings of fast growing legumes, the interplanted terrace crops are given a more sheltered, stable environment in which to grow, and erosion is reduced by deeper rooting tree species. In the most degraded terraces saltbush and brooms take over the role of trees; grown as soil improving hedgerows saltbush in particular can be regularly harvested for forage.

To reverse the process of erosion on catchment slopes, a range of approaches is required. To halt soil movement easily constructed barriers have been developed using locally available "cana". Once the soil movement is slowed, revegetation ranges from transplanting of succulents and grass species to native leguminous herbs and shrubs. In order to provide economic incentives for restoring the natural climax forest, fast growing timber trees (such as the Australian Acacia) are grown as nurses to native oaks and pistachios. Having aided establishment through nitrogen fixing, shade and leaf-litter, they are felled after 5-1C years as a valuable crop.

These on-going projects can act as experimental and training grounds for arid land workers en route to the developing world. In this way gaps can be bridged from scientifically trained horticulturalists adapting to low-tech nursery conditions to grass roots development workers making use of western ecological research.

(2) Regeneration of Forests and Waste Lands Reclaimation

The School of Fundamental Research (SFR), founded in Calcutta by B.B, Basu in 1971, initiated ecodevelopmental management programmes in the most environmentally degraded in drought-prone hilly areas of Parulla, West Bengal, which have a very high percentage of tribal population. Villagers and volunteers formed Village Forest Protection Committees to implement an inexpensive programme for reviving natural forest through social fencing and suitable endogenic technological management. They have regenerated over 3,000 ha of Sal (Shorea robusta) forest, and revived the prospect of alternative livelihoods based on forest products for tribal and forest dependent communities.

Ecodevelopment programmes have added over a million utility trees with high survival rate, in the degraded terrain of the project area. The SFR has prepared an innovative input model for wasteland reclamation that uses less irrigation and fertilizer, with successful field trials and extension programmes. A unique participatory model for Rapid Rural Appraisal has promoted mass awareness about interactive scientific principles in natural resource management.

Since 1991, a collaborative Research and Development programme on biological reclaimation of wastelands, land-spoils and mining over-burdens has been operating, aimed at breaking the dormancy of the rock surface and converting it into the production base for biomass generation through biological reclamation, Over 125 ha of such degraded areas have been reclaimed.

Over 100 youth training camps, involving experts, activists, and government officials, have produced an SFR workforce of over 200 barefoot ecologist-volunteers.

Having understood that tribal and forest-dependent communities are essentially land-locked people, the SFR worked to revive a non-alien interest in deforestation problems and to develop a combat strategy without dependence on government, so that people's own initiative could manage and reverse the impact of drought and expanding wasteland. The SFR has generated not only hope but an alternative livelihood for forest dependent communities, independently of internal initiatives and assistance.

(3) Seeds Against Erosion

Reforestation is very important, especially in mountainous areas which are endangered by erosion. It is suitable to use tree species which are native to the environment. But in certain areas it is impossible to achieve successful reforestation, either because of the high game population or because the soil has already degraded too much. In the latter case it is advisable to reestablish the "Preforest community" in order to stabilize the soil. Once a year since 1980 gardeners, other volunteers and people like Mr. Karl Partsch collect seeds of more than 20 alpine plants. Seedlings are raised in lowland nurseries and planted, the following spring, in eroded areas on the Walmendinger Horn and on the Furschiesser (AllGau, Germany).

In the forest cultivation project above Hinter stein (Allgau, Germany) we deliberately created a "pre-forest" environment with small trees and fast growing crops. They initate nature.

(4) Green Belt Movement

On 5 June 1994 the Green Belt Movement (GBM) will celebrate 17 years of a campaign to raise public awareness of the urgent need to protect and rehabilitate the physical environment. GMB wants to move people to do the right things for the environment to eching their hearts and convincing their minds.

The GBM is an indigenous grassroots environment campaign with tree planting as its basic activity. The tree has been used as the focal point around which other environmental issues are discussed.

The projects we developed under the auspices of the National Council of Women of Kenya. The GBM is rooted in the "Harambee development philosophy, with women's participation as a driving force. This participation is encapsulated in the recitation invoked at each tree planting ceremony.

The GBM approaches the issues of development holistically, endeavors to build on local expertise and abilities and to curb all desertification processes in Kenya and in Africa, encouraging tree planting, soil rehabilitation, water harvesting, reafforestation, etc., creating jobs in rural areas, making tree planting an income-generating activity especially for women, encouraging extensive tree farming by private small-scale farmers, and promoting zero-grazing and organic farming as a means of improving soil fertility and food production.

The accomplishments of the GBM have been far reaching: over 1,000 tree nurseries have been established, and about 50,000 women are involved at these tree nursery sites. GBM is active in 10 central and eastern African countries.

(5) UNESCO And Desertification

UNESCO work on arid lands and desertification under the UNESCO Man and Biosphere (MAS) Programme and the International Hydrological Programme (IHP) focuses on finding solutions to local land management problems, while providing a core of knowledge that can be applied throughout the world's arid and semi-arid zones. 'UNESCO's early work in arid zones revealed the complexity of the interactions between natural' phenomena and human activities in these zones and the need for an inter-disciplinary strategy to understand and manage these interactions. It also indicated the need to increase scientific capacities and the application of research results in arid zones in order to improve land management. For these reasons, UNESCO promotes projects that combine natural and social science research with training for scientists, technicians and decision-makers, as well as dissemination of research results through publications and seminars.

Beginning with the Arid Zone Programme in 1951, UNESCO has undertaken numerous projects in arid zones, including the preparation of six case studies on desertification for the 1977 UN Conference on Desertification, the development of a resource management plan for the Marsabit District of Northern Kenya, a 10 year training programme in integrated pastoral development in the Sahel, and a study of water resources in the Northern

Sahara leading to proposals for the extraction of groundwater to develop irrigation, extend existing oases and/or create new oases in the desert. UNESCO activities are increasingly centered on Africa and the Saheiian countries, which are experiencing the combined effects of growing human populations and recurrent droughts.

(6) UNDP and International Priorities

- Strengthening the knowledge base and developing information and monitoring systems for regions prone to desertification and drought, including the economic and social aspects of these ecosystems.
- Combating land degradation through inter alia, intensified soil conservation, afforestation and reforestation activities.
- Developing and strengthening integrated development programmes for the eradication of poverty and promotion of alternative livelihood systems in areas prone tc desertification.
- Developing comprehensive antidesertificatior programmes and integrating them into national development plans and national environmental planning.
- Developing comprehensive drought prepadness and drought-relief schemes, including self-help arrangements, for drought-prone areas and designing programmes to cope with environmental refugees.
- Encouraging and promoting popular participation and environmental education, focusing on desertification control and management of the effects of drought.

TROPICAL GRASSLAND

The tropical grassland biomes or savanna lands arc regions of marked seasonal changes. Temperatures are high all the year round, seldom falling below 21°C (70°F), but the crucial climatic factor is the rainfall, which comes in summer Rainfall varies widely and there is a gradation from over 60 inches (1.524 mm) on the forest edge to 15 inches (381 mm on the desert margin.

The association of savanna vegetation with areas of the

vorld having marked wet and dry seasons, with constant warm emperatures and generally high isolation, led earlier workers o talk of a "grassland type of climate', Schimper (1903)) a notion upported by some climatologists as in the 'Aw' climate lassification of Koppen (1923), but it seems preferable and ertainly more practical to restrict the term savanna to vegetation lescription.

Although a correlation between plant type and climate does exist, it is not as consistent as the Equatorial climate: rainforest ssociation (which is far from universal in any case). There are reas which appear to have a 'modal' savanna climate but which upport forest (where for example there is ample groundwater), or which support only thorn scrub, In addition there are quite lifferent climatic regions which contain patches of similar-looking grassland and grass-woodland vegetation. Such localized avannas occur for example, in the Amazon Basin and in parts of the African rainforests, or along the coasts as in West Africa, or amongst more arid vegetation types in for instance, South-Nest Africa. On the whole there is no appreciable change in the nacroclimate discernible across the forest-grassland or grassland-leserts vegetation boundaries. Thus a particular pattern of limate does not, by itself, result in savanna vegetation; other nvironmental and biotic factors have to be taken into account.

The majority of savannas are nonetheless fairly consistently ssociated with some aspects of climate. Savanna vegetation normally demands a warm, continental type of climate with ariable humidity according to the season (less than 50 per cent n dry periods and near saturation in wet) together with elatively abundant, if irregular rainfall. Total rainfall tends to be in the range 500 to over 2000mm per annum while emperatures rarely drop below 20°C. These relationships may be illustrated in the Brazilian savanna, known as cerrado, because his formation covers many different geological outcrops tretching over different types of topography at varying altitudes rom sea-level to 1300m Yet the average annual temperatures ange from less that 20 to 26°C and the mean annual rainfall aries from around 750 to 2000mm. With changes in floristic omposition and structure, the savannas can withstand dry seasons of up to 8 or 9 months in length. In the Americ tropics, savannas do not seem to occur with totals less th 500mm, at which stage the vegetation alters towards deciduo and thorn forest. One of the clearest sequences from forest progressively- drier savanna zones is found in West Africa,

Though the climate is usually described as being one hot, wet summers and hot, dry winters, it is possible to recogni three seasons: a comparatively cool, dry Season, a hot, d season; and a warm, rainy season.

'Parkland' areas are often mosaics of grassland and fore which cannot be easily placed under either heading. Some these parkland areas, as in East Africa, have trees on the upraise mounds of old termitaria, a striking feature which has bee given the name 'termite savanna' (Hesse, 1955). Thus with predominantly forest areas, there may be patches of savanna, within predominantly savanna there may be patches or mo continuous stretches of forest. A good example of the latter the fringing forest found along streams, rivers and lakes know as gallery forest.

The margin is often sharp but irregular. There are ma natural reasons for this including the extension of forests alo streams and rivers and wetter depressions (fringing or galle forest), the local influence of topography, drainage and wat availability, and the effects of fire. Further, the dynamic natu of the boundary tends to result in one system advancing a1 th expense of the other (in this case savanna upon forest).

Not only is there a long dry season but the evaporati rates are high; these conditions are not suited to tree growt there is, in fact, a wide variation in savanna which ranges fro entirely treeless grassland to thickly wooded grassland.

However, the vegetation of most savannas is dominate usually, by tall perennial Graminaceae. Grasses grow quickly the wet season and may reach heights of 6 feet (1.8 m) ar more; the tall grass is commonly called "elephant grass". Grass tend to be thick and hard-stemmed and when they die dow form a dense, coarse mat in many places. In some areas the is a scattered tree growth which gives rise to a land scope 'parkland view'. The trees found in association with the grasslands are quite distinctive: they are relatively low-growing, umbrella-shaped or flat topped, and of a more or less xerophilous nature but may be either deciduous or evergreen; they comprise, also, species which are quite different from those found in the rain forest. On the African grasslands acacias are common as are the baobabs, with their swollen trunks in which they store water, while frequently palms dot the landscape. During the dry season the grasses become desiccated and often burn, and because of the frequent fires grasses, and trees, too, must be fire-resistant. Another feature of the savannas is that it is not uncommon for single species of both grasses and trees to be dominant over quite extensive areas. Floristically, however, the savannas differ greatly since there are so many different kinds of savanna scattered so widely throughout the tropics.

The tropical grasslands are, or were before man intervened, the home of a rich fauna; this is especially true of the African grasslands. The larger animals are of two chief types: the herbivores, grass-eating and browsing creatures which are fleet of foot, e.g. antelopes, of which there are numerous types, wild beast, zebra and giraffe; and carnivores, beasts of prey such as lions and leopards which hunt the first group. The number and variety of hoofed mammals found on the African savannas is un-excelled anywhere else in the world.

Some of the larger ungulates are of special interest. The elephants, forming a sub-order of ungulates, are the largest living terrestrial mammals. There are two main species, the African elephant (Elephas africanus) and the Indian (E. maximums); the former is the larger and may weigh over 6 tons and is also distinguishable by its larger ears and hollow back. The rhinoceros, which is allied to the elephant, is the second-largest and most powerful land mammal. It is one of the oldest surviving animals and in some respects may be regarded as a living fossil; scientists believe it has not changed in 60 million years. Specimens of the white or square-lipped rhinoceros have been known to weigh 3 tons, to stand 6 feet (1.8 m) high at the shoulder and to bear a horn 5 feet (1.5 m) long. Rhinoceroses are now rare. Though heavy and clumsy, they are capable of running at a great speed. The hippopotamus (Hippopotamus amphibious) is river-banks or lake edges. Only slightly smaller than the elephant, this ugly creature, encased in thick hide and possessing very short, stout legs spends most of its time wallowing in mud and water.

An interesting facet of animal life in the savanna lands is the animals' remarkable adaptation to their environment. In this environments of characteristically wide open spaces most animals display remarkable camouflage, e.g. the town; colours of antelopes and lions and the stripes or spots o zebras and cheetahs, which help to disguise them in grassland country. Again, the ungulates are agile and swift footed to help them escape the sharp-clawed, sharp toothed predators such as the lions, leopard and hyenas.

Although the mammalian herbivores are the most conspicuous animals, there are many other animal types Birds are numerous, often occurring in great colonies, such as the flamingoes. There are, too, scavenger birds such as the vulture. Ants, locusts and other insect pests are numerous. They are most abundant during the wet season and provide food for the birds at nesting time. The tsetse fly carrier of sleeping sickness and animal diseases, infests large parts of Africa and prevents cattle rearing. In the savanne lands of South America, the cattle-tick is a pest.

The tropical grasslands of Africa are unique in their possession of numerous species of large mammalian herbivores. The Campos and llanos of South America are poverty stricken by comparison and do not seem ever to have had a wealth of herbivores. The tropical grasslands o1 Australia lacked the variety of animals, although kangaroos and kindred marsupial types were very numerous.

Man has had a much greater impact upon the tropical grassland biomes than he has had upon the tropical forests; there has been much disturbance as a result of firing, hunting and tillage by man, although the extent of this disturbance has varied quite widely from region to region. Firing, too, has affected the species composition of the grassland and, doubtless, many of the original plant species which were intolerant of fire have been culminated. Large-scale hunting, both by native peoples and by "big game" hunters using guns, has led to the decimation, and sometimes near-extinction, o1 many native animals.

Man in the savanna lands has traditionally been a hunter but in many areas he has become a pastoralist herding cattle. For example, the Fulani of West Africa and the Massi of East Africa herd cattle, unfortunately they count their wealth in terms of the numbers rather than the quality of the animals they possess and this has often led to the over-grazing of the pastures and their consequent deterioration and, sometimes, destruction.

In many parts of the savanna lands crop cultivation is carried on, but arable farming has to face two main physical problems: first, water is a limiting factor since, unless irrigation is practiced, and, second, soils are seldom very fertile and useless. Most of the soils fall into the latosol group. One the other hand, in the dry season, when there is intense evaporation, the water-table falls abruptly and the less soluble elements in the soil are precipitated and give rise to the development of a hard-pan. For example, soils over much of the Brazilian Plateau, which is largely savanna country, are poor. Since the predominant parent rock is sandstone, the weathered material produces porous, dry, sandy soils. These, incidentally, are greatly inferior to the soils developed on the crystaline rocks as, for example, in southern Goyaz, and especially those derived from volcanic rocks as in Sao Paulo State. The sandy and gravelly, accumulations of the Planalto of central Brazil are subject to the occurrence of canga, i.e. latosols and which is sometimes so hard that it cannot be broken by heavy steel ploughs.

Farmers in savanna regions are often primitive cultivators, of either the shifting or the sedentary type, growing crops such as millet, maize, yams, groundnuts, beans and peppers. Native cultivation in Africa is commonly done by the womenfolk. In some parts of Africa, notably in East Africa, large single-crop plantations established by Europeans, but worked by native labour, produce coffee, cotton, sisal and tobacco.

TROPICAL DECIDUOUS FOREST

Seasonal drought in winter produces the same deciduous characteristic among many woody plants in the tropics. If the rainfall is greater or more regular, a well-developed deciduous forest occurs. The tropical deciduous forest biome is associated with tropical monsoon regions and attains its greatest extent in southern and south-eastern Asia.

Many areas experience monsoon winds in summer but the only area where the climate is completely dominated by them is southern and south-eastern Asia. Northern Australia is strongly influenced by them, as is Ethiopia, while the coastal margins of East Africa feel the effects of the Indian Ocean monsoon system. Similarly, parts of tropical America suffer monsoonal influences. In those lands experiencing the true monsoon conditions the winds are emphatically seasonal, blowing from land to sea in winter and from Sea to land in summer. 'The Indian subcontinent provides the classic example of an area having a tropical monsoon type of climate; winters are cool or warm and dry, early summers are hot and dry, and late summers hot and wet. The year is divisible into three seasons instead of the usual four. Temperatures during the months of April, May and June are high, commonly between 27° and 32°C (80°- 90° F); this period of great heat immediately precedes the "burst" of the monsoon, which usually occurs in June. The onset of the summer rains, brought by the south-west monsoon, is typically sudden, and violent storms with torrential rains introduce the "wet season", on the other hand, the rainfall is extremely variable in both amount and incidence from year to year.

The regional variations in the amount of precipitation result in corresponding wide variations in the natural vegetation: this ranges from rain forest, through deciduous forest and jungle to thorny scrub vegetation and savanna. Much of the original forest and woodland in the Indian subcontinent and southern China has been cleared for cultivation, but in Burma, Thailand and the countries formerly comprising Indo-China much monsoon forest remains. The true monsoon forest, i.e. the tropical deciduous forest, is less dense and less luxuriant than the equatorial rain

›rest, though it bears some resemblance to it. In this biome the anopy is not as continuous nor as thick as in the rain forest, the ees are smaller, and there are fewer creeping vines. But, pically, the monsoon forest has much more ground vegetation nce sunlight is able to filter through to the forest floor. As a esult, dense, tangled undergrowth with patches of grass occurs, roducing what might be called "jungle". At the beginning of ie dry season there is a well-marked leaf fall and the ndergrowth dies down. Teak, sal, pynkado (ironwood), banyan nd sandalwood are typical representatives of the monsoon orest. Many of the trees are of great commercial value. Remnants f the original forest occur in the Indian subcontinent and, on greater scale, in South-east Asia. Where the forest has been leared and then abandoned, dense bamboo brakes or jungle rowth occur.

There is a rich wildlife, especially in the forested areas vhich have suffered little disturbance. Of the carnivores, tigers nd other members of the cat family are most important. They re, of course, mainly confined to the more remote and wilder reas. Deer, a few antelopes, wild pigs, rhinoceros and elephants, ll ungulates, are to be found in various parts of the region. Aany kinds of monkeys occur and insects, bats, birds and reptiles re numerous. Many beautiful and brilliantly coloured birds are o be found and the peacock is native to the region. It is also f interest to note that the jungle fowl is the birds from which nodern domestic poultry have been developed. Lizards; snakes, ncluding a large number of poisonous varieties, crocodiles and urtles are common.

Insect life is especially important not only because of the uisance insects cause by infesting dwellings and attacking food ut also because they are often carriers of disease. Most important rom the human point of view are the malaria-carrying nosquitoes. Malaria caused high death-rates throughout much f the region. Where properly controlled, as in Ceylon, malaria vas practically culminated with a consequent drastic fall in the leath-rate.

Ways of life in the monsoon region are mostly bound up

with the cultivation of the soil, and the agricultural village is th characteristic form of settlement. Agriculture is primaril subsistence faming and many peasants still live a self-containe and self-sufficient existence, it explains, too, the "character" c the oriental civilization: "Monsoon Asia is the home of 'vegetable civilization', where wood and plan materials hav been the basis of everyday things from houses to domesti utensils, farm implements and clothing". Apart from som exploitation of the forest wealth, especially hare timbers such a teak, and some plantation agriculture, is dominant.

The tropical deciduous forest biome occurs elsewhere in th world but on a more reduced scale. There is, for example, a extensive area in eastern and southern Africa -roughly th Zambezi Basin and the Tanzanian Plateau - which is clothed i the main with dry deciduous woodland, known as miomb woodland, composed of Brachystegia-isoberlinia trees attainin heights of 30 to 50 feet (0.9 - 1.5 m); the this woodland i sometimes quite dense and at other times more open witl tussocky grass. This area may be said to fall within the biom type. Coastal Queensland, parts of eastern Brazil and smalle areas in Ecuador, Colombia and the Central American area als fall into this category.

TROPICAL SCRUB FOREST

Tropical scrub forest or thorn forest also occurs where ther is seasonal precipitation but where the rainfall generally is lower more capricious, and the rainy season is shorter Characteristi of this biome type is the caatinga of the northeast of Brazil, th so-called Dry North-east Region which covers nearly (6,50,00 km^2) and includes parts of the states of Maranhao, Piaui, Cerara Rio Grande do Norte, Paraiba Pernambuco, Alagoas, Sergip and Bahia. Topographically it is a hilly, upland region, a peneplained plateau with resistant masses forming mountair ridges known as serras. The region is distinguished by th irregularity and uncertainty of the rainfall and its partial aridity The total annual precipitation varies between approximately 3C and 60 inches (762-1,524 mm). This is not unduly low, but four factors affect its efficiency: first, the rainfall is highly erratic and completely undependable in its occurrence; second, the rain tends to come in a few violent downpours of brief duration; third, the high temperatures result in a high rate of evaporation; and, fourth, the disposition of the relief produces rain shadow effects.

Most of the precipitation falls between December and April, but in any given locality its occurrence and amount varies" widely from month to month and from year to year. Periods of drought alternate with heavy rains. A long, dry, hot season prevails between May and October when the skies are clear, the sun burns down, the temperatures are over 27° C (80° F), and the intensity of evaporation is high. The climatic conditions cause the region to be subject to the recurring calamities of flood and drought, and by both of these the North-east is sorely tried and frequently hard hit.

Over most of the region the natural vegetation is a kind of scrub forest, termed caatinga. This consists of drought-resisting vegetation of small or dwarf hardwood trees, frequently twisted in a grotesque fashion, and thorny shrubs. The trees and shrubs usually bear small leaves which are shed during the dry season. Thorns, spines and prickles are common plant features. In some moister areas the caatinga forms dense, intermingled, and sometimes impenetrable, thickets; in the more arid localities the twisted trees disappear altogether and cacti and bromeliads predominate. In aspect the caatinga varies greatly between season and season. During the rainy period the vegetation is green and luxuriant and grasses grow; as the dry season sets in, the verdant aspect disappears as the grasses wither and the trees lose their leaves; and at the end of the dry season the caatinga has a bare, harsh, desolate and hostile look about it. Large areas of caatinga have been cleared, sometimes as a result of the need for charcoal, sometimes to assist the growth of pasture grasses since cattle rearing is one of the economic mainstays of the region.

The Chaco region of the interior of South America is an extensive plain covered with scrub forest or xerophilous woodland over much of its extent of some 95,000 square miles (247,000 km2). In summer, temperatures are high and there are heavy rains, which result in flooding of extensive areas. During the cooler winter season there is drought; the lane dries out and becomes parched and baked, and the streams over their poorly defined channels, are reduced to mere trickles, sometimes drying up completely to form salt marshes. Generally speaking, the Chaco becomes drier westwards, and parts of the north-west are almost waterless This decrease in rainfall is reflected in the vegetational cover near the Rio Paraguay there is considerable forest cover, with grassy areas and clumps of palms; farther west scrub forest prevails with acacias, mimosa and palms broken by patches of rough savanna; in the far west the scrub forest degenerate; and thorny thickets mixed with coarse grassland occur. The Chaco is a zoological sanctuary, and innumerable species o animals, reptiles, birds and insects haunt the land. Jaguars armadillos, alligators, monkeys, snakes, toads, rheas, storks parrots, ducks, bats and butterflies, as well as warms of insect pests, such as ants and locusts, inhabit the area. The Chaco is not an attractive environment in its raw state, and it is sparsely populated. In the Americas, other small areas o tropical scrub forest occur in the Caribbean coastlands o Colombia and Venezuela and in the Sierra del Sur and Pacific Coast lowlands of Mexico.

Similar areas of tropical scrub forest occur in southern Ethiopia, Somalia and northern Kenya in Africa and in the India subcontinent where a belt surrounds the Thar Desert on the east and north.

TROPICAL RAIN FOREST

The tropical rain forest biome occurs in equatorial latitudes within a few degrees north and south of the equator which are always hot, humid and wet. The average monthly temperatures are always about 27°C (80°F). The diurnal range of temperature is greater than the annual range. Heavy convection rains fall daily. The average annual rainfall is usually about 80 inches (2,032 mm) but two periods of exceptionally heavy rainfall commonly occur a little after the equenoxes. It is a salient feature of tropical rain forest that there is no seasonal change of rhythm; the same sequence of weather repeats itself day after day, and conditions are more pleasant-in coastal localities where sea breezes bring air movement.

The constantly high temperatures and the plentiful and regular moisture provide optimum conditions for plant growth: such conditions promote a rapid and luxuriant growth of vegetation which expresses itself in forest. The flora is extremely varied and the tropical rain forest biome probably possesses around 1,00,000 species: we have referred earlier to the Malay archipelago which alone is said to have some 45,000 species. Since natural life thrives in the hot, humid climate, the outstanding characteristic of this biome is the richness of the natural life, not only plant life which because of the uninterrupted growing period proliferates but animal and micro-organic life as well. Vegetationally, forest is dominant although, as mentioned previously, diverse types of tropical forest make up this biome. The tropical rain forest occurs in three main areas, in the Amazon Basin, one the coastlands of West Africa and in the Congo Basin, and in the Malay-Indonesian region; smaller outliers occur elsewhere in intertropical latitudes.

The diverse forests which make up this biome, whether occurring in South America, Africa or Australasia, posses certain features in common: they are evergreen because, owing to the lack of any dry or cool season, there is no general period of leaf fall-germination, growth, flowering, fruiting and dying go on side by side; they are characteristically dense and difficult to penetrate as a result of the rampant growth and profusion of foliage; they show a wonderful wealth of plant species comprising trees, shrubs, ferns, epiphytes and parasites; and they usually exhibit a stratification into tiers, with sometimes as many as five different storeys.

Further in this concern some biogeographers and botanists gave a classification of tropical forest.

A classification of tropical rain forests. (Modified from Longman and Jenik, 1974).

Tropical evergreen or rain forests: Rainforests composed mainly of evergreens with little or no bud protection against drying or cold.

1. **Lawland forest**: multilayered structure with many trees exceeding 30m in height; discontinuous ground herbaceous layer.
2. **Mountain forest** : tree sizes markedly reduced and few species exceed 30m; abundant undergrowth, often represented by tree ferns, small palms, vascular and other epiphytes; ground layer rich in herbs and bryophytes.
3. **Cloud forest**: closed structure with numerous gaps and liana thickets; trees often garlaned, rarely over 20m; burdened with epiphytes, lianas and herbaceous climbers; extensive ground coverage of mosses, liverworts, broad-leaved herbs and herbaceous ferns.
4. **Alluvial forest** : multilayered closed structure with numerous gaps, distinctive herbaceous undergrowth and palms; can be subdivided into (a) riparian forests occupying the frequently flooded narrow strip along river banks, (b) occasionally-flooded forests which can contain emergent trees over 50 m with buttresses and numerous climbers, and (c) seasonally-waterlogged forests with an uneven tree cover where water stagnates for several months.
5. **Swamp forest**: tree species limited and usually less than 30 m high; stilt roots and air-breathing roots common; located in depressions and smaller valley bottoms with permanently excessive soil moisture and poor soil aeration.
6. **Peat forest** : stands generally less than 20m high with a few, slow-growing, broad-leaved trees or palms; few ground plants-mostly ferns; air-breathing roots and stilt roots common; found on nutrient-poor soils covered by an accumulating organic layer.
   a. This stylized diagram represents a typical evergreen forest where the top stratum (A) consists of emergent trees, some woody climbers and epiphytes, the (B) stratum is made up of large trees and many woody climbers and epiphytes, the (C) stratum consists of smaller trees and saplings, whilst in the lower strata, there are mainly shrubs and saplings with many small stem less palms and tree-seedlings (D) and the ground

layers (E) consists of shade and moisture-loving herbs and forbs (herbs other than ferns and grasses) tougher with small seedings, a small number of mosses, lichens and liverworts (thallophytes), but no carpet of plants typical of more open conditions. The root layers are also distinctive, usually consisting of a dense mat of roots in the surface 5-10cm, a less abundant mass of tree roots from 10cm downwards with only scattered roots in freely-drained conditions below, which seek out groundwater.

b. The forest is of a lowland type although the area is at 380m. All the trees taller than 4.5 m are shown. The climbers are shown in solid black. The symbols represent the following genera and families: Ac - Acalphya; Al - Araliacea; Cl - Clusia; Ch -Chomelia; Do - Dialyanthera; Gu - Guarea; Mr -Metteniusa; MX - Malmea; My - Myrtaceae; Qu -Quariribea; Sa - Sapindaceae; So - Socratea; Tr -Trichillia; Va - Virola.

The variety of trees within a short distance illustrates the diversity of the area. (After Grubb et al. 1963)

The plant species show a wonderful adaptation to the ever-hot, ever wet environment. In the struggle for light and air, trees grow tall and trunks are usually supported by tremendous buttresses. The foliage forms a canopy at foot top level and leaves are often large and leathery. Tree-perchers frequently suspend their roots thought the air, securing food and water from the atmosphere. In coastal localities the forests often terminate in mangrove swamps where the stilt-like roots of mangroves hold the trees firm in the oozing mud of the tidal-flats.

Just as the vegetation shows adaptations to the climatic conditions so, also, animal life is adapted to the vegetation. Dobby has remarked how "the tropical rain forest has complicated ecologies of living creatures associated with the various storeys and the variety of these creatures parallels the variety of the vegetation." Except in the more open forest, ground animals, other than reptilian and amphibian forms, find movement difficult; large animals are relatively few and ar usually confined to the marginal and more open areas. On th other hand, reptiles and amphibians are numerous, being adapte to life in the dapper and more swampy parts of the forest.

Arboreal forms and flying creatures are especially abundar and there is a great wealth of bird and insect life. The prolif tree life is a response to the unfavourable living conditions a ground level. Many of the birds, e.g. the parrot, toucan an bird of paradise, vie in their brilliant coloration and unusu forms with some of the exotic flowers. Birds, for the most pa are thoroughly arboreal, possessing well-developed climbing fee short stout legs, and strong hooked beaks which are as usef for climbing as for nut-cracking. Among the myriads of insec are brightly coloured butterflies, moths, malarials mosquito and armies of ants. Such mammalian forms as exist are typical tree-dwellers and show remarkable adaptations, especially i the form and freedom of their limbs, to life on the trees, e. long arms and short legs, prehensile tail, opposable thumb Mammals are normally non-fur bearing and subsist on frui and leaves. Characteristic of the larger mammals are the slot tapir and certain predatory cats, such as the South Americ jaguar which is a good tree climber and which in swampy are may be almost entirely arboreal in habit. Especially numero among the arboreal mammals are the primates: these a represented by the New and Old World monkeys, the goril and chimpanzee of the Congo Basin, the orang-utan of Borne and Sumatra and the gibbon of Malaya. The rivers often tee with fish and also provide a home for the African crocodile ar the South American alligator.

The accelerated decay of organic matter has, also, importa effects upon the formation and characteristics of the so Weathering is fairly uniform in equatorial latitudes and und the constant conditions of warmth and abundant moisture t process is more chemical than mechnical. Rock is rapidly brok down and rotted at depth under the attack of warm and we carbonated rainwater. Moreover, under the heavy rainfall ar high temperatures of equatorial latitudes, the soil tends to suff from pronounced leaching and from laterisation. Although t heavy leaf fall does sometimes produce tropical humus soils, usually the rapid bacterial decomposition prevents much humus accumulating.

The conditions prevailing in the rain forest environment exert a profound influence upon man and not infrequently limit his activities. The climate, essentially unhealthy and evervatin, saps man's energy and has debilitating effect. The persistently high temperatures, combined with high atmospheric humidity, not only undermine the human constitution and predispose towards skin complaints but also provide ideal conditions for the vectors of disease. Many diseases, such as malaria, leprosy, yellow fever, dysentery and dengue, are prevalent in the tropics and would appear to be associated with hot, humid conditions, Parasitic worms may infest the intestines causing irritation, deblitation and sometimes death. Many medical problems of the tropics, debilitation and sometimes death. Many medical problems of the tropics, however, arise from unsatisfactory and inadequate diet, hygience and sanitation rather than climate, and the problem of the acclimatization of white people has been shown to be concerned as much with these practical matters as with the climatic conditions themselves. Nevertheless, in general terms, it may be said that the rain forest environment is an unhealthy one and that the people living in it frequently show a low state of health.

Agriculture is difficult for a variety of reasons: except in the more open areas, plant growth is rapid and lxuberant and this poses a problem of clearing and keeping clear the ground; soil fertility is impaired by the excessive leaching and the accelerated bacteriological^ activity and soils quickly become exhausted; and many kinds of blights, rusts and plant pests exist and make cultivation a hazardous business. Again, while plant life is exceedingly rich, useful species seldom are found together in numbers and this militates against the exploitation of plant resources where as in a animal resources especially domestic animals, pastoral life and were imported stock field difficult to survive because lack of, suitable border wealth and prevalence of dangerous pest's insect i.e. tests.

Transport and communications have never been easy in the rain forest, and waterways, if conditions of navigation permitted, have always provided the chief lines of communication. Overland transport has always been very difficult because of the largely impenetrable forest and even today the construction and maintenance of any land highway-road or rail - presents a problem. In view of these difficulties it is not surprising that the rivers have provided the principal avenues of movement, although communications by water may be hampered by aquatic plants, floating tree-trunks, braiding channels and sandbanks.

Amazonia provides the most extensive area of tropical rain forest in the world. Although there are vast areas of unbroken forest the selva also embraces extensive stretches of savanna, grassy enclaves where the forest is thin (usually where there are patches of porous oil), and areas of swampland on the flood-plains which frequently carry only coarse grasses and the forest may be said to be the dominating feature of the region. Amazonia offers a poor home for man and the region is sparsely peopled. Of the total estimated population of around 2 million, the aboriginal peoples number perhaps 30,000 to 50,000 and live in widely scattered tribal groups in the depths of the forest. Immigrant settlers, mainly Jesuit missionaries and Portuguese adventures, entered Amazonia from both the west and the east very early,-not until the nineteenth century, with the growth of the importance of rubber, did immigrants begin to move into Amazonia in appreciable numbers. The greater part of the settlers, who include those who have come into the region since the rubber era, live in the eastern section of the basin-below Manaus-and especially around the mouth of the Amazon.

Opinions about Amazonia's possibilities very widely: from A.R. Wallace writing in 1853 to John Gounther writing a century later, the region's potentialities for settlement and production have been enthusiastically, even extravagantly, proclaimed; others have been much less sanguine. The prodigious forest wealth of Amazonia has not been touched and the present economy of the region is dominated by the gathering of forest products-the collection of latex for rubber, chicle for chewing gum, kapok for fiber, coca leaves for cocaine, cinchona bark for quinine and Brazil nuts. The Brazilian Government, conscious of the possibilities of Amazonia, their lost horizon, have begun to plan the conquest of the region, but, whatever success the Brazilians may have in Amazonia, there will be difficulties and setbacks, and progress will be slow. One and a half million square miles (3,900,000 km^2) of selva cannot be tamed in a decade, not even in a century, and such highly coloured statements as "the future home of a thousand million people" and "the chief hope of a plundered planet" show little appreciation of the geographical fundamentals of Amazonia.

In Africa the rain forest is neither so extensive nor in general so dense as the South American selva: moreover, it is more densely peopled and more economically developed. Although equatorial Africa as a whole cannot be said to be even moderately densely populated, except in southern Ghana and southern Nigeria, densities in the Central African republics are at least five or six times those in Amazonia. In Africa, disease and malnutrition go hand in hand and these, in turn, by sapping his energy, make the African an indifferent and inefficient farmer, shifting cultivation and bush fallowing are the traditional farming practices carried on in tropical Africa. However, some tree crops of economic value, such as oil palm, cacao, bananas and rubber, are grown in the rain forest zone, often on a plantation basis, and there are a number of areas producing agricultural commodities for export. There has also been some exploitation of mineral wealth, e.g. petroleum, bauxite, diamonds, manganese. Although the rain forests are not suitable for stock rearing, the presence of the tsetse fly, which is responsible for the spread of sleeping sickness (trypanosomiasis), a disease which can be fatal to animals and man alike, makes it almost impossible to raise stock.

In the Australian area the occurrence to tropical rain forest is more fragmentary because of the topographical fragmentation and the varied relief, but, partly because of these conditions and partly because the area lies between the main Asian and Australian centres of plant dispersal, it possesses a diversity of flora which is probably without parallel anywhere else on Earth. The true rain forest is largely restricted to the coastal, lowland

and mountain, areas of South-east Asia, most, though by no means all, of the Indonesian region, and the narrow coastal fringe of northern Australia and Queensland.

MOUNTAIN BIOMES

There are areas in the world which, because of their high relief, create complex biotic conditions and it seems necessary to accept high mountains and high tablelands as forming a distinct biome type. High altitude, often extreme ruggedness, thin and stony soils, frequently interior drainage, and an 'alpine' climate usually found characteristic feature over these mountain areas physically. Altitude induces temperature changes and it is the drop in temperature with height which is largely, if not entirely, responsible for the climatic zonation which is characteristic of mountain areas. Such climatic changes react upon plant life and there is a zonation of vegetation which is more or less in sympathy with the climate. Nevertheless, there is an associated zonation of climate and vegetation which is probably best exemplified in the Andes, where distinctive zones, tierra caliente, tierra templada, tierra fria and tierra nevada (or helada), are clearly recognizable.

At high altitudes the climates are designated alpine and these bear a fairly close relationship with the tundra climate, but there are differences, that the tundra climate, as we have already seen, is controlled by the annual cycle of solar radiation which gives two strongly contrasting seasons, winter and summer. Alpine climates differ in having winter sunshine and summer night-time. They tend also to have higher rainfall, a greater snowfall, and more wind and a much higher degree of solar radiation which gives intense sunlight with a high amount of ultraviolet light. Both generally experience low temperatures and usually at times there are keen frosts.

As in the tundra regions, plant life is handicapped by the low temperatures and strong winds, and plants are characteristically small although there are exceptions, as in the tropics where the local climatic conditions are different and give rise to tall plants. The number of plant species in any mountain area is typically somewhat limited although alpine flora as a whole is much richer than tundra flora. Many plant species are common to both biomes. Grasses and sedges, mosses and lichens are abundant. In temperate latitudes the alpine pastures show a wealth of brightly coloured flowers in summer. On the puna of the Andean plateaus ichu grass is dominant with drought-and wind-resistant yareta and tola scrub. On Mount Kilimanjaro and some of the other mountains of tropical East Africa tufted grasses are interspersed with giant flowering herbs such as giant groundsel (Senecio johnstonni) and giant lobelia (Lobelia bequarti). Why such gigantic forms should develop in this tropical montane environment is something of a puzzle but it seems possible that they may be linked with the rarefied atmosphere and the increased intensity of ultraviolet light. Again, because of varying local conditions, resulting from aspect, shelter, drainage, soils, etc., the plant life varies from locality to locality within short distances. Only on the great, high, level plateaus such as the altiplano of Bolivia or the Tibetan Plateau is there a measure of uniformity.

The productivity of alpine vegetation is small and animal life, accordingly, is limited. Animals are mostly herbivorous and with a few exceptions, such as the yak of the Himalayan-Tibetan region, are small. The rocky habitat of many mountain areas has led to the development of herbivorous creatures which are extremely fragile, capable of climbing and jumping with ease, such as the chamois, the ibex and the American mountain goat. On the Andean plateaus and mountains the llama family (llama, alpaca, vicuna) is characteristic and unique, although the variants of this family would appear to be domesticated forms of the guanaco which was native to Patagonia; if this is so, the llama family represents an extension of a lowland form into the highlands. This is not uncommon, for, as a result of the altitudinal zonation, an example of this interchange is the puma, found in the Andes and the Rocky Mountains, which is an entrant from adjacent lower lands. The only large carnivore which is endemic to high-altitude regions would seem to be the snow leopard which inhabits the Himalayas.

With the notable exceptions of the Tibetans and kindred peoples such as the Sherpas of the Himalayas and the Andean

Indians of South America, few people make their homes in mountain environments. In some cases such use has resulted in overgrazing and serious modification of the alpine vegetation. In recent times some of these alpine lands have found a new utility as centres of tourism, catering for mountaineering and winter sports and serving as sanatoria, while in a few places the occurrence of mineralized zones has also led to mining activities.

■■■

13

Biogeographical Regions of the World

INTRODUCTION

A biome or biotic region is a major terrestrial community; it is the largest land community which can be conveniently recognized from geographical spread point of view. The unit comprise both vegetation and animal life forms. Each and every biome is the product of the interaction of regional climates with regional biota (plant and animal life). In a broad and fundamental sense a biome might be described as an area possessing a particular set of climatic conditions i.e. its own distinctive temperature and rainfall regime and its own diurnal and seasonal changes-for these conditions give rise to a particular kind of vegetation which, in turn, provides a home for a particular kind of animal life. The biomes are the equivalent of the plant ecologist's plant formations and of the geographer's major vegetation regions-indeed, the biomes are named after the predominant vegetation in any given region-but they include the characteristic animal life of those vegetation regions as well. The point which must be emphasized is that the biome is a total community and not merely a vegetation unit.

A particular combination of temperature, moisture and soil conditions conspires to produce a distinctive type of vegetation which may be forest, grassland or desert. Whatever type of vegetation results, it will have its own characterizing assemblage of animal life. The totality of life forms resulting from particular physical conditions results in a unique biotic region. The biomes which we can distinguish at the present time may be said to characterized by four principal features:

1. They have their own diagnostic combination of plants and animals.
2. They have each passed through a series of development stages to attain their present biotic character istics.
3. They have each attained an approximate condition of equilibrium with the regional environment.
4. Each displays a condition of natural balance which differs from the equilibrium reached in any of other biomes.[23]

It should be noted, however, that although biomes are more or less complete communities of plants and animals, they are seldom sharply separated from one another: it is more usual for one community to grade gradually into another. Thus in Central Asia what is some times known as the "grove belt", a transitional zone of wooded steppe, separates the coniferous forest from the temperate grassland. Such a transitional zone is known as an ecotone.

"Since the life form of the vegetation, on the one hand, reflects the major features of climate and, on the other, determines the structural nature of the habitat of animals, it provides," says Odum, "a sound basis for a natural ecological classification. "The major biomes of the world are as follows:

1. Tundra.
2. Northern Coniferous Forest.
3. Temperate Deciduous Forest.
4. Temperate Grassland.
5. Broad-leave Evergreen Forest.
6. Mixed Sub-tropical Forest.
7. Desert.
8. Tropical Savanna.
9. Tropical Deciduous Forest.
10. Tropical Scrub-Forest.
11. Tropical Rain Forest.
12. Mountain.

These are all familiar as the geographer's principal regions of natural vegetation. There is some approach to a zonal arrangement, more particularly in the northern hemisphere, but only the tundra and coniferous forest exhibit a measure of continuity. Other biomes of the same type, such as temperate grassland, desert or tropical rain forest, are more discrete because there is less geographical continuity in the land areas. Since such biomes occur in different continental areas with their species of plants and animals are often unrelated taxonomically, although they may show ecological equivalents.

It may be noted, also, that the pattern of the major biomes shows a broad correlation with, though it is not identical with, the principal soil groups.

1. Biogeographical Realms

As already indicated, it is possible to recognize three great associations of living things-vegetation, animal life and soil. The three are interrelated and interdependent. Plant life serves as a shelter for and provides sustenance for animal life, while both contribute to the formation of the soil. Animals, in turn, may influence plants through their selective eating habits and may be necessary for the fertilization of some plants. The soil, through its physical and chemical characteristics, affects vegetation and animals also since they are directly or indirectly dependent upon plants.

Vegetation may be said to hold a key position in our understanding of all life forms within the biosphere because of its function in soil formation and its support of animal life. Fauna (man excepted) fulfils a lesser role: the occurrence and distribution of animal life are determined essentially by the location of food supplies; both directly (in terms of the herbivores) and indirectly (in terms of the carnivores) the major animal associations are intimately linked with the patterns of established vegetative associations. Thus there is, as one might expect in view of this interdependence, a broad correspondence between distinctive areas of natural vegetation and particular associations of animal life. But more than this there is a broad correlation between floral realms (areas characterized by distinctive plant species and often plant genera) and faunal realms (areas possessing their own special fauna). Using these floral and faunal distinctions as a basis we can divide the earth up into a number of distinctive biogeographical realms, as follows:

1. Palearctic,
2. Nearctic,
3. Neotropical,
4. Ethiopian,
5. Oriental,
6. Australian.

Man, because he is a rational being and possesses a creative imagination, has destroyed, modified and improved, according to his wills and needs, the animal life and the soils of his planet. The influence of man has made itself very widely felt: steadily, laboriously, unremittingly, he has transformed large areas. Species of plants and animals have been exterminated, often ruthlessly; species of plants and animals have been transported from one habitat to another, sometimes with good, other times with unfortunate, results; and some species of plants and animals, as a result of man's scientific expertiseness, have been transformed almost out of all recognition.

In view of these changes it may be questioned whether the concept of biogeographical realms is still valid. However, it does remain true for many groups of plants and animals and has validity in explaining the historical biogeography of the Earth.

FLORAL REGIONS AND ZOOGEOGRAPHICAL REGIONS OF THE WORLD

Before elaborating these contrasts between the northern and southern land-masses we must pause to inquire how far plant distribution corresponds to that of mammals, that is to what extent we can correlate Floral Regions with their great Zoogeographical Realms already defined. There is a measure of correspondence, but botanists have not reached the unanimity as regards even major divisions which is so marked with the zoologists, while different schemes vary notably in regard to the number and status of the subdivisions.

It is not difficult to understand why this should be so. In the first place, the fossil record is very imperfect in the case of plants. Biogeographers have little direct knowledge either of the main centres of evolution or of the stages by which differentiation occurred in the higher forms. Mammals present a great contrast in this regard. As we have seen, the teeth which are readily fossilized, give clause to the diet and habits while the markings on the bones which show where the muscles were attached make it possible for the anatomist to make some reconstruction of form and function. Thus mammals are not only well represented as fossils in some Tertiary beds, but the material is such as to make it possible both to draw valid conclusions as to the areas in which they occupy.

BIOGEOGRAPHICAL REGIONS OF THE WORLD

So far as non-Volant terrestrial mammals are concerned also we can recognize quite definite barriers to their migratory movements. Though a number of the land mammals are good swimmers and take voluntarily to the water, yet there is little reason to believe that even these are likely to cross "belts of water exceeding some twenty miles in worth. Floating ice or raft-like masses of vegetation may be responsible that the mammoth crossed from Asia to Alaska either over a frozen surface or on broken masses of ice. In the general case, however, we can be reasonably sure that when several identical or nearly allied species of mammal occur on either side of a wide belt of water, then there must have been in the not very distant past some kind of land link. It is very different with plants. The fruits and seeds of some kinds are definitely adapted to water transport so that it is water and not land that functions as the track of migration. The coconut palm is the outstanding example, for it is distributed throughout the warm zone and is one of the few genera of palms with such a range, for it is true generally that the parts of that zone have endemic, that is peculiar, palm genera. Thus the doum palms (Hyphaene) are limited to Africa and the wax-palms (Copernicia) to tropical America. Thus, one cannot lay any particular stress, however, upon the wide range of the coconut, for the trees tend to occupy coastal sites and the fruit is capable of floating long distances uninjured and will then germinate if cast up on a beach. The members of the screw-pine family or Pandanaceae (not to be confused with the coniferous pine) also have fruits adapted for sea transport and are widely distributed in the inter-tropical belt of the Old World. Thus, the members of the genus Freycinetia extend from Ceylon to New Zealand and the Polynesian Islands; but we cannot regard this as a proof of affinity between the flora of Ceylon and that of New Zealand.

There are other possible ways in which plants may be transmitted across the belts of water or even over those deserts and transeverse mountain chains which seem to block the movements of most mammals. Fruit-eating bats or birds on migration may have within their bodies seeds which when finally voided are still capable of germination. Thus, the Bermuda Islands contain an endemic 'cedar', really a species of juniper whose nearest ally is found in Cuba, nine hundred" miles distant. But we need not here assume a former land connexion, for birds eat juniper "berries' freely and the Bermudas are visited by a number of migrant forms. Seeds and fruits may also cling to the bodies of flying animals and be thus transported, or, when small or furnished with a parachute, may be carried great distances by air currents. Man also is a potent if often unwitting agent of dissemination and it is much less easy than with animals to trace the effects of his influence. If again we recall the fact that the single large and cosmopolitan order of the Composites among the Dicotyledons contains more species than the two classes of birds and mammals put together, it is not difficult to realize that to make a satisfactory subdivision of the globe into floral regions based even on the Angiosperms alone, is a problem of great complexity.

We have already seen that conifers tend to accumulate towards the poles, largely avoiding inter-tropical areas. As positive features of the latter we have the tendency for arborescent forms of Monocotyledons to occur, as exemplified by palms, bamboos, screw-pines and many others, while in the higher latitudes even monocotyledonous shrubs are rare. Again, if the names of most of the tropical dicotyledonous orders are unfamiliar the fact that they sound strange to ears well accustomed to hear of the Ranunculus groups, the poppies, the saxifrages, the crucifers and so on, but serves to emphasize the greatness of the contrast between tropical and temperate plants. Among the numerous families which are mainly or wholly tropical we may note the Sterculiaceae, which include the South American cacao tree, the Anonaceae, including the custard apples, the Piperaceae or peppers widely spread in tropical latitudes, the Sapotaceae also with a wide range within the African tree from the fruit of which the butter is made.

But if tropical America, much of tropical Africa and at least the eastern section of tropical Asia fall in this way into a wide pan-tropic belt, with a number of common features so far as orders are concerned, tropical Australia, as indeed one would expect, stands markedly aloof. Not only has the continent in the main a flora of its own, very different from that of the other land-masses, but there is not that contrast between tropical and extra-tropical families and genera which is so marked in South America and Africa.

Thus we get as a first region a Pantropic or Inter-tropical Belt stretching right across the globe, but excluding most of Australia save a comparatively small area round the Gulf of Carpentaria and in Cape York peninsula. Within this Pantropic region, however, again as we might except in view of what we have seen occurs in the case of mammals, the signs of affinity between the floras of tropical Africa and tropical Asia are much closer than between the former and the plants of tropical South America. So great are the contrasts indeed that most systematic botanists find it convenient to divide the Pantropic Belt into an Old World and a New World section. At the same time, and for us it is a significant fact, the sharpness of the contrast is blurred by finding that there are a few-a very few-genera common to West Tropical Africa and Tropical America but absent from other parts of the Old World tropics. Two examples are the related genera Vismia and Symphonia, tropical trees belonging to what is apparently a somewhat old-fashioned family. Vismia has a fairly wide range in tropical America and a very limited one in West Africa, while Symphonia with a not dis-similar range in America is more widely spread in tropical Africa and reappears, after a gap, in Madagascar, but not elsewhere. There is a certain analogy to the range of a group of frogs (Aglossa), represented by two genera and several species in the Guianas and lower Amazon area. The Aglossa posses certain primitive features and the living kinds are apparently related to a fossil form found in mid-Tertiary beds in Europe, suggesting that the group had a northern origin. Such facts are important because they confirm the rather less definite evidence derived from the mammalian fauna that there has been in the geological past some kind of link between West Africa and Brazil despite the present width of the Atlantic ocean.

The second region shown on the map includes the southern part of the Sahara, much of Arabia and the continuation of this arid belt eastwards to the Indian desert. It may be called the Northern Palaetropical Deset Region. From the floristic standpoint it is characterized by the negative feature of the absence of endemic orders, while even the genera are shared with the bordering areas to the north and south. On the other hand the species, remarkably few when the extent of the area is borne in mind, are mainly endemic. This means in effect that the region is now so arid that it supports plant life with difficulty but that the onset of the present extreme drought or the extension of the drought area or both must have been sufficiently gradual to make it possible for a certain amount of adaptation to take place, involving the rise of a number of new species.

It is only when we consider the subdivisions of Arctogaea that the full significance of this floral region becomes clear. Africa south of the desert forms for the zoologist the Ethiopian Region of the Arctogaeic Realm, but he draws his limit as a straight line, corresponding mainly to the tropic, across the Saharan and Arabian desert. Straight lines of the kind, whether as political or administrative frontiers or as distribution limits, mean two things. They mean firstly that at the time of drawing there is little knowledge of detail; almost always there is also a secondary implication that the detail is not worth troubling about. In this particular case the point which interests the zoologist is that to the north of the desert, in the lands bordering the Mediterranean Sea and sharing the Mediterranean type of climate, there are deer and sheep, both absent from the south, while the characteristic Ethiopian mammals do not occur. For him then the desert as a whole is a kind of no man's land separating areas with characteristic faunas and having too few mammals of its own to need special consideration. It is therefore very important that the botanists on the other hand emphasize rather the transitional or 'island' character of the southern section of the desert belt, which at once links the Mediterranean flora of the north with the tropical flora of the south, and has also served as a minor centre of evolution. If, as the zoologist believes, the present mammals of Ethiopian Africa entered from the north, he has a problem to solve in the question of how the forest-haunting forms got across the desert. Some botanists maintain that the 'Europear' element in the Desert Floral Region is so pronounced as to prove that during the height of glaciation the Sahara cannot have been nearly so arid as at present, and that there must have been at least relatively moist areas which served as migration tracks. Clearly this view aids the zoologist in facing his own problem.

North of the Desert Floral Region the botanists recognize a Mediterranean one, using the term in a some what wider sense than is usual with climatologists. That is, the Mediterranean Floral Region includes not only the Mediterranean Lands as usually defined but extends southwards to cover part of the Sahara and eastwards into Persia. The essential floristic feature is the presence throughout of at least some of the plants characteristic of the true Mediterranean lands, combined with the absence of the endemic species which distinguish the Desert Region. The limits are thus necessarily somewhat vague, especially to the east. Southwards, however, there is a good deal of evidence to show that some of the mountain massifs of the Sahara form a kind of floral divide, the northern slopes bearing plants of definitely Mediterranean character and the southern ones endemic desert plants.

This enlarged Mediterranean Region is of much interest to the zoologist, who would fain recognize a similar zoological division if he could find a logical basis. This is partly because, as we have already suggested, the American zoologists divide North America into a northern and a southern section, the one characterized by mammals with strong affinities to those of temperate Eurasia, the other by those common to Neogaea. There is no doubt that the mammals present round the Mediterranean Sea do differ from those found north of the Alpine chains of Europe and their continuations in Asia. The difficulty is that this "Mediterranean" fauna has neither the measure of unity which can be recognized in the southern or Sonoran section of the fauna of North America, nor that which can be recognized for the plants. For example, Syria shares with Ethiopian Africa the rock coney (Hyrax); here we seem to have an obvious analogy with the peccary present in the southern United States and extending also into South America. As against this we find that the monkey, the so-called Barbary ape, found in the Atlas Lands and one the Rock of Gibraltar belongs to a genus (Macacus) found not in Africa but in eastern Asia (India, Father India and some of the Malay Islands with an extension into Tibet, China and Japan). Generally the mammals found round the Mediterranean Sea show a great mixture of elements, their nearest allies being widely scattered.

This is the more remarkable in that during the Pleistocene period the mammalian fauna of southern Europe and its borderlands was at once much richer than at present and the contrasts between it and that of the region north of the mountain belt much greater. The pre-glocial mammals, aided it would seem by land-links, scattered widely ; many became extinct in their former habitat, a few lingered on in isolated areas, but great numbers found their way into Ethiopian Africa or into tropical Asia south of the mountain belt. The result is that while we have to-day very definite contrasts between the faunas of temperate Eurasia on the one hand and those of Ethiopian Africa and what is called the Oriental Region of Asia on the other, the area which forms for the botanist the Mediterranean Floral Region is not zoologically a unit.

It should be noted that what is rather loosely called the "migration" of plants necessarily takes place in a very different fashion from the actual migratory movements of mammals. Numbers of plants which once grew round the shores of the Mediterranean Sea, as well as farther north, have disappeared. But certain areas-the Balkan peninsula seems to have been one-served as refuges from which a measure of re-colonization of lost ground took place, the beautiful Judas tree (Cercis siliquastrum) seems to be an outstanding example of a plant which survived glaciation within the Balkan peninsula and spread westwards again as the climate improved. Such instances of survival are sufficiently numerous among plants to make it possible to define a separate Mediterranean Floral Region; they are too infrequent among mammals for it to be possible to erect a similar zoological region.

Apart from these two interrelated Floral Regions in the eastern hemisphere there is no real difference between the botanists and the zoologists as egads the recognizable biogeographical regions of the northern extra-tropical lands. The botanists accept the view of the zoologists that despite minor and local differences temperae Eurasia shows remarkable resemblances in its life to North America. Many botanists indeed take over from the zoologists the term Holarctic to cover a wide belt in both hemispheres, the name being intended to emphasize the fact that the farther north one goes the closer are the resemblances.

Turning next to the southern hemisphere we find that all botanists separate off from the great Pantropic Region extra-tropical South America and South Africa and also, as already stated, virtually the whole of the Australian continent. Are these three separate regions or merely subdivisions of an interrupted Austral Region? The point is debatable and we need only note that there are clear signs of affinity between the floras of South Africa has no marsupials and Australia no placentals the mammals of the two areas cannot show any relationship and there is no definite evidence of this among other faunal elements. On the other hand traces of affinity certainly exist between the faunas of South America and of Notogaea. Generally we may say that the distribution of plants in part confirms and in part supplements the zoologists' view that there has been at one time some kind of connexion between the now widely separaed southern continents.

We may now sum up the general conclusions arrived at. zoologists and botanists are agreed that it is possible to divide up the lands of the world on the basis of the taxonomic affinities of their plants and animals. There are also at least certain resemblances between the divisions recognized. The differences can be explained in part by the fact that the zoologists have, so far as the mammals are concerned, far more fossil material at their disposal than is available for the botanists; in part also by the contrasts between the modes of dispersal open to mammals and to land plants. The number of kinds of land plants is also much greater than that of land mammals so that the botanical problem is far more complex.

Because of the wealth of fossil material the zoologists in their first division of the globe into Realms lay stress upon the fact that a wide tract of land, including sections in both eastern and western hemispheres, and extending in Africa far south of the Equator, seems to have had some measure of unity throughout later geological time, and, so far as its northern section is concerned, to have served as the main centre of evolution for the higher living mammals. Notogaea has been long isolated and has served as the centre of evolution for the majority of living marsupials. Neogaea was similarly for long isolated, and there special types of mammals evolved; but at least since towards the close of the Tertiary era it has been connected with North America.

Arctogaea is so wide a Realm that it must needs be divided. To the north there is a contrasts between the eastern (or Palaearctic) sub-region and the western (or Nearctic) are much less marked than the resemblances. This leads to the recognition of one large Holarctic Region. In North America this passes, not without intermixture, into the Sonoran Region, where mammals with Neogaea affinities are mingled with Arctogaeic ones. In the eastern hemispehere the desert belt on the one hand and the mountain chains, of which the Himalayas are the most conspicuous element, on the other, make the separation of Ethiopian and Oriental Regions an easier matter.

Neogaea scarciy needs subdivision, but partly to get a completely logical arrangement and partly to emphasize the fact that many of its most peculiar forms are limited to the tropical areas, it is regarded as including a single Neotropical region. Notogaea is more complex, for various island areas, including some of the Malay islands, which contain mammals, and New Zealand, the Polynesian Islands and the Hawaiian Islands, which have none, have to find a place here. For the moment it is sufficient to say that continental Australia, New Guinea and Tasmania form the Australian Region.

Turning next to Floral Regions we find that the botanists tend to simplify their problem by laying the first stress upon climate. A number of orders are virtually limited to the tropics, and, apart from the Conifers, which are geologically old, there is a general tendency both in the class of Monocotyledons and in those orders of Dicotyledons which are both tropical and temperate, for arborescent forms to predominate in the tropicas and herbaceous forms in the temperate regions.

As against this tendency for the botanists to run their major divisions across the globe, and specifically to recognize a great (Holarctic) North Temperate Region as contrasted with an almost equally wide Pantropic one, they are constrained to separate off certain special regions. In the estern part of the northern hemispehre we have a Northern Palaeotropical Region and a Mediterranean .Region of more limited extension. The southern hemisphere presents difficulties. We cannot say that an Austral temperate region is recognized, for the Austral Floral Region includes tropical as well as temperate Australia. If we call this area 'Australian' we have to remember that the botanist is not using the word in quite the same sense as the zoologist.

The divisions may be put for convenience in the following tabular form:

Table 13.1

Floral Region	*Zoological Realms*	*Regions*
1. Holarctic (including Sonoran zoological Region)	1. Arctogaea	1. Hoiarctic. 2. Sonoran. 3. Ethiopian. 4. Oriental.
2. Mediterranean	2. Neogaea	5. Neotropical.
3. Northern Palaeotropical Desert	3. Notogaea	6. Australian and others.
4. Pantropic		
5. Australian	(a) Extra-tropical (b) Extra-tropical Ethiopian (c) 'Australian'	

ECONOMIC BEARINGS OF BIOGEOGRAPTIY

The final, and it might be supposed the most important aspect of biogeography, is the economic one. Here, however, we find that at least so far as the chief cultivated and useful wild plants are concerned, much of the material already finds a place in the ordinary text-books, and does not require special consideration. Certain problems, it is true, are inadequately treated there and demand fuller discussion in the light of biological principles. In the main, however, the economic side need be treated only in summary fashion.

Lastly by summing up, then, we have three main topics to discuss in this book:

1. The influence of natural conditions on the distribution and outstanding features of the great terrestrial plant communities and the animals associated with them.
2. The outstanding facts of the taxonomic distribution of organisms over the land surfaces, in so far as this distribution throws light upon the present features of these and on their probable past history.

3. The response made by marine organisms to the ocean habitat in relation to the conditions existing there, and the similar response in the case of the fresh-water habitat.

In particular, we must have a clear if generalized notion of the main living kinds of plants and animals, which involves a study of the elements of taxonomy also.

■■■

14

Biodiversity

INTRODUCTION

Biological diversity (or biodiversity) comprises all species of plants, animals, and micro-organisms and the ecosystems and ecological processes of which they are part. It is usually considered at three different levels: genetic diversity, species diversity, and ecosystem diversity. Genetic diversity is the sum total of genetic information, contained in the genes of individual plants, animals, and micro-organisms that inhabit the Earth. Species diversity refers to the variety of habitats, biotic communities, and .ecological processes in the biosphere, whereas the tremendous diversity within ecosystems is based on, terms of habitat differences and the variety of ecological processes.

Biological diversity or Biodiversity is the characteristic of living things to be formed by many and different entities. So, for example, our body is formed of many and different cells, and no two human being are identical, not even identical twins. Biodiversity is a basic property of life. It manifests itself at all levels of biological organization from cells to ecosystems. It is considered essential for the proper functioning of living systems since it provides populations, species, and ecosystems.

Populations, species, and ecosystems can differ very significantly in diversity. So, while most individuals of a species are genetically very dissimilar, some populations of plants and animals such as dandelions or cheethas are formed by genetically very uniform individuals. The same is true of ecosystems. While some ecosystems such a the vegetation of the Cape of Good Hope known as "feinbos", tropical rainforests, or coral atols have hundreds of species, others such a the northern taiga, the Antartic sea-shelf, or heath communities, are very poor in species. In general tropical ecosystems are more variable than temperate ones.

We do not yet know precisely what factors explain these great variations in diversity. We do not even know whether some general principles determine the biodiversity of a region, or whether each local situation is unique, the result of unpredictable historical factors.

If the principle role of biodiversity is to provide the biological materials to cope with inevitable environmental change, both gradual and sudden, it may be hypothesized that the greater the variation the more capable a biological system is able to deal with change.

Can it said that tropical regions with their greater biodiversity are better equipped to deal with change than temperate regions? Empirical evidence appears to discount such an assertion.

Planet Earth is endowed with a rich variety of life forms and the teeming millions of these living organisms have been well-knit by the laws of nature. The inter-dependence of the various life forms-starting from the uncelular primary producers to the complexly built higher plants and animals is a unique feature of this green planet.

Biodiversity, as this assemblage of life forms as referred to, has now been acknowledged as the foundation for sustainable livelihood and food security. Scientists have estimated that more than 50 million species of plants and animals, including invertebrates and micro-organisms, occur on earth and hardly 2 million of them have been described by man so far. Scientists are also aware of the immense potentials of various life forms, especially in the context of recent advances made in science and technology. The incessant human assault on forests has left indelible scars on nature. One result on the United Nations

Conference on Environment and Development held in Riode Janeiro in June 1992 was a "Convention on Biological Diversity" which was signed by 156 countries and European community.

DEFINITION

Biodiversity refers to the variety of forms-the different plants, animals and microorganisms. It also includes the genes they contain and the ecosystems they form.

Biological diversity refers to the variety and variability, among living organisms and the ecological complexes in which they occur. Diversity can be defined as the number of different items and their relative frequency. For biological diversity, these items are organized at many levels ranging from complete ecosystems to the chemical structures that are the molecular basis of heredity. Thus, the term encompasses different ecosystems, species, genes and their relative abundance.

BIODIVERSITY IN THE WORLD

On the planet earth, there are about 30 million insects, 15,210 mammals, reptiles and amphibians, 9,225 birds 21,000 fishes, about 4,80,000 plants and 3 million other invertebrates and micro organisms. Many among them have not been identified. For example, out of 30 million insects, only 7,51,000 have been identified. Other organisms identified (total number of species in brackets) are: mammals, reptiles and amphibians 14,484 (15,210), birds 9,040 (9,225), fish 19,056 (21,000), plants 3,22,311 (4,80,000), other invertebrates and micro organisms 2,76,594 (3,00,000), making a total of 1,392,485 (33,525,435).

Most of the 1,700 million hectares of tropical forest, rich in biodiversity, were located in poor countries. While such forests covered barely 7 per cent of the land surface, they harboured half of the species of the world's flora and fauna. For instance, in a 15-hectare patch of rain forest in Brunei, 700-odd species of trees have been identified as many as in all of North America. Much of the world's agricultural and pharmaceutical needs-from developing hybrid seeds to herbal cures-come from such prime forests. Famous Hard ward biologist E.O. Wilson estimates that the choping down of tropical forests leads to extinction of at least 50,000 invertebrate species every year-about 140 facing extinction every day.

BIODIVERSITY IN INDIA

India is exceptionally rich in biodiversity and is one of the 12 mega-diversity centres of the world. With 10 bio-geographic zones and 25 biotic provinces, all major ecosystems are represented here. The bio-diversity hotspots include mainly the Eastern Ghats, the Western Ghats and the North-Eastern hills. The estimates figures of plant species and animal species, representing 7 percent of world's flora and 6.5 percent of world's fauna, of which 33 percent flora and 62 percent fauna are endemic.

Thus, India is recognized as a country uniquely rich in all aspects of Biodiversity-ecosystem, species and genetic. For any one country in the world, it has perhaps the largest array of environmental stipulations by virtue of its tropical location, varied physical features and ckunatuc types. India has the widest variety of biomass, it attribute further enhanced by the meeting of three major biogeographic reamis, namely, the Indo-Malayan (the richest in the world), the Eurasian and the Afro-Tropical. The plant wealth of India is about 45,000species, i.e. 12 percent of global wealth of plants and nearly 33 percent of these are endemic, mainly located in 26 endemic centres. These include 5,000 species of algae, 1,600 lichens, 20,000 fungi, 2,700 bryophytes, 600 pteridophytes, and 15,000 flowering plants. Roughly one third of the flowering plants are endemic and nearly 1000 species are endangered. The animal wealth of India is about 75,500 species which includes 60,000 insects, 1,693 fishes, 372 mammals, 1200 birds, 420 reptiles and amphibians and 4,000 molluscs, Endemic among these are 33% reptiles and 62% amphibians. There are very few estimates available of India's marine life (765 starfish, brittlesthar, sea urchins although it has a coastline over 7,500 km long. The marine-life-data has yet to be systematically recorded.

The Indian region alone has given to the world nearly 167 economical plants whose centre of origin/diversity lies in India, along with their 320 species of wild relatives and land races, for example, rice, sugarcane, minor millets, brassicas, rice-bean, asiaticvignas, egg plant, banana, citrus, mango, cardamom, jack fruit, jute, edible diascorea, black pepper, seed amarnathus, turmeric, ginger, several umbetlifers and cucurbits, colocasia, and many herbal drugs, rhododendrons, jasmine, some bamboos, some orchids and betel nut. Further, the opportunities and scope provided by genetic engineering, which allows the transfer of genes among the species, will increase the opportunities which the genetic diversity provides for enhancing agricultural productivity.

Livestock diversity is also high: 27 breeds of cattle, 40 of sheep and 22 of goats are available in India.

1. Distribution of Species

No one knows the number of species on Earth, even to the nearest order of magnitude. Estimates vary from 5 to 80 million species or more. Only about 1.4 million of these living species have been briefly described. Of these about 750,000 are insects, 41,000 are vertebrates and 250,000 are plants; the remainder consists of a complex array of invertebrates, fungi, algae and other micro-organisms.

Like other natural resources, the distribution of living species in the world is not uniform. Species richness increases from the poles to the equator. Freshwater insects, for example, are 3 to 6 times more abundant in tropical areas than in temperate zones. Tropical regions have also the highest richness of mammal species per unit area, and vascular plant species diversity is much richer at lower latitudes. Forty-to one hundred species of trees may occur on one hectare of tropical rain forest in Latin America, compared to only ten to thirty on a hectare of forest in eastern North America. In one area of about 15 hectares of rain forest in Borneo, about 700 species of trees were identified, as many as in all of North America. A region in lowland Malaysia near Kuala Lumpur has some 570 plant species greater than 2 cm in diameter per hectare.

In comparison, all of Denmark possesses less than twice as many species of all sizes- as there are in one hectare in Malaysia. Global patterns of species diversity in the marine environment resemble those on land. The number of tunicate (sea squirt) species increases from 103 in the Arctic to some 629 in the tropic, the diversity of plank tonic foraminifera increases from only two species near the poles to some 16 in tropical water, and deep sea species diversity also tends to be higher at lower latitudes.

Tropical forests are not, however, the only highly diverse ecosystems. Mediterranean climate regions also have very rich flora with high levels of endemism. For example, of the 23,200 species of plants estimated to occur in South Africa, Lesotho, Swaziland, Namibia and Botswana (which are temperate areas), 18,560 (i.e. 80 percent) are endemic to the region. This gives the area the highest species richness in the world, 1.7 times greater than that of Brazil. Some 30 per cent of California's 5,046 plant species and 68 percent of south west Australia's 3,600 plants are endemic to these regions.

2. Importance of Biological Resource

Biological diversity provides the basis for life on Earth. The fundamental social, ethical, cultural, and economic values of these resource have been recognized in religion, art, and literature from the earliest days of recorded history. Wild species and the genetic variation within them make substantial contributions to the development of agriculture, medicine, and industry. Perhaps even more important, many species have been fundamental to stabilization of climate, protection of watersheds, protection of soil, and to the protection of nurseries and breeding grounds. It is difficult to determine the total economic value of the full range of goods and services which biological diversity provides.

Biological resources have made substantial contributions to human welfare, especially in rural areas of developing countries. For example, fuel wood and dung provide over 90 percent of the energy needs in many areas in Nepal, Tanzania, and Malawi and more than 80 percent in many other countries. In Botswana, over 50 species of wild animals provide animal protein, which constitutes up to 40 percent of diet in some areas. In Ghana, about 75 percent of the population depends largely on traditional sources of protein, mainly wildlife.

Human beings have used about 7,000 kinds of plants for food, but only 20 species supply 90 percent of the world's food, and just three - wheat, maize and rice - supply more than half. Although the major food crops in use today were domesticated thousands of years ago. Numerous locally important less known species of wild and domesticated plants could be cultivated and used much more widely. For example, quinua, a staple grain of the highlands of Bolivia, Chile, Ecuador, and Peru, yet it is one of the world's most productive sources of plant protein. Biological resources are also major industrial feed stocks, and can have a major impact on national economics.

3. Loss of Species

Throughout the geological history of the Earth, species of plants and animals had been subjected to various evolutionary processes. Some species became extinct during the different geological periods, the length of which is measured by millions of years. The last major extinction of some species occurred at the close of the Cretaceous Period, some 65 million years ago, when birds and mammals were particularly affected. The total disappearance of all dinosaurs occurred during that great extinction. Although the causes of those extinctions are a matter of scientific speculation, it is generally agreed that they were triggered by natural environmental phenomena during the geological evolution of the Earth. In recent history, biological resources have been lost at an accelerated rate, mainly due to anthropogenic causes.

No precise estimate can be made of the number of species that have been - or are being - lost in major habitats. This is mainly due to the lack of systematic monitoring and baseline information. Many species may become extinct before they are even discovered or described. The extinction of other species may be detected years later because of inadequate monitoring. Most experts have concluded that perhaps a quarter of the Earth's total biological diversity is at serious risk of extinction during the next 20-30 years. Between 1990 and 2020, species extinctions caused primarily by tropical deforestation (tropical forests cover only 7 percent of the Earth's land surface, but contain more than hall of the species in the entire world biota) may elimate between 5 and 15 per cent of the world's species. This would amount to a potential loss of 15,000 to 50,000 species per year, or about 40 to 140 species per day. The World Conservation Monitoring Centre has recorded that some 22,000 species of plants and animals are actually threatened with extinction.

THREATS TO BIODIVERSITY

As Gandhiji once said, The Mother Nature has every thing to meet our needs and not to satisfy our greed. Failure to consider this aspect has resulted in the threat to biodiversity as a whole. There exists an overall lack of any sustained effort to preserve the ecosystem. As genetic diversity erodes, out capacity to maintain and enhance agricultural forest and livestock productivity decreases. The major factors leading to decline of biodiversity are:

1. Over-exploitation

Indiscriminate killings have dragged many animals to the verge of extinction. The inability to site even a single tusker in Periyar Sanctuary of Kerala is a case in point Animals are hunted for many precious commodities, notable ivory, fur, skin, horn etc.

2. Habitat Degradation

Loss of breeding habits may endanger the species. The banning of buffaloes into the famous Koeladeo National Park of the Bharatpur Bird Sanctuary since 1982 has led to an overgrowth of grass in wetlands, disrupting the aquatic habitat. The overgrowth of the weed, Paspalum distichmm forming an aquatic mat have made feeding very difficult for birds. Number of migratory birds like the Siberian Crane Herons and Water-Fowls have greatly declined due to this Habitat fragmentation may be due to several reasons of which, deforestation and pollution rank foremost.

3. Deforestation

Large forest areas have been cleared for constructional as well as extensive agricultural purposes leaving the native animals home-less. Construction of dams has destroyed many large sections of rivers and streams and their ecosystems. Coastal zone development is responsible for wiping out the reefs near the shores. Jhum cultivation has led to considerable decline in the North Eastern forests. Earlier, the Jhum cycle was 25 to 50 years, now it is just 5-8 years, almost doubling the deforestation. In Nagaland alone, 4.4 lakh tonnes of fertile topsoil are lost every year from areas of Jhum practice. Over 300 sq. kms of forest cover has been lost in the North East, while the figure for India as a whole is 5482 sq. kms.

4. Pollution of the Land

Pollution strains ecosystem and reduces sensitive species. The Barn owl population of U.K. is under great pressure due to extensive use of rodenticides. Toxic amounts of pesticides through the process of bio-magnification have reached the body of even the arctic and Antarctic inhabitants. The 6017 sq. km Sunderbans designated as a World Heritage site in 1997 is now in danger. Tops of thousand of trees are dying. Even the soil micro flora and fauna suffer from pollution as industries shed huge quantities of deleterious chemicals.

5. Global Climate Change

A sea level rise of 1 to 2 metres is expected in the next century due to global warming. The shape of the map of India at that time would be difficult to predict since many coastal regions and islands would be submerged in the sea. Often introduced species may result in the extinction of native species. They may multiply due to lack of predators and outnumber the natives, resulting in a final withdrawal of the latter.

Four main causes have been identified for the loss of biological diversity. The first is habitat loss, fragmentation and modification. As forests are cleared, wetlands drained, valleys flooded and roads built, so habitats are transformed and effectively lost for certain species. It has been estimated that 11.1 million ha of tropical forests are eliminated each year (i.e. 21 ha every minute). A reduction of say 70 per cent of a tropical forest leads not only to the elimination of entire species restricted to the removed part of the forest, but also reduces the number of other species living in the forest to 30 per cent of their original population size, rendering them more vulnerable to future extinction. Habitat changes in sub-Sharan Africa and in tropical Asia have caused a loss of 65 per cent and 76 per cent of wildlife, respectively. (54,55)

The second reason for the loss of biological diversity is over-exploitation of resources. Commercial harvesting has been a threat to many marine species. Overexploitation has been the cause of extinction of some large terrestrial animals, and well known species like the African Elephant are under threat today.

Pollution is the third reason for the growing loss of biodiversity. Pesticides have affected several species of birds and other organisms. Both air and water pollution stress ecosystems and reduce populations of sensitive species. For example, air pollution and acid rain has resulted in the loss of a number of fish species in Northern European lakes. The excessive use of agrochemicals and the release of many compounds of heavy metals and other toxic substances from industrial processes have caused ecological imbalance in' water bodies, wetlands and land areas with various detrimental effects on plant and animal species. A recent report by IPCC on climate change due to greenhouse gases pointed out that because species respond differently to climate change, some will increase in abundance while others will decrease. Over time some species may be displaced to higher latitudes or altitudes. Rare species with small ranges may be prone to local or even global extinction. Global warming would raise sea level and this could threaten almost all existing wetlands in the world.

The fourth reason for the loss of biological diversity is the impact of introduced exotic species as they threaten natural flora and fauna by predation, competition or altering natural habitat. Introduced species of plants have virtually replaced native species in many areas. The introduction in the Middle East and Asia of new high-yielding wheat and rice varieties since the mid 1960s has caused a loss of the gene pools in such centres of crop diversity as Turkey, Iraq, Iran, Afghanistan, Pakistan and India. In some of the African Rift Valley lakes, which have remarkably high levels of endemism, introduced species offish have threatened most native species with extinction. The introduction of herbivores such as goats and reindeer can extinguish that introduced species threaten 19 per cent of all endangered, vulnerable and rare species of vertebrates particularly on islands.

Biological resources are the basis of human life. The intense pressures on biological diversity are a direct reflection of increasing human numbers. These pressures are expected to increase until populations stabilize as projected by the United Nations by about the year 2050-2070 at about 10 billion. Such stabilization will be achieved only if present efforts to curtail population growth are pursued vigorously. As population grows, however, the pressure on biological resources will reach levels far beyond those prevalent now. The continued erosion of these resources poses a serious threat of ecosystem collapse. Biological diversity losses have serious worldwide implications for agriculture, medicine and industry; in fact for human welfare and his very existence.

Bilogical diversity is threat end because people are out of balance with their environment; benefits are being gained from exploiting natural habitats without paying the full costs of such exploitation. Current human populations and standards of living are subsidized by non-renewable resources that have accumulated over hundreds of millions of years, yet are being consumed in a few generations.

CONSERVATION OF BIOLOGICAL DIVERSITY

Conservation of nature implies protecting nature from the impacts of development, while bio-diversity conservation essentially safeguards even the genetic diversity of cultivated/ domesticated as well as wild flora and fauna. There are three distinct levels of biodiversity though all of them are components of a much intricate web.

Habitats are endangered by human activity. No one can predict the actual numbers of lives becoming extinct as rain forests are continuously cleared. So the urgent need to study and preserve the ecology and biodiversity of what remains has become an important issue of international priority. The need for preservation lies in the value of the components of biodiversity. It includes the indirect benefits arising from the conservation of these components, viz. ecosystem services, biological resources and social benefits.

AMONG THEM FOLLOWING ARE OF WORTH IMPORTANCE

1. Protection of Water Resources

The natural vegetation cover in water catchments helps in maintaining^ hydrological cycles, regulating and stabilizing water run off and acts as buffer against extreme events like flood and drought. It also helps to regulate underground water tables and prevent dry land stability. Thus a pointer to degradation of habitats is the depletion of ground water levels. In India, the last 25 years have seen a decline of water level by 30 feet in the entire eastern coast, and can be reasoned for the occurrence of frequent floods and drought.

2. Soil Formation and Protection

Biodiversity also helps maintenance of soil structure and increases the moisture retention capacity as well as nutrient level of soil. Non-existence of any sustained effort to preserve the ecology has resulted in denudation and soil erosion. Thus Stalinization of soils, leaching of nutrients, topsoil erosion etc. lead to over all decline in soil productivity. Trees also help in soil formation, their root system enables deep penetration of water and transport mineral nutrients to surface. Litter formation by the organic matter enhances the microbial activity.

3. Nutrient Storage and Cycling

Nutrient recycling is an essential event concerned with maintenance of the ecosystem. Biological diversity is inevitable for this. Microorganisms in the soil by decomposing dead and decayed wastes replenish the soil's nutrients. The function of nitrate bacteria and that of a nitrifying bacterial being different, diversity of the microorganisms is also essential.

4. Pollution, Breakdown and Absorption

The many pollutants including sewage, garbage, oil spills etc. are all deleterious to the balance of the ecosystem. The diverse components of ecosystem with special mention of the decomposers break down and assimilate these wastes. Wetlands breakdown and absorb pollutants, also filter effluents and remove nutrients, heavy metals, reduce BOD and also destroy harmful microorganisms. Atmospheric pollutants often pollute sites even far away from their actual source. The acid rains shower destruction usually on places far away from their actual site of emergence. Deleterious DDT levels have been reported in seals have been reported in seals and other aquatic inhabitants of the arctic and the Antarctic.

5. Climatic Stability

Vegetation influences climate both at the micro and macro levels. Forests maintain rainfall by recycling water vapour steadily into atmosphere and through canopy's effect in promoting atmospheric turbulence. There happens an increase in temperature due to increase in levels of CO_2 in atmosphere and is accounted for due to the inverse proportion between human activities including population rise and total spread of forests and trees. Only trees can absorb Co_2 and maintain a stable Co_2-O_2 balance. Some researches of the Indian Institute of Science have pointed out that globa warming, a consequence of green house gas emision, may result in a shift in forest types in Western Ghats.

6. Maintenance of Resources

The animal-plant interrelationship is essential to allow survival, and to maintain balance between living things and the needful resources Thus vegetation is integral to maintenance of water and moisture levels as well as a stable O_2-CO_2 balance. The web of life is so intricate that removal or disturbance of one part of the ecosystem could affect the smooth functioning of many of its other components.

AMONG BIOLOGICAL RESOURCES FOLLOWING ARE IMPROVEMENT

1. Food

Heterotrophs depend on autotrophs, the primary producers for food. Only through conservation of floral biodiversity can global food capacity be met with since nutritional value is different for different groups. Further diversity of food crops increases opportunities for enhancing agricultural productivity.

2. Medicine

The Ayurvedic system of medication is entirely dependent on the biodiversity of the flora. Diverse plants have diverse medicinal values. Plant products are immense ranging from Quinine, Cinchona Tyiorebrine, to the vine Tyiophra (for the treatment of serious tymphoid leukemia). Thus to provide resource for searching new medically active compounds, at least some part of the nature has to be left undisturbed. The Silent Valley Forests of Kerala are preserved since it was known to hoard diverse endemic varieties with immense medicinal value.

3. Population Reservoirs

Natural areas support many living systems. Some habitats support crucia life stages or elements of wild life, without which they are unable for existence. Thus if mangroves and wetlands are cleared, many commercial fish species which depend on these mangroves for breeding sites also perish. In India, the Sunder bans enjoy a protective status, being important for maintaining stocks offish, crustaceans, such as prawns, mud crabs, many other aquatic fauna and migratory birds.

4. Horticulture and Wood Requirements

For developing new hybrids and strains of ornamental plants, preservation of biodiversity is essential. Wood is a basic commodity and is harvested from the wild. The timber industry forms a significant part of our modern economy. Hard woods, soft woods etc. are put to entirely different uses, others are used as fuels, for paper manufacturing etc. So to meet differen needs, biodiversity has to be maintained.

AMONG SOCIAL BENEFITS IT INCLUDES MAINLY

Natural serves as the best laboratory for studies. It's harc to duplicate strictly a natural environment. So research, educatior and such extension works can progress only with the help o nature and its inherent biodiversity. Unaltered habitats help u: to evolve indexes to formulate different management levels.

1. Recreation

The aesthetic qualities of natural habitats are a result of it: biological diversity. No two spots in a forest can exactly b alike in all aspects. Since time immemorial, nature has satisfiec recreational pursuits of the humans. The gifted nature and th rich biodiversity have made India one of the important touris attractions of the modern world.

2. Cultural Value

There are ample evidences to prove that human culture ha co-evolved with the environment. For this reason itself conservation of biodiversity is important for his cultural identity For, it has been found that nature has always providec inspirational, aesthetic and educational needs of the people, natur also contributes to our emotional and spiritual well being.

The World Conservation Strategy I and II, (58,59), the repor of the World Commission on Environment and Developmen (11) and the Environmental Perspectives to the Year 2000 anc Beyond (60) have stressed that the conservation of natura resources has to be provided for within strategies for sustainabl development because these resources are the essential base fo such development. Meeting the needs of the present withou compromising the ability of future generations to meet thei own needs implies prudent management of available resources. Inter-generational equity requires each generation to conserve the diversity of the natural and cultural resource base, so tha it does not unduly restrict the options of future generations;

each generation is entitled to diversity comparable to that of past generations.

Four kinds of actions have been taken by the international community and by governments to promote the conservation and sustainable use of biological diversity: (a) measures to protect particular habitat as National Parks, Biosphere Reserves or other protected areas; (b) measures to protect particular species or groups of species from over-exploitation; (c) measures to, promote ex situ conservation of species in botanic gardens or in gene banks; and (d) measures to curb the contamination of the biosphere with pollutants. Several national, regional and global conventions and programmes have been formulated to implement these measures. For example, the Convention on Wetlands of International Importance (Ramsar, 1971), the Convention Concerning the Protection of World Cultural and Natural Heritage (Paris, 1972), the International Convention for the Regulation of Whaling (Washington, 1946), the Convention on International Trade in Endangered Species of Wild Fauna and Flora (Washington, 1973), the Convention on the Conservation of Migratory Species of Wild Animals (Bonn, 1979), Regional Seas Conventions and Programmes, the Convention for the Protection of the Ozone Layer, and others.

All these conventions and programmes have provided important means of promoting the conservation of biological diversity. Yet none of these has the explicit purpose of conservation of global biological diversity. Most nation efforts for conservation and management are not adequate five main obstacles have been identified: (a) national development objectives give insufficient value to biological resources. Development tends to emphasize short-term exploitation to earn income or foreign exchange rather than long-term sustainable utilization of such resources; (b) the species and ecosystems upon which human survival depends are still poorly known; (c) the available science is insufficiently applied to solve management problems; (d) the narrow focus of most conservation activities; and (e) the grossly insufficient resources (human as well as financial) allocated to conservation of biological resources. An example of the inadequacy of national efforts can be given by protected areas. Legally protected areas in the world cover 485 million ha, or 3.2 per cent of the Earth's land surface area. Yet most of these areas exist on maps only. It is unlikely that such areas provide adequate protection from a biogeographic perspective.

Recognizing the growing severity of threats to biological diversity and the increasingly international nature of the actions required to address the threats, a global strategy dealing with all aspects of biological diversity is being prepared by the World Resources Institute, IUCN and UNEP in collaboration with WWF, the World Bank and other governmental and non-governmental institutions in both tropical and temperate nations. The strategy which will be launched in 1992 aims to: (a) establish a common perspective, foster international co-operation, and agree to priorities for action at the international level; (b) examine the major obstacles to progress and analyze the needs for national and international policy reform; (c) specify how conservation of biological resources can be integrated with development more effectively and identify the linkages with others related issues facing humanity; and (d) promote the further development of regional, national, and thematic action plans for the conservation of biological diversity, and promote their implementation Furthermore, IUCN, FAO and UNEP have embarked on the preparation of an International Convention on the Conservation of Biological Diversity.

The time has come to appreciate the Earth's biological resources as assets to be conserved and managed for the benefit of all humanity. All nations have the duty to safeguard species within their territories, on behalf of everyone. But there is a need for a global effort in which developed and developing countries infuse a new spirit of co-operation for the conservation of biological diversity as a fundamental element of environmentally sound and sustainable development. It must protect the interests of the States in which the resources are located and provide incentives for conservation of biological diversity without inhibiting growth or sustainable development. Yet the agreement should cover inter alia; (a) measures for conservation of the full range of biological diversity; (b) measures for sustainable utilization of biological diversity; (c) research, training, education and public awareness; (d) environmental impact assessments; (e) access to biological diversity; (f) transfer of technology for the conservation and utilization of biological diversity; (g) technical and financial co-operation with developing countries to allow them to participate fully in the conservation of biological diversity; and (h) institutional arrangements at the national and international levels.

BIODIVERSITY AND INTELLECTUAL POPERTY RIGHTS

Biodiversity leads to diversity in products. Transformed microorganisms, plants and animals can be patented and made a private property under the Intellectual Property Rights (IRPs). For preservation of biodiversity, a detailed survey is undertaken to assess the flora and fauna of a habitat or a country. Specialists in particular fields could identify each group upto the species level. Systematic is the only tool with which identification is possible. A through knowledge on the particular ecosystem, its components, possible energy cycles and nutrient flows, the status of the animals weather predator or prey, their mode of life, feeding habits etc., is needed prior to seeking reasons for their decline or extinction.

It is imperative to demonstrate the economic contribution biological resources make. Conversion of their services in terms of money gains can give an accurate assessment. This can be done through consumptive use valuation, where the value of direct nature products like fuel, fodder etc. is considered. The non-consumptive valuation assesses the direct value of the function of the ecosystem. Periodical monitoring is also necessary. Reliable information on earth's resources is reported, using remote sensing technology. IRS 1C and IRS-2D can provide detailed images of landscape and can be used to characterize potential bioprospecting zones. Only 19 percent of India's land area are under forest cover.

■■■

15

Remote Sensing in Biogeography

INTRODUCTION

Remote sensing is the process whereby information is acquired about the earth or other planets by non-contact methods using electromagnetic energy or seismic, gravitational, vibrational or magnetic forces. More specifically, remote sensing is now regarded as the sensing of electromagnetic energy, particularly visible and infrared light, thermal energy and the microwave or radar regions of the spectrum. For the remote sensing of vegetation the most useful parts of the spectrum are the visible and near infrared: from 0.4 um to 2.5 urn, but in this spectral region cloud cover can be a major problem so, in areas of the world prone to cloudiness, radar imagery is sometimes favoured.

REMOTE SENSING AND MAPPING OF SOILS, VEGETATION AND ANIMALS

The global patterns of soil, vegetation and animal distribution have long been appreciated and their limits determined in this aspect. Paradoxically, on a national scale, the distribution are far less completely known, the reason being that at the larger scales of mapping appropriate to national surveys, more detailed classifications with more exact areal coverages are required. The state of national mapping of vegetation and soils varies greately in different parts of the world: for the developed countries of Europe and North America plus a handful of other countries, national maps do exist, often in conjunction with topographical map series. But for the great majority of nations in the developing and undeveloped world, such maps do not exist or the basic surveys have only recently been undertaken.

In cartographic terms, the distribution of these components represent thematic maps, in which the theme is portrayed as a superposition over a pre-existing base map complete with a grid reference system and other locational devices. The based map commonly existed beforehand as a standard topographical map, and the data have been compling, comparison, classification and field mapping onto this topographical base. Many such thematic maps are still produced in this way, especially in smaller projects, but since the 1950s these traditional ground methods have been increasingly supplanted by remote-sensing methods. In some of these newer methods the traditional base map is dispensed with, the thematic map together with its locational base being produced together as a single operation. As a consequence a number of countries now have accurate and detailed vegetation surveys but no topographical map sheets.

Remote sensing is a term coined in the early 1960s to describe the acquisition and interpretation of all photographic and other imagery acquired from air and space platforms. Remote sensing includes conventional aerial photography, photographic interpretation and photogrammetry. With respect to the survey of the biosphere, remote sensing has developed in three overlapping phases. First came the use of black and white aerial photographs, increasingly supplemented by colour aerial photographs. This usage started in the 1930s for civilian surveys such as in Canada and East Africa, but was not implemented regularly until the post-war period Aerial photography using various filrr emulsions and filters is still the standard method of obtaining high quality material, Aerial photographs are often used directly as mosaics in the form of photomaps, which have the property of showing vegetation distributions unclassified and exactly as they occur on the ground.

Secondly, in the 1960s, special purpose airborne devices became available, such as the multiband camera, the multispectral scanner (MSS) and side looking airborne radai (SLAR). The multiband camera is used to sense several separate portions of the visible electromagnetic spectrum, thus providing extra discrimination of ground objects for the interpreter. This is particularly helpful in specialist vegetation studies, because plant species vary in their spectral responses not only between species but also within species according to season of year and state of health. The MSS works on the same principle of selective sensing but can operate over wavebands outside the range of human vision and produces data in either graphical or digital form, so similarly allowing greater scope for analysis. The SLAR has developed from a military reconnaissance system into a general purpose small-scale mapping tool, of special relevance where perpetual cloud cover makes conventional aerial photography impossible.

The third phase, remote sensing from space, started in the early 1970s with the launching of satellites in low-altitude global orbits carrying sensors designed for monitoring and mapping the earth's surface. The earlier manned satellites of the Mercury, Gemini, Apollo and Skylab space programmes provided results mostly in the form of colour photographs which have proved of less consequence than the results from the more recent unmanned satellites, particularly the LANDSAT programme with new types of sensors. Satellite sensor imagery, both graphical and digital is now available in great quantities, and is being energetically investigated. Although the imagery is not yet internationally implemented in a global mapping and monitoring system, it has already produced a total reordering of ideas concerning global surveillance of vegetation, soils and land use, as well as short-term management of agriculture, forestry and rangeland. Rudd (1974) rightly described remote sensing as a quiet revolution which, if it lives up to its potential, will affect the lives of everyone. An excellent modern account of the acquisition of all kinds of remote-sensing data and image interpretation and its processing for environmental purposes is given by Lillesand and Kiefer (1979), while Avery (1977) concentrates on more traditional imagery.

Remote-sensing methods are very satisfactory for surveys

of vegetation for a number of reasons: the normally vertical viewpoint ensures that vegetation distributions are seen in approximately plan position; boundary decisions are easily made; different types of sensors can be employed according to the scale and coverage required; and changes can be registered by repetition of the sensing. Although no remote-sensing technique has the immediacy or accuracy of direct ground observation, it is often more economical in terms of both time and labour costs, and may well yield a better overall result.

For soil surveys, which normally include soil profiles, a vertical sequence is involved, just as it is for vegetation surveys of more than one continuous canopy. Here, remote sensing provides no direct assistance, as all sensor data are of reflectance or emittance from the uppermost surface only, what ever that may be. Therefore supplementary field surveys must be arranged. Soil types may however be inferred by considering topography, geology, vegetation and drainage by remote-sensing means, together with background knowledge of climate and economic activity. Although imagery derived from LANDSAT sensors is of limited resolution, the detailed mapping of soils, even allowing identification of specific series and types of soil, is possible.

So far nothing has been said about mapping the distribution of animals by remote sensing. As animals are mobile, permanent distribution has no meaning, except in the broadest regional terms, and the most common practical questions that are likely to be posed concern the numbers and distribution of wild or domesticated ungulates at any one particular time. There are no inherent difficulties to this sort of monitoring by remote sensing, given sufficient logistical and financial support.

Whether the information on the distribution of vegetation or soils or animals is obtained from space or from air-borne seasons or by direct ground enquiry, for mapping purposes numerous decisions have to be made as to how to assemble the discrete areas into types or classes. As a first step the map compiler will normally choose the information classes according to some prior framework. Boundaries between the classes are then drawn on the imagery, and the areal units are each allocated to a class. Drawing boundaries and allocating to classes are both subjective processes; and the distribution map will inevitably be a simplification of reality, to a degree depending on scale of mapping and the complexity of the original.

The type of classification used to survey vegetation depends or should depend on the requirements of the customer. In the developed countries where thematic map series are relatively common there is little natural vegetation remaining and the most common thematic maps have therefore traditionally been of land use and soil types. But due to customer demand there has been a move from these purely descriptive documents towards predictive maps of land capability, land value or biophysical land types, such maps using classifications involving a range of physical elements including aspects of soils and existing land cover. Most recently, remote-sensing methods have played a positive role in determining the types of classification used. For example, a methodology for producing land-use maps from LANDSAT imagery has been given by van Genderen and Lock (1976). Also a recent paper by Anderson et al. (1976) provides a revised land use and land cover classification system for use with remote sensor data. This system is hierarchical on four levels, the first level having nine general categories determinable from imagery generated by satellite or high-altitude aircraft. The second level has 92 categories, by subdivision of the original nine, visible on larger-scale imagery, and so on.

Before considering national and local examples of mapping of the biosphere, some further brief points will be made to set the scene. The distributions of vegetation and soils are generally stable, but interference by man is causing changes at an increasing rate. man's interest in these distributions is widening as, on a planet that is rapidly shrinking in economic and political terms, more and more data are required for effective planning and management. Through developments in remote-sensing sensors and in high-altitude aircraft and spacecraft, the demands for distributional data are capable of being met, and original remote sensor data of the biosphere are currently being acquired faster than ever before. There is no international agreement for mapping of the biosphere to a common basis, but the global satellite imagery now available may stimulate cartographic co-operation in this direction.

GENERAL PURPOSE SOIL AND VEGETATION SURVEYS

1. Ground Techniques Supplemented by Aerial Photographs

Many national mapping schemes began in the era before remote sensing products were available and so were carried out entirely by direct field sampling and field mapping. The earliest systematic soil surveys in the UK were carried out by ground methods in the 1930s with aerial photographs used experimentally. When aerial photographs became generally available, following World War II, they improved the quality of the soil mapping programme in three main ways: by increasing the speed of mapping and hence lowering costs; by greater accuracy in boundary location; and by greater understanding of soil distribution and variability within a map unit (Carroll et al., 1977). Aerial photographs are used both for preliminary analysis and for field checking, experience showing that in the UK, for example, to achieve field maps at 1:25000 scale, the best photographic scales are 1:15000 or 1:20000.

A land use map series at 1:25000 scale is also currently under production in the UK. This has similar descriptive classifications to those used in an earlier land use and land use capability series at 1:63360; both series being based on ground collection supplemented by aerial photographs.

In terms of European example of vegetation mapping, pride of place must go to the Carte de la Vegetation de la France, published in sheets at 1:200 000 scale, the first sheet for Gap in the French Alps dating from 1974 (CNRC). These are detailed maps of vegetation communities, both natural and modified. The compilation of recent sheets has been assisted by aerial photographic interpretation. A recent map of potential vegetation communities at 1:200 000 scale has also been described for the Netherlands, based on a study of the relationship between soil, ground-water and vegetation.

Vegetation mapping in Canada has followed several different styles. Apart from map series for topography and land use, which are purely descriptive, a number of predictive map series at 1:250000 and 1:1000 000 scales have been published, based on Canada Land Inventory data. Maps on land capability for forests, soil capability for agriculture, land capability for ungulates, among others, point the way for modern mapping of practical interest. In the USA the US Geological Survey has embarked upon a new programme to provide land use and land cover maps and ancillary data for the country by the mid-1980s.

2. By-product of Topographical Mapping by Photogrammetry

The national topographical map series of Great Britain, published at six scales by the Ordinance Survey, carry some information on vegetation in accordance with a long mapping tradition. The topographical maps are produced by photogram metric mapping, the vegetation details being obtained at the same time by aerial photographic interpretation. Vegetation types currently distinguished in Ordinance Survey Maps are: braken, coniferous woodland, orchard trees, reeds, rough grassland, salt marshes and scrub. Insofar as Ordnance Survey maps provide complete national coverage and' are regularly revised, the vegetation information is accurate. However, vegetation is not given pride of place, as the classes of vegetation chosen are simple ones, easily identifiable from aerial photographs by the map compiler and likely to be understood by map readers (Harley, 1975). To map minor variations would impose too much work on the organization, even if the maps could carry the extra details. The same position is true of many other developed countries, the vegetation distributions being shown on topographical maps at levels of generalization commensurate with the scale of mapping.

3. Photomaps and Orthophotomaps

These are essentially mosaics of single black and white aerial photographs joined together to form a longer composite view of the whole area. The continuous total variation of the original photographs is retained so that the vegetation patterns can be seen at first hand. On some photomaps, little editing has taken place, so that decisions on vegetation classification have still to be taken by the map reader. On other examples, different colours are used to register different cover types. This is possible because photomaps are finally produced by offset lithography, allowing multiple colour printing. The original photographs can be subjected to a range of geometric improvements before being compiled into a mosaic and printed, including being rectified, scaled to ground control points and converted to orthophotographs. Orthophotography is a process of differential rectification whereby a new photography free .from displacement errors due to relief is produced from the old. Orthophotomaps are therefore essentially correct in scale all over (Petrie, 1977).

Attractive photomaps and Orthophotomaps have been produced for many countries of the world often at great speed in response to some economic requirement. The most impressive example is that of Sweden, which has been producing photomaps since 1937 and Orthophotomaps since 1966 at 1:10 000 and 1:20 000 scales in a series labeled the Economic Map of Sweden (Johansson, 1969). The photographic tones are reproduced in green colour and cultivated land in yellow, with much other information overprinted in black. West Germany also has been producing Orthophotomaps since 1969 in standard series at 1:5000 scale, and these have been found particularly useful for land use and forest management. In Canada five different types have been published, ranging from uncontrolled mosaics to Orthophotomaps (Sebert, 1968), and are of special value as reconnaissance documents of the biophysical resources of the Canadian northlands. In the USA many experimental Orthophotomaps series have been developed, as well as blocks of 1:24000 scale sheets of parts of Florida, Georgia and Louisiana and Alaska, by the US Geological Survey as part of the standard national topographic series. These areas have in common difficult terrain conditions that effectively defer both ground surveying and cartographic representation by conventional line work. The colours chosen for the photomaps vividly reflect the vegetation types.

Mention must here be made of the thematic mapping produced by the Directorate of Overseas Surveys (DOS) based in England, for the developing countries of the world, often deficient in any form of large-scale map. Photo mapping techniques have been used by DOS, for example, in South Arabia at 1:100 000 scale, The Gambia at 1:50 000 scale and Botswana at 1:50 000 scale to produce reconnaissance map series very rapidly. The Botswana map series comprises a block of 49 sheets of the seasonally in undated Okavango Swamps, publication beginning in 1970 for the express purpose of assisting hydrological investigations by United Nations team.

4. Radar Mapping

Radar is a microwave sensor, described as active because it supplies its own source of energy. The SLAR system produces small-scale imagery in graphical form which, although superficially attractive, requires a great deal of complicated processing if detailed information is to be extracted. The application of radar to vegetation studies is still at an early stage of experimentation but it does have special importance in the tropics because of its capability to penetrate cloud. Persistent cloud cover over most tropical countries has frustrated aerial photography as well as repetitive satellite ground conditions have obstructed ground surveys. Consequently the tropical regions, particularly the forests, have been among the worst mapped areas of the world. Three major projects have been completed, beginning with a SLAR survey of the Darien province of Panama in 1968 covering 20 000 km^2 from which a reconnaissance vegetation map was prepared. In the early 1970s most of the rainforest of the Amazon basin was surveyed by SLAR in Project RADAM, from which have emerged a range of studies on natural resources and management potential. Similarity the NIRAD Project commissioned by the Federal Government of Nigeria in 1976 for the survey of the vegetation of the whole country has produced SLAR imagery at 1:250 000 scale from which the results to date are promising (Parry and Trevett, 1979).

5. Small Project Biophysical Surveys

Many examples of smaller, frequently research orientated schemes exist and the few that are mentioned here are chosen to illustrate the range of techniques employed, and involve both aerial surveys and a combination of ground and aerial surveys.

6. US Coastal Marshlands

Coastal zones contain a variety of natural ecosystems and research and management interests in them has steadily increased. In the USA, many different coastal zone mapping programmes have been initiated, although to no common plan. One of the most fully documented is that of Sapelo Island, coastal Georgia, designed to monitor the natural ecological habitats, especially extensive areas of Juncus and Spartina (McEwen et al., 1976). Ground sampling of vegetation and tidal conditions was linked to aerial sensing carried out by black and white and colour infrared photography and by thermal scanning. This approach to mapping coastal resources via remote sensing produced dynamic maps of marshland systems as well as agronomic yield estimates for the marsh.

7. Scottish Coastal Biophysical Habitats

More specific than the Sapelo Island experiments and carried out entirely by conventional aerial photographic interpretation, an inventory was made of about 2000 1-km National Grid squares along the Scottish coastline. For each square, data were systematically collected on vegetational and ecological habitats, such as sand dunes and salt marsh, and made available to provide tabular and graphical computer output (Kirby, 1977). The results give 3,00,000 items of ecological information that can be organized into simple map distributions according to customers' requirements.

SUPPLEMENTARY FOREST PHOTOGRAPHIC STUDIES

Cameras of 35 mm and 70 mm format are frequently used to produce rapid aerial photography of forest, marshland and other inaccessible areas. Such low-cost non-metric photography is suitable for revision mapping and large-scale monitoring processes. Among many examples in forestry may be cited the extensive work by Zsilinszky (1966) in determining tree species in Ontario, and Murtha (1972) in describing morphological and physiological damage to forest trees in Canada generally.

ANIMAL INVENTORIES

Counts of wildlife and rangeland animals from low-altitude aerial photography, most often using small-format photography from helicopter or light aircraft, has became a fairly standard process. Photography offers a permanent record and when taken at an altitude that will not disturb the wildlife below, allows very accurate counts, for example for white-tailed deer, caribou, ungulates on tropical game reserves, snow geese on migration and even sheep, cattle and ponies an Dart moor, South-West England (Goodier, 1971). Thermal sensing by registration of the body heat of the animals compared with their surrounding has also been used experimentally for ungulates in Alberta, and could ultimately be developed as a civilian practice by thermal sensors on satellites. Applications of this process are some way off yet.

THE POTENTIAL OF SATELLITE-BORNE SENSORS

Most of the examples so far described are of stable vegetation and soil systems so that the airborne surveys, if satisfactorily completed, should have long validity. Airborne sensors, with the exception of SLAR, also commonly give imagery at scales sufficient to allow medium to large scales of mapping. Satellite-borne sensors differ from air-borne sensors in both these respects: the nature of satellite orbits provides repetitive imagery, best suited for monitoring short-term changes, while the altitudinal height of satellites means that the imagery will always be at very small scales. Furthermore the totally different magnitude of costs and technology involved in putting satellites into orbit and recovering and processing the sensor data means that far fewer satellites than aircraft will be in operation and the work of each will be planned most carefully.

The few satellites designed as terrestrial environmental satellites so far launched have provided a great deal of information in both quality and quantity, so that the position has been rapidly reached when data are being acquired faster than they can be assimilated.

Satellites are global systems, their sensors registering conditions beneath their orbital paths without regard to national boundaries, and nations are beginning to consider the legal and political issues consequent on the acquisition of resource information from countries other than their own. At present all satellites are controlled by the USA and USSR, the USA environmental satellite data being made available without restraint and at minimal cost to any customer. As the French and other nationalities come forward with independent environmental satellite systems, so resource surveys will require further international review.

Although a number of early spacecraft monitored vegetation, agriculture and earth resources, as Colwell et al. (1971) makes clear, the first satellite programme devoted primarily to earth resources has been the LANDSAT programme, initiated in 1967 for which LANDSAT-3 was launched on 5th March, 1978. The LANDSAT programme was conceived as an experimental reconnaissance system, to collect data on a systematic and repetitive basis and it has already more than fulfilled the original objectives. Many of the uses for early LANDSAT imagery were described by Williams and Carter (1976).

The LANDSAT satellites have all carried two sensor systems, a MSS operating at four wavebands and a three-channel return beam vidicom (RBV), both systems covering the visible and near infrared wavelengths. The output from each system is either in graphical form as photographs (Sheffield, 1981) or in digital form as computer-compatible tapes. The MSS and RBV products are not easy to deal with beyond the first cursory look, requiring computer-based radiometric and geometric corrections followed by some form of image classification to achieve spatially correct mapping (Holkenbrink, 1978). Currently the sensor resolution is coarse and processing techniques are not fully standardized in spite of a great deal of progress in a very few years. The next generation of satellites should see improvement of resolution and superior processing, as well as several more national data-receiving station in operation. Further new experimental sensors are also planned (Doyle, 1978).

The developments in global monitoring consequent to the inception of LANDSAT and other environmental space programmes are so rapid, at the time of writing, that the state of the art in resource surveys will require to be revised frequently. A number of examples have been chosen simply to illustrate the current range of developments.

SOIL SURVEYS

Studies to determine whether LANDSAT data could provide useful soil and land system surveys have been encouraging. Variation in soil characteristics can be identified on specially processed LANDSAT imagery, and ultimately soil association maps can be produced, at scales ranging from 1:50 000 to 1:250 000. Based on the demonstrated capability of the present LANDSAT sensors, it should be possible to provide many of the developing countries with semi-detailed soil maps that would be impossible to obtain in the foreseeable future by conventional ground and aerial methods (Cleveland, 1977). An uncomplicated example of reconnaissance soil mapping in India from LANDSAT imagery is given by Allan (1978).

LAND USE SURVEYS

LANDSAT imagery is being used in countries all over the world to develop land use or land classification maps whose practical value lies in the synoptic impression they convey. As early as 1975, a land use map of North-East China was published at a scale of 1:600 000 based on LANDSAT MSS imagery (Welch et al., 1975). In Canada, an ecological land classification of Labrador was published in 1977 with a map at 1:1000 000 scale, and utilized visual interpretative information derived from LANDSAT imagery. More recently, a LANDSAT mosaic of the entire country of Bangladesh at 1:500 000 scale has been published by the World Bank (1981), with a symbol overprint of crop and natural vegetation types, and most of the crop and natural vegetation types, and most of the land use boundaries are derived from satellite imagery.

THE LARGE AREA CROP INVENTORY EXPERIMENT (LACIE)

LACIE was established in 1974 as a major project to predict the yield of the world's major wheat crops from a merger of LANDSAT data with climatic data and some ground verification. Project LACIE involved a commercial company in joint undertaking with the US Department of Agriculture, the National Oceanographic and Atmospheric Administration, and the National Aeronautics and Space Administration (NASA), and is a good example of the co-operation ideally required for analyzing LANDSAT data at a global level (MacDonald and Hall, 1980). Wheat is relatively easy to monitor because it is grown a single crop over large blocks of land and LACIE has achieved encouragingly accurate predictions. In more complex environments with mixed cropping in smaller units, crop identification from LANDSAT is much less accurate.

RANGELAND AND FOREST MANAGEMENT

The 18-day global cycle of LANDSAT sensing is the basis for monitoring short-term and seasonal changes in land use, although for many parts of the world, repeat imagery is not obtained at this frequently, due to the presence of cloud, or sensor malfunction or closedown. For rangeland and forest management, large blocks of territory can be examined from LANDSAT imagery as a preliminary to more detailed aerial investigations where necessary. In the USA, satellite imagery has been used in rangeland management to produce inventories of range vegetation types, to evaluate the biomass conditions at particular dates and to monitor the rangeland changes (Williams and Carter, 1976). In the Arusha region of Tanzania, LANDSAT data been used to delineate different grassland types of varying suitability for forage as the basis for identifying promising areas for range and agricultural development (Cleveland, 1977). For tropical timber resources LANDSAT data are generally inadequate for inventory purposes, as it has not proved possible to separate the diversity of tree species. The imagery has been useful, however, in monitoring the rate of forest clear-cutting in British Columbia (Lee, 1975) and for monitoring the areas of clearing by landholders in newly settled areas of Brazil (Carneiro, 1980).

Satellite imagery might not be thought to have much relevance to monitoring animals as the current generation of MSS or cameras do not have the resolution to detect livestock. However other sensors are proving successful. Caribou and polar bears have been fitted experimentally with collars containing radio transmitters that send locational signals capable of being detected by satellites, and attempts are under way to monitor locust swarm breeding areas from satellites. This latter work carried out by the Food and Agriculture Organization (FAO) further illustrates the need for combining techniques in dynamic environmental studies. For the broad strip from western Africa to the Middle East, geostationary weather satellites give frequent indications of where rainfall is sufficient to cause suitable soil moisture conditions for locust breeding, and to promote plant growth. 'The LANDSAT satellites can give less frequent but larger scale indications of the growth and density for more direct reconnaissance for correlating vegetation cover on the ground with its recorded satellite spectral response (Howard, 1977). Complete surveys on the ground of potential locust breeding sites are virtually impossible, and the future use of satellite in locust detection and control seems assured.

In this type of international operation, as in so many other global biophysical schemes made possible for the first time by high-resolution satellite sensors, the emphasis will increasingly be on funding, delicate diplomacy and good management rather that on technical capabilities.

THE ROLE OF REMOTE SENSING IN THE DETECTION OF GEOBOTANICAL AND BIOGEOCHEMICAL ANOMALIES

Remote sensing has many different roles in biogeographical studies. In this section and the next its specific use as a mineral exploration tool in vegetated terrain will be analyzed. The use of remote sensing in this context is a recent addition to the sciences of geobotany and biogeochemistry. Geobotany is concerned with the affinity o1 particular plants, plant associations or plant morphological aberriations to soils containing higher than normal contents of heavy metals, such as copper, lead, zinc or tin. Biogeochemistry enables the analysis of plant tissue to assess its heavy metal content. Geobotanical indicator species, plant association changes and biogeochemical anomalies can all be distinguished from the synoptic view of a remote sensing platform: so, during the last fifteen years, remote sensing, as an exploration tool, has become increasingly popular.

The introduction of high-resolution spectroradiometers to detect plant spectra associated with heavy metals has also yielded results of great significance to mineral exploration in vegetated terrain. Healthy green leaves have a low visible and a high near infrared reflectance while' physiological disturbances, such as excesses of heavy metals, cause changes in leaf pigmentation, structure and water content which leads to aberrant leaf reflectance. A number of studies have used spectroradiometers to record the changes in plant reflectance over natural geochemical anomalies (Table 15.1). Data collection in these studies has been achieved by elevating a spectroradiometer on a platform above the plant canopy. (Table 15.2) This position is near-vertical but is not entirely complementary to the true vertical angle achieved by a satellite or aircraft. Nevertheless, the results gained by these studies show a trend towards higher visible reflectance of the anomalous vegetation, together with a change in the near Infrared reflectance; the results of Yost and Wenderoth (1971), and Yost (1975) are the exception.

The most successful detection of biogeochemical stress has been achieved with high spectral resolution spectroradiometers. Collins (1976) and Collins et al (1979, 1980) have developed such an instrument which scans in 500 narrow bands between 0.4 um and 1.1 urn. In addition to allowing studies of reflectance changes in each narrow band, this instrument also allows for an interpretation of reflectance changes that occur on the red edge. It has been shown that the slope of the red edge is determined by chlorophyll concentrations and that chlorophyll concentration

Table 15.1
The effects of heavy metals on plant reflectance, as measured in the field with a spectroradiometer

Author	*Mineral*	*Species*	*Decreased Visible*	*Increased Visible*	*Decreased Near IR*	*Increased Near IR*
Birnie & Dykstra, 1968	Cu & Mo	Pinus contorta		×	No data	
Canney, Yost &	Cu & Mo	Picea balsamea		×	×	
Wenderoth, 1971	Cu & Mo	Juniperus sp.		×		
Yost& Wenderoth, 1971	Cu & Mo	Abies balsamea			×	×
	Cu & Mo	Picea rubens	×		×	
Press, 1974	Pb&Zn	Quercus sp.		×	×	
Lyon, 1975	Mo	Pinus ponderosa	No Data		×	
	Mo	Juniperus utahensis	No Data		×	
Yost, 1975	Cu	Quercus sp.	×		×	
	Cu	Pinus portderosa	×		×	
	Cu	Juniperus sp.	×		×	
Collins & Chiu, 1979	Cu, Pb &Zn	Conifers (species not stated)		×		No Data
Howard *et al*, 1971	Cu	Pinus ponderosa	No Effect	×		

Table 15.2

The effects of heavy metals on plant reflectance, as measured in the laboratory with a spectrophotometer

Author	*Mineral*	*Species*	*Decreased Visible*	*Increased Visible*	*Decreased Near IR*	*Increased Near IR*
Press, 1974	Pb, Zn	Beans		×		No Change
Horler *et al*, 1980	Cd, Cu	Peas		×	×	
	Zn	Soybean	No Data		×	
Chang and Collins,	Cu, Zn, Ni	Sorghum		×	×	
1980	Cu, Zn, Ni	Mustard		×	×	

is affected by a plant's heavy metal content (Horler et al 1980, 1983); in particular, an increase in the concentration of heavy metals in plant nutrient environments causes a reduction in chlorophyll production and a correlatable and progressive shift towards the blue part of the spectrum. It follows that, for mineral exploration in vegetated terrain, the red edge is an important feature of plant reflectance, particularly as it is not prone to shifts due to background noise. Collins et al (1979) have already shown that conifers, growing over a metal sulphide-ore body, display a preliminary red edge shift to longer wavelengths, followed by a permanent shift to shorter wavelengths as chlorophyll production ceased. Laboratory experiments using spectrophotometers have also shown that it is possible optically to detect geochemically-stressed plants even when no visual signs of foliage damage are apparent. But, as Knipling (1970) stated, although studies of single leaves are basic to the understanding of the reflectivity of an entire plant canopy, single leaf measurements are not directly applicable to the natural environment. However, in the studies of geochemical stress, the association of these two types of measurements are complementary.

16

Future Aspects of Biogeography

INTRODUCTION

In 21st centaury the scope of the subject i.e. future aspect of biogeography is divided into two parts - A. Pure and theoretical, B. Applied and behavioural as being described in the following pages of this chapter.

BIOGEOGRAPHY-AN INTERDISCIPLINARY SUBJECT

It is a well known fact that, Biogeography is associated with both the geographical (Simmons; 1980) and the biological (Vuilleumier, 1977) sciences which continue to nourish its development. It has also acquired a separate identity on its own terms, not only within geography but also within biology. Thus, as a two-way, interdisciplinary sub-field, it has been enable to develop reciprocally within the orbits of the parent sciences with which it shares some common, if constantly changing, ground. There is nothing unique in these interdisciplinary borderlands which are essentially a means of expansion or contraction of adjacent sciences. At its positive best, such adjacency sparks off innovation and creates new hybrid sciences i.e. like biogeography.

In beginning from natural history, several interdisciplinary subjects origin take place with the development of scientific studies by their workers from time to time in which biogeography is also one of them. The injection of chemistry into biology has created the biochemical science and new penetrations in the field of microbiology to internet relationships between environmental signals and physiological responses in plants and animals. Geological research has been transformed by the introduction of geochemical and geophysical techniques. Civil engineering and geomorphology have together advanced hydrological research and teaching, not least in geography departments (Ward, 1980) almost the extinction of the flame of traditional Wooldridgian geomorphology.

In contrast, climatology continues to live dangerously, perhaps sinfully, with meteorology. Atmospheric physicists have achieved more rapport with biologists, agonomists and environmental scientists than with climatologists, with the exception of a very important few (Atkinson, 1980). Pedology, too, exhibits continual turbulence as Soil Survey hovers between taking international taxonomy too far for field survey purposes, on the one hand, and mixing Rothschid-derived, force-fed research programmes, with the target of achieving a national soil survey coverage within a few years, on the other hand. Academic pedology has found diverse lodgings in departments of agriculture, biochemistry and geography but prospers best when a wide range of specialists, e.g. soil chemists, soil physicists, soil medium under one roof. But the fact remains that in geography departments at least, soils are best taught, understood and researched as integral parts of the physical and cultural landscapes with which they have evolved.

The buoyancy and longevity of an interdisciplinary sub-field is guaranteed if its practitioners are equipped, collectively as well as individually, with expertise in both adjacent sciences. It is over-qualification and over experience in the one rather than the other which can create the undesirable ill balance and malformed growth of the sub-field. This may win scientific acceptability from the one science but invite professional hostility from the other, respectively.

Inevitably, interdisciplinary sub-fields tend to be more controversial and often charismatic than may long-established core disciplines, and their practitioners are heavily committed to the scientific demands of at least two major study areas. But Chaucer's oft-quoted cri de coeur: 'The lyf so short-the craft so long to learn' must not be used as an excuse for not attempting a definition of any busy sub-field, let alone biogeography itself.

BIOGEOGRAPHY AND ITS IDENTITY

Subjects and their sub-fields in volve continuously over time and experience episodes of convergence or divergence and sequences of ever-changing technology and affiliation. At any time, the evolutionary stage attained is reflected in the research outputs and teaching profiles of the contemporary practitioners involved. For the achievements of British biogeography or, more properly, British biogeographers, Simmons (1980) has usefully complied a comprehensive survey but is forced to conclude that there is no such thing as 'a distinctive British school of biogeography'. In fact, therein lie the three basic ingredients for a definition of the scope of biogeography as practiced by geographers: (i) natural ecosystems, (ii) how they have changed by man and (iii) the relationships between (i) and (ii). Simmons' two major texts (1974 and 1979) detail his central concept of biogeography which may be expressed simply as an evaluation of the modification of natural ecosystems by man's activities. Simmon's material is drawn extensively from the biological rather than geographical literature. The shortage of biogeographical textbooks, once bemoaned by Old fields (1967), has since been partially corrected. Watts (1971) presented the first major comprehensive study (since Dansereau 1957) and Polunin (1960) of the principles of biogeography as focused in ecosystem mechanics. Pears (1977) presented a 'basic' volume derived very much from the experience of teaching biogeography to undergraduate geographers but previously Seddon (1971) and Cox et al (1976), and later Jones (1980), ail produced texts more oriented to the style of biogeography teaching in biology departments. Jones' earlier chapters smack of the kind of traditional, global pale botanical (and palaezoological) approach which characterizes the type of palaeoecology researched and taught by biologists (Gould, 1981). A recurrent theme within these numerous texts, since Eyre (1964) and Stoddart (1965,

1967) promoted its importation from ecology, is the ecosystem, first proposed by Tansley in 1935, intone concept or model, the flora, fauna, man and environment and their collective interactions. Kellman (1980) and Stott (1981) have reached to this excessive regurgitation of the one idea. Stott elaborates his views volume, to which we must now refer to trace the roots of biogeographical studies from the last century through to understand the stage they have reached in the late twentieth century.

Stott concludes, as does Simmons (1980), in effect, 'that there can be no such thing as the 'definitive' approach or the 'final' biogeography, implying that an eventual explicit identity will remain illusory. In that context, the complexity of the history of biogeography reflects its current dilemmas and debates. Prior to the impact of Fleure (1951) and Newbigin (1936), both zoologists, on pre-World War II developments in British biogeography, the pioneering of the subject was the exclusive domain of biologists, including some with an acute environmental awareness. Alexender von Humboldt (1969-1859) is regarded as one of the founder fathers of geography, as an explicit study, and also of biogeography as a systematic study (Humboldt and Bonpland, 1805).

The impact of Darwinism on later geographical thought has been summarised by Stoddart (1967) in cementing ideas on evolutionary timescale changes, competition between species, and the coexistence of both association and randomness in nature. Haeckel's broad concept of an ecology involving interactive organisms and environment, anticipated the expanded scope of modern biogeography as it is studied in geography departments, where it was natural (de Candolle's, 1882 visionary work apart) that, following de Martonne (1932), Fleure (1951), Morgan and Moss (1965), Eyre and Jones (1966), Harris (1969) and Taylor (ed.) (1980), for example, the study of man should be integrated with the study of plants and animals in their respective ecological settings. The distinctive commitment to the taxonomy and functioning of the "raw materials' of biogeography, i.e. the plants and animals themselves, has remained, and does remain, very much the prerogative of departments of botany and zoology. Brown (1975) compares the relatively easy and accessible vocabulary of geomorphology with the more demanding and detailed vocabularies of plant and animal taxonomy, including simple identification.

It is essential to point out that British university geography was introduced by a diverse range of non-geographical specialists from both the arts and sciences, including Fleure (zoologist), Roxby (historian), Stamp (geologist-originally!), Miller (geologist) etc. in the early decades of this century and at least three or four academic generations ago. These were the 'first-generation' geographers (Fisher, 1959). The general objective was to achieve an integrated study of man and environment as expressed in traditional regional studies. Again, although biogeography achieved some representation before 1939, it languished in the 1940s and 1950s, as geomorphology assumed its vast dominance of physical geography but became less and less adaptable as the 'physical basis' of the subject in its human context (Martin, 1951). Intense specialization in aspects of physical and human geography was also rampant at this stage, thus creating a divided, compartmentalized subject, and much disillusionment with integrated regional approaches. Consequently, geography was in no condition to respond to, and capitalize on, the remarkable reawakening of environmental awareness dating from the mid-60s, an awareness which was to lead to the creation of Environmental Science departments at several, in particular the newer universities. However, internally within established geography departments a minority of specialists, coming in, as Oldfieic (1967) explained, from the 'pedological, geomorphologica or climatological margins' (of biogeography), initiated and expanded biogeography options from about the mid-1960s These 'first generation' biogeographers have now producec an increasing number of 'second generation" specialists among whom it is obviously premature to look for a common philosophy (Simmons, 1980).

Nonetheless, recent (1976-81) surveys, reported in Simmons (1980), reveal that two major and related interest dominate contemporary British biogeography. These are (i) the study of palaeoenvironments and (ii) the ecological basis of land-use which, taken together, create a focus on a broad-based kind of environmental history and on the ecological condition of the derived, modern environment: in other words environmental and man-induced changes over time, their successive cyclical stages, their impacts and their management. Palaeoecologists, in particular those trainee in the Cambridge sub-department of Quaternary Studies pioneered pollen-analytical research in British in the 2 40s and '50s, and it is significant that Godwin (1975) subtitles his classic work on the history of the British flora 'A factual basis for phytogeography.'

Biogeography then is more than the study of the distributions of flora and fauna. Yet the spatial dimension has varied remarkably in its importance to geographical, as distinct from biological, investigations. Geographical to the non-geographer means spatial, fundamentally, and therefore distributional and, ipso facto, locational. To the geographer then, 'geographical' is as much as spatial and is ultimately and embarrassingly encyclopedic in its terms of reference. To the biologist, 'geographical', traditionally and persistently means spatial and often global, and his explanations of the development of distributions. It follows that biogeography for geographers is destined to be an expanded combination of plant ecology, animal ecology and human ecology, whilst biogeography for biologists is essentially a spatial platform for the debate on the manner in which modern plant and animal distributions are related to their antecedents, in both biological and geological terms.

Hare (1969) has remarked how developments in geography (and physical geography in particular) has been persistently out-of-step with scientific fashion and trend during this century. The geologists and historians, etc. who founded the first departments of geography in the inter-war period, promoted integrated, cross-Faculty studies but the 'nineteenth-century fixation for separating the arts from the sciences was generally to persist. The new technique of air photo interpretation was pioneered but it did not flourish in geography departments until the '50s. 'Second-generation' (Fisher, 1959) geographers became committed so increasingly intense specialization, especially in geomorphology, historical and urban geography, and the stage was set for the decline, slow at first and very rapid later, of integrated, including regional, studies. In the meanwhile, the statistical revolution which encompassed the biological science in the '50s could not penetrate into geography until the "60s. Human geography, in the meantime, through the auspices of Harvey (1969), Haggett (1965) and Hall (1970) et al, went through a fundamental reappraisal in the late '60s and "70s and has emerged with a well developed, if also well debated, theoretical base (Johnston, 1983). Physical geography, including biogeography, still awaits this methodological and philosophical renaissance (Haines-Yound and Fetch, 1980). Nonetheless, biogeography, by virtue of its biological data source, together with climatology and hydrology, has embraced the full range of statistical techniques now available, although the 'opportunist' or adhoc nature of much geomorphological, palaeoenvironmental and pedological field data means that strict sampling procedures for site selection are of limited application. The analysis of pollen diagrams, relating to the prescribed and self-selecting locations of organic deposits, is a nice case in point. Techniques like cluster analysis may achieve unbiassed zonations, and computer programmes are available to take the labour out of pollen diagram construction.

Again, since the 1950s, physical geography (and human geography) has become obsessed with studies of process rather than form (the latter being the focus of the '50s), and a switch in emphasis to the time-scale from the space-scale was inevitable. Moreover, adopted the featureless isotropic plane as the theoretical platform on which their human distributions are displayed, thus symbolizing the complete demise of the one-time scared 'physical basis of geography.' In the meanwhile, economists and sociologists have tended to adopt their own spatial and regional approaches, especially when concerned with planning problems, and regional synthesis survivors under the umbrella of new agglomerations styled as 2†area studies' or 'development studies'. 'Regional Science2† now applies mathematical measures to spatial distributions. Geography, thus, retains the doubtful privilege of taking the wrong direction at the wrong time.

Biogeography, however, has been fortunate in two respects. First, it reasserted itself in geography departments at the time of the environmental reawakening in the 1960s (but could certainly have contributed more than it did in the '70s to environmental research in biology departments, being the beneficiary not only of a promopt statistical transformation in the '50s but also of a theoretical renaissance in the '70s, albeit now clouded in fundamental controversy in the '80s. At the same time it must be conceded that the kind of biogeography which has been nurtured in geography departments over the last two decades has been so obsessed with applications of the ecosystem concept, on the one hand, and palaeoenvironmental reconstructions, on the other, that the response to the 'new biogeography' being so fiercely debated by the biologists has been muted.

THEORETICAL BIOGEOGRAPHY

Stoddart has made regular appraisals of recent developments in biogeography with particular reference to theoretical advances. He quotes extensively from the biological literature, in particular the zoological sources from which the major innovatory thrust has recently come (May ed., 1981).

MacArthur and Wilson's (1967) pioneer development of the equilibrium theory of particular by Gilbert (1980), has been constructively reviewed by Diamond and May (1981) and Higgs (1981) with particular reference to the design of nature reserves, an application which Gilbert regards as premature. Islands are naturally well defined, biophysical units or prescribed theaters of biological operation with measurable and controllable dimensions, discrete locations and accessibilities, and less complex histories than is usual for less well circumscribed habitats. Moreover, the island concept is equally applicable to any geographically isolated area, e.g. a lake, a mountain peak, a peat bog or the detail of the type of mosaic landscapes developed, for example in periglacial environments, deciduous forest clearings, or within the savannas. The quilibrium theory of island biogeography is based on the postulate that a dynamic relationship exists between (1) the species arriving and colonising, which is a function of distance of the island from source, and (2) species becoming extinct, which is a function of island area. There are logistic problems in data assembly. Can one differentiate between resident, seasonal and chance species? Are simple positive sightings reliable population indicators? Are varying arithmetic totals of parallel varying ecological significance? Extinction as such is a difficult stage to define. Again, the physiography and habitat potential of islands varies spatially and also eventually over time, e.g. if climate changes or ocean currents deviate.

But is not the modification and eventual replacement of hypotheses of the very essence of progress in the scientific method? Ball (1975) calls for this development by the introduction of hypothetico-deductive procedures a la Popper (1968) to supplement the empirical-descriptive (i.e. the establishment of distributions) and the so-called 'narrative' (explaining the distributions) methods already well practiced. Cracraft (1975) makes a parallel three-fold recommendation. Much biogeographical work requires to progress from the inductive to the deductive and, ultimately, the predictive (Haines-Yound and Fetch, 1980). The current Darwinist/cladist debate is very intense and often ad hominem between the (a) traditional school, which assumes centres-of-origin, dispersal or migration tracks, and the availability and applicability of many different explanations, e.g. continental drift and not vicariance alone, and (b) the new school which assumes only the one explanation, i.e. the fragmentation of antecendent distributions (i.e. vicariance), generalized "tracking" of species and continental movements. As Stoddart (1981) comments, biogeography would be "weakened by neglecting either school of thought".

Equally ripe for revision are the traditional ecological concepts of "succession" and "climax". Clementsian succession is rare in the real world and palaeoecological work is revealing that what was thought to be the largest, established and most stable of the vegetation climax formations, the tropical rain forests, is vulnerable to climatological, pedological and physiological changes over the short-term and over relatively short distances. Whitmore et al (1982) recommend that the tropics, rather than, conventionally, the temperate latitudes, might be considered as the norm in both biogeographical and geomorphological studies. The uniformitarian-inspired, nineteenth century-style, latitudinal zonations of vegetation and soils may now melt away into more detailed calibrations over time and space of Quaternary environmental oscillations. Multivariate statistics enables the analysis and interpretation of massive if localized data sets. The probability of plants being replaced in a specific time period can be estimated and future community compositions can be predicted. He suggests that, where successional convergence occurs, it is a statistical phenomenon rather than a biological one. Again, as Matthews (1979) has shown, plant succession may be divergent. Linear models have proved most successful, especially for predicting forest successions, but many interesting non-linearities must occur due to varying sensitivities to disturbance, for example.

The climax theory, a sympton of the old, unicycle, ternary model, must also subside with the decline of the parallel and analogous concepts of 'grade' in river profile development 'maturity' of soil profile development and long-term 'stability' of climate regimes. These concepts were developed and applied in the context of "closed systems'. Following Stoddart (1965, 1967), Chorley (1971) and Bennett and chorley (1978), the 'dynamic equilibrium' concept may now be applied in the 'open-system' context, allowing the operation of continuous change in both process and form. Oldfield (1983) has proposed a 'steady state' model of ecosystem change as an additional alternative to the standard successional and cyclic models.

Biogeographers, very much a minority group in geography departments, have been concentrating on extending the research frontiers in the study of British vegetation and environmental history. The parallel reconstructions of edaphic, climatic, topographic and hydrological historic and related archaeological and historic successions are testimony to the broader expertise in palaeoenvironmental science which physical geographers are usually more able to apply than palaeoecologists, among whom, nonetheless, is often displayed an equally penetrating environmental awareness. As with the spatial dimension, geographers have no automatic case for monopoly or even priority in expertise, so also it is apparent that palaeoclimates, palaeohydrologies demand the combined interpretations of palaeoenvironmentalists of different training and backgrounds.

Ironically, the global space dimension, now adjustable in the light of place tectonics, has provided the ideological battle ground for the zoologists. The new biogeography incorporates welcome contemporary theories on the short-term and episodic nature of climatic and geological changes, and updated Darwinism provides a temporal framework for theoretical comparison and context. Biogeographers in geography departments must work now towards their own hypothetico-deductive models to calibrate and predict the environmental changes with which they are so obsessed.

APPLIED BIOGEOGRAPHY: WITHIN PHYSICAL GEOGRAPHY

Biogeography, being concerned to study biological and man-derived processes operating in both natural and man-made environments, is bound to contribute to interpretation of pattern and change in both physical and cultural landscapes. It follows that it has applications (a) within physical geography as a whole, (b) within human geography as a whole, (c) in areas involving both physical and human geography. Along with climatology, pedology and hydrology, biogeography has comprehensive linkages throughout the length and breadth of the subject and especially at what has been allowed to become its central divide between the human and physical sectors. Wooldridge once described as "an ugly monocular squint' (Woodridge, 1945, 1950), it is, however, biogeography, with pedology, that provides the biophysical arena where land-use systems convert natural energy for man's dietetic and technological consumption. This biosphere is the engine room where biogeological exchanges take place and where man's cultural adaptations are concentrated and focused within physical geography.

The full interpretation of the physical landscape must include the delicate veneer of soil, vegetation and land use that covers its surface. In the micro-detail of this veneer are the residual effects of both long-term and short-term geomorphological, hydrological and climatological processes and the abundant evidence of recent environmental history. Gerrared (1981) has presented an integrated view of geomorphology and pedology and Dimbleby (1962) and Smith (1970) pioneered investigations in soil palynology. Equally, palaesol horizons containing residues of associated flora and fauna allow the identification of warmer interstadial or interglacial periods, and thus contribute to the reconstruction of environmental histories, especially of the late Quaternary where the major thrust of current geomorphological research is located (Bowen ed., 1977).

Lockwood (1983) has outlined the role of vegetation cover in the operation of the world's climatic systems. Currently, there is probably more agreement among climatologists and meteorologists on the impact of rapid deforestation (through changes in the carbon dioxide content of the atmosphere), on the direction (if not the scale) of climate trends, than on other factors affecting those trends. Fossil polen, snails and beetis remains etc., have been used to reconstruct past climates but the exercise is in some ways presumptuous and generates its own interpretational controversies. According to variations in (a) relief, soil conditions and associated ground hydrology, (b) the state, vigour and continuity of the vegetation cover, (c) above all, in the inherent sensitivity, including mobility in fauna, of the biota involved and (d) finally, the site-impact of prehistoric man. This hypothesis could be applied to explain some of the time discrepancy between the onset of warming and cooling phases in the Devensian Late-glacial. A fuller explanation, however, must lie in a broader biogeographical awareness of the varying rates of colonization opportunities and migration rates from southerly sources between circa 14,500 and 10,000 BP for (a) grasses, (b) trees, (c) animals like the deer, (d) insects like the beetle. The summers and afternoons of British-style, relatively cold, periglacial phases (Williams, 1975) could well have been micro climatically warm enough to provide very early, if patchy, habitats for grasses and insects well before the ungulates and, later, shrubs and trees, could respond to a fuller-scale climatic warming with tree-canopies enjoying the required levels of maximum temperatures. The fullest bioclimatic interpretations are possible when palaeoecosystems are reconstructed, an example of which is provided (Taylor, 1980). The collective interrelationships within and between environmental and cultural factors, in terms of change and response, is fully displayed, thus promoting equilibrium and accuracy of interpretation of the initial causes and consequences of change. However, the inferential nature of such models must be stressed since the basic biological, pedological and archaeological and radiometic evidence is adapted to reconstruct other components of the environment for which direct data are not as available, e.g. the climate, the hydrology and, to a great extent, the fauna. Such palaeoecosystematic models are as yet inductive and must survive the accumulation of further Ecosystem model for the Middle and Late Bronze Age (after Taylor, 1980).

The model has been contracted on the basis o1 palaeoenvironmental and archaeological evidence available for sites in Wales and adjoining Welsh Borderland. It should be emphasized that much of the evidence for climatic hydrological and geomorphological changes has beer inferred from the more directly available evidence on the history of flora, fauna and soils, environmental an(archaeological data and the development of new dating techniques in the future.

Smith and Taylor (1969) and Taylor and Smith (1972, 1980) have shown how the analysis of vegetation history can aid the explanation of soil profile development, especially when organic layers are present either at the surface in the form of peat (at first, soil-induced, and termed pedogenic but, later, climatically controlled, and hence termed climatic peat), or within the profile, for example as the more layer of a buried podzol. Biological processes, in collaboration with physical and chemical processes, continuously create (and successively destroy) the soil medium.

The hydrological cycle involves losses, gains, surpluses and deficiencies by courtesy of the vegetation/land-use layer which lies at the interface with water-usage by plants, animals and man. Panman (1948) pioneered evaporation studies from different vegetation surfaces and Law (1956) was to discover that as much as 30 per cent of incident rainfall can be intercepted by a closed tree canopy. This statistic was derived for conifer plantation in the central Pennines. Later, New son et al (1982) confirmed that the afforested upper Severn catchment, near the summit of Plynlimon in mid-Wales, also intercepted rainfall at comparably high rates which did not apply in the grass lands of the adjacent headwaters of the River Wye. Again, Taylor et al (1980) usefully combined data for soil moisture storage with data for potential soil moisture deficits for a 20 km^2 grid network covering Great Britain for the 1976 drought. This gives a more refined local measure of 'functional drought' as both soil and climate parameters are built into the distributions. The biospheric component of the hydrological cycle is the 'operations room' where both quantity and quality water resources are continuously required. Rapid vegetation change, whether it be in Amazonia or in the Southern Uplands of Scotland (Robinson, 1980), has immediate hydrological repercussions on land use, especially in the context of drainage costs and water quality. The afforestation of water-supplying catchments beyond, say, 50 per cent of their land area is increasingly being challenged by Water Authorities since the type of remote countryside and localized water supply options in summer. Clearly, the long-term planning of water resources over the coming decades should fully incorporate extrapoiated land use and vegetation changes to reduce and perhaps avoid the recurrence of such friction.

BIOGEOGRAPHY WITHIN HUMAN GEOGRAPHY

The abandonment of any traditional 'physical background' in favour of isotropic surfaces may be excusable for theoretical studies in human geography. Otherwise what human geographers do, if they confine their objectives to explaining human distributions in exclusively human terms, might as well be located outside, as well as inside geography departments. The way forward is in a reassessment of, first, the way environment factors encourage or discourage the taking up of options and, second, the cost-benefit, operationally, socially, economically and technically, of accepting or refusing such options. Advanced and sophisticated, urbanized and industrialized cultures are not immune from such a reappraisal which may be deceptively more applicable to the rural and developing worlds.

It is patently obvious that the cruder physical underpinnings of the past which have been used to explain settlements (e.g. physical site and position, regionality, gaps, accessibility, defensibility, simple area and distances available, spring-lines, water and other natural resource availability, bridging and fording points, etc.) are basic geomorphological, hydrological and strategic factors which operated functionally in the dark and distant past in the foundation of pioneer settlements. Such associations have now been overprinted by new economic, social and political forces which have re-shaped settlement patterns and industrial locations. More pertinent, however, as argued by Taylor, is the pattern of evaluation over time of land (=biophysical) resources, which may present some degree of consistency along cultural successions from the most primitive and prehistoric to the most modern and intense Again, non-rural landscapes and cities are equally interpretable as ecosystems (Douglas 1981, 1983) with energy exchanges, biogeochemical cycles balances and imbalances, storage requirements and pollution hazards.

Human systems involve the circulation of information as well as the fundamental cycling of energy in both is natural and converted forms. Birch (1972) has modeled the farm unit in this context where both energy transformation and information flows combine to produce outputs for transfer of marketing systems for the negative or positive feedback into the original system. The use of the same concepts; models and methods enables a new liaison to be established with human geography.

Historical geography (Thomas, 1963; Darby, 1977), history and archaeology have long laboured without the benefit of a contemporary environmental settings to provide context when attempting to account for those epregrinations and predicaments of prehistoric and historic man which hint of environmental inducement, steering or constraint.

Thus, the final burial of any vestiges of direct physical determinism may be followed by an historical application of behavioural geography in the context of the contemporary environmental conditioning. Lynch (1975) has discussed imaginatively the possible landscape appraisals attributable to Bronze Age man in his decision about the location of his settlements and burial places. Parry (1978) and Taylor (1980b) have examined behavioural attitudes to environmental changes, initially climatic but also eventually biogeographical, pedological and hydrological, in prehistoric and medieval times, respectively, in Wales and the Southern Uplands of Scotland, respectively.

At the same time, new direct environmental linkages are emerging from studies in medical geography, in particular the incidence of environmentally-related diseases and the occurrence of selected dietetic deficiencies (Howe, 1963, and Howe and Loaraine (eds.), 1980). Recent research in Wales and Scotland is confirming that the bracken fern (Pteridium aquilinum) is a source of toxins, in particular the carcinogenic shikimic acid which, when transmitted via water or milk, is capable of including cancers in animals and possibly humans also. Taylor has presented initial evidence that the bracken areas of Wales have doubled since the 1930s and the collation of local rates of expansion for a number of representative but well scattered sites in Britain indicates a national average rate of increase of 1.0 per cent, but on selected common lands it is in excess of 3.0 per cent. This rate of land-loss is all the more serious as bracken occurs mostly on well drained, sunny, sheltered slopes of high grazing potential. This land-use change will rank with the more familiar rural land-losses to afforestation and urbanization, as a major twentieth-century event of both economic and ecological significance (Taylor, 1978). The problem is so interdisciplinary in nature as to require balanced and broad-based biogeographical solutions.

It follows that an alternative biophysical basis is available as a backcloth for selected studies in human geography where environmental constraints, inducements, resources or relationships are explicitly involved.

AN INTERGRATING APPROACH ASPECT BETWEEN PHYSICAL AND HUMAN GEOGRAPHY

The current fissiparous tendency throughout geographical studies has created an estrangement between physical and human geography that is unprecedented and ill-advised from the point of view of maintaining the intellectual identity and integrity of the subject which must include a commitment to study both man and his environment and ipso facto, their interrelationships as well. Johnston (1983) has reviewed the possible role of resource geography in achieving some integration between physical and human geography, and concludes that such a role is both 'unlikely' and 'unnecessary' because, he argue, resource geography is basically 'a social science' which can import environmental considerations as and when required. He argues that both sets of processes should be fully the explicity involved in such attempts at integrative study. This is very much the blinkered view of the systematic. Integrated studies involve much retailing as well as wholesaling, and much secondary evaluation of facts as well as primary establishment of facts.

Resource management is not an exclusively social science and does possess an ecological basis. Natural resources have inherent qualities and rankings prior to assessment for usage by man. Usage in nature provides a pre-existing hierarchy, be it air, land, water, slope, soil, nutrients, flora, fauna, etc. Pre-use assessments of inherent productivity provide a base-reference for subsequent land-use performances and alternates. Fully integrated studies must involve both the environmental base and the land-use activity performed on it. Such a perspective is eminently appropriate for biogeographical analysis, a point to which Hohnston (1983) pays scarcely any attention.

The work of Isard (1969) and his co-worker (1967, 1972) and of Clarke (1981) point the successful integration of ecological and economic systems as an example of a man/land combination. Both systems may be conceived in budgetary terms, with inputs and outputs which are variably interchanged and converted, some within either system and a few in both. Using coefficients, the processes and commodities of both systems can be evaluated in comparative accounting terms. Thus the 'combined operation room' at the heart of the two systems is identified and penetrated. Information follows interlock with converted energy flows in land-use systems and industries in general, and inputs and outputs can be expressed in the common language of either energy equivalent or monetary values and related productivities derived. Isard establishes a numerical ecological classification system and derives ecological interrelation coefficients as applied to some more accessible case-studies such as selected fisheries.

The upper part of Table 16.1 expresses typical inputs and outputs of economic commodities as coefficients. For example, the first coefficient listed, -0.612006, is a dollar's worth of input of crude petroleum or natural gas per dollar output of the industry. Similarly, the coefficient next to last, -0.89378, is the input of wages and salaries per dollar output of the industry. Concerning inputs/outputs other than economic ones, a classification for water intake from, and pollutants discharged via water to, the environment is presented in Table 16.3. For example, the fourth item is water intake for cooling purposes expressed in 1,000 gallons per dollar intake, and the" penultimate item is radioactive waste. The set of non-economic commodities in is listed in the lower half of in the form of coefficients. These tabulations are not complete (e.g. air and air pollution inputs/outputs are excluded) but at least the first empirical linkages between economic and ecological systems are demonstrated.

Note: SIC = Standard Industrial Classification
WPC = Water Pollution Classification

RECIPROCATION WITH THE BIOLOGICAL SCIENCE

Whitest biogeography in geography departments has become the beneficiary of the statistical and theoretical advances achieved in biology in recent decades, a reciprocal contribution can be identified in the injection of a broader environmental expertise both in the field and the laboratory. This derives from a training in physical geography as a whole, including geomorphology (and geology), climatology, hydrology and pedology as well as biogeography and their individual technologies. In addition, traditional and new skills in survey, cartography and remote sensing have been brought to bear on the problems of representing and interpreting biological distributions.

Table 16.1
Input-Output Coefficients : RIS Sector 2911 Petroleum Refining

Sector			*Coefficient*
RIS 1311	Crude Petroleum and Natural Gas		-0.612006
1509	Construction, Maintenance and Repair		-0.001410
2652	Set-up Paperboard Boxes		-0.008054
2655	Fibre Cans, Tubes, Drums and Similar Products		-0.001557
2812	Alkalis and Chlorine		-0.000935
2818	Industrial Organic Chemicals, n.e.c.		-0.027180
2819	Industrial Inorganic Chemicals, n.e.c.		-0.009190
2911	Petroleum Refining		+0.954950
2992	Lubricanting Oils and Greases		-0.014954
3411	Metal Cans		-0.005294
4811	Telephone Communications		-0.001210
4890	Telegraph and Other Communications		-0.000100
4911	Electric Utilities		-0.007629
4920	Gas Companies and Systems		-0.012336
4941	Water Supply		-0.001082
4990	Sanitary and Other Systems		-0.000142
6020	Interest		-0.005088
6301	Insurance, Nonlife		-0.001242
6510	Real Estate Services		-0.007680
7301	Business Services, excluding Advertising		-0.017228
7310	Advertising		-0.002312
7400	Research and Development		-0.000390
7500	Automotive Repair		-0.001040
9000	Local and State Taxes		-0.008049
9100	Federal Income Tax		-0.014755
9826	Office Supplies		-0.000280
9842	Transportation Costs		-0.040831
9888	Wages and Salaries		-0.089378
9899	Residual		-0.063589
WPC1001	Water Intake, Sanitary Use,	1 ,000 Gal/$ Output	-0.000455
1002	Water Intake, Production	"	-0.022827
1003	Water Intake, Cooling	"	-0.114861

1011	Water Discharged, Sanitary Use	"	+0.000323
1012	Water Discharged, Production	"	+0.070219
1013	Water Discharged, Cooling	"	+0.050100
1031	Biochemical Oxygen Demand BOD, 5-Day	1 ,000 Lb/$ Output	+0.000065
1032	Ultimate Oxygen Demand, UOD	"	+0.000076
1033	Chemical Oxygen Demand, COD	"	+0.000169
1041	Suspended Solids	"	+0.000084
1042	Settleable Solids	"	+0.000124
1047	Turbidity	"	+0.000365
1051	Alkalinity	"	+0.000051*
1052	Acidity	"	+ n.a.
1061	Oils and Greases	"	+0.000012
10951	Phenols	"	+0.000003

* The pH factor for this industry is the range of 4.5-10.7, with 7.0-8.0 most likely. Source : Isard *et al* (1967).

Pollen-analytical studies of inorganic and organo-mineral sediments as distinct from organic ones have been expanded by geographers as well as ecologists. Many palaeoecologist; have restricted their pollen sources to organic profiles. Ye mire sites, like lake basins, blanket peats or soil profiles also exhibit their own 'site bias' in pollen records, and much more research is required into the variability of pollen records from different but proximate sites to calibrate such bias. Birks et al (1975) has pioneered the way with a series of isopollen maps of Britain for circa 5,000 BP and an atlas containing similarly derived maps for north-west Europe has beer complied (Huntleyand Birks, 1983). However, these studies adopt the large-scale, cartographic base beloved of the ecologist, with the background of the map consisting merely of coastlines (Dunnet, 1982). For such maps to be of biogeographical use in the fullest environmental sense significant contours and other gradients (climatic, pedagogical for example) should be selectively shown, as indeed the would enhance the interpretation of much needed, small-scale, isopollen maps, e.g. of Wales or county size (Smith 1970; Moore, 1971). The reconstruction of significant biogeographies of the past as local maps offers an eminently worthy challenge to the expertise of both biogeographer and ecologist, and would provide new spatial perspectives for archaeological research.

Table 16.2
Proposed Water Pollution Classification (WPC) Code

WPC Code	*Water in take, Total**	*Units*
1000	Water Intake, Total*	1,000 Gal/$
1001	Sanitary Use	"
1003	Cooling	"
1004	Boiler Feed	"
1008	Irrigation	"
1009	Other, n.e.c.	"
1010	Water Discharge, Total	"
1011	Sanitary Use	"
1012	Production	"
1013	Cooling	"
1019	Other, n.e.c.	"
1020	Water Consumed	"
1031	Biochemical Oxygen Demand, BOD 5-Day	1,000Lb/$
1032	Ultimate Oxygen Demand, UOD	"
1033	Chemical Oxygen Demand, COD	"
1040	Solids, Total+	"
1041	Suspended Solids	"
1042	Settleable Solids	"
1047	Turbidity	"
1048	Colour	"
1051	Alkalinity	"
1052	Acidity	"
1061	Oils and Greasses	"
1062	Surfectants	"
1070	Pathogenic (Disease Causing) Organisms	-x
1080	Temperature	-x
1090	Other Pollutants	
1095	Toxic Material**	-x
1096	Radioactive Waste	-x
1099	Not Classified	"

* Cost of water intake is given by SIC code 4941 -water supply

\+ 1041 = 1041 + 1042 (i.e. WPC Codes)

\# In addition, colour should be specified by kind by its wave length

x No one satisfactory measure was decided upon, although thermal pollution may be specified most satisfactorily in terms of millions of BTUs per dollar output

** Phenols, which fall in this category, may be identified by a five-digit code such as WPC 10951

Source : Isard *et al* (1967)

A similar technological overlap occurs in the methods now available to map modern vegetation distributions which may be recorded at three different levels. First, on the micro-scale, quadrats or releves may be taken according to a prescribed spatial sampling procedure (stratified random is usually recommended), the size, shape, intensity and frequency distribution of the quadrats being very much determined by the degree of floristic variability of the study area and the scale required (and utility) of any proposed, derived map. Second, on the meso-scale, reconnaissance mapping of visible vegetation distributions can be attempted in the field on, for example, the scale of 6" to the mile (1/10560) provided the vegetation pattern is so standardized as to be legible in panoramic view (Taylor, 1968). Thirdly, using conventional air photography or satellite sources, the vegetation canopy can be remotely-sensed and checked for ground truth but the spatial continuity and unbiased quality of this source goes hard-in-hard with an unaviodable dependence of interpretation on the scale and standards of the initial photography (Darch). The bridging of the two extremes (that is, between intensely taken ground quadrates and very remotely sensed satellite sources with pixels of, say, 50 m^2, and even the bridging of quadrats and conventional air photographic sources), is not by any means a straight forward task (Davies, 1974). It is one where geographers could contribute professionally, especially from 1984 when the French satellite imagery source, SPOT, will be supplying new photography with a much finer resolution of 10 m^2 pixels.

It could be argued that bioclimatology as applied to both animals and plants is a sub-field shared between climatology and biogeography or biology. Ollerenshaw's successful work (1966) on role of weather factors in disease incidence and prediction for farm animals is applied bioclimatology at its most effective. In crop climatology a major contributor has been W.H. Hogg, as reported by Taylor (1967). Without doubt, interdisciplinary qualifications for work in this area are a necessary prerequisite for its advancement.

IN SERVICE OF CONSERVATION

In contrast to conventional and systematic biological arguments for conservation (e.g. on the basis of individual species of plant or animal at risk), a broader-based biogeographical view could incorporate rock, soil, climate and total land-use, past and present, to derive a measure of the distinctiveness of the landscape or habitat concerned. Such a view would keep conservation policies in touch with the economic, social and technical realities of land usage and, in the end, protect heritage sites within the tempo of land-use change. No ecosystem can survive in any form of suspended animation. Changes is a natural process within ecosystems as well as being imposed externally by man. Catering for both is preferable to the all too familiar friction between positive and negative policies when the forces of conservation and land-use are allowed to oppose each other. O'Riordan's (1982) bureaucratic prescription too reconcile the problem, as manifested in the British countryside, takes too little account of the institutional inertia (which already exists in the form of complex land ownership and tenure), open-market competition for land purchase, hierarchies of protected or conserved areas and sites, and incompatibility of local and national priorities. Real local conflicts between users, conservationists and planners in the British context (and probably elsewhere) are normally soluble only on a local scale. Nonetheless, O'Riordan certainly shapes the problem and its possible national solution, but inevitably from a conservational viewpoint, initially, rather than a developmental one.

On the theoretical side, both the theory of island biogeography and its application in conservation have been criticized (Gilbert, 1980). Wilson and Willis (1975) make four recommendations on the design of nature reserves. First, they argue that reserves should be as large as possible, initially for strategic reasons, to allow fall-back positions in relation to specific extinction rates. Second, they suggest that unique habitats are best protected in closely adjacent multi-reserves since extinction has a strong random component. Thirdly, because of additional vulnerability of peninsula shapes, reserves should be as round, regular-shaped and as continuous as possible. The designs on the left in each case result in lower spontaneous extinctin rates than their counterpart designs on the right. Fourthly, comprehensive surveys of both the least vulnerable and the minority species should be completed as soon as practicable as well as the urgent construction of extinction models for vulnerable and conspicuous organisms. Diamond and May (1981) offer four qualifications. First, several smaller reserves in lieu of one large one may be preferable in that each smaller reserve may favour the survival of a different species. Higgs (1981) has exposed arguments for and against a single large reserve may favour the survival of a different species. Higgs (1981) has exposed arguments for and against a single large reserves (SLR). (Table 16.4) Second, many scattered small reserves are less susceptible to the spread of epidemic diseases or some analogous disaster, e.g. fire. Thirdly, 'edge' preferring species will thrive better in irregular-shaped and smaller reserves with a high perimeter-to-area ratio. Fourthly, non-random priodic changes in species population dynamics could help to determine the 'optimal size of reserves and the time-scales of management policies.

The continuing debate on the application of island biogeography theory is dramatically highlighted in two contemporary events. First, the well documented deforestation of Amazonia evokes the challenge as to best programme to be devised for the partial survival of the last major area of tropical rain forest on this planet. The survival plan would be well concentrated on the 'islands' of greatest ecological stability where the greatest continuity of forest cover occurs. The second refers to the annihilation or evacuation of the entire 17 million bird population of Christmas Island in the mid-Pacific which has reported early in 1983 by the Los Angeles County Natural History Museum. This is possibly the largest island extinction ever recorded. It may have been due to the aberrant timing of the warm surface EL Nino ocean current which not only deprived the birds of access to food supplies in the immensed, cooler waters but also has been associated with climatic anomalies on the American Pacific seaboards and also possibly worldwide climatic repercussions in 1983. The events on Christmas Island make two. The design of nature reserves (after Wilson and Willis, 1975).

Table 16.3

The arguments for and against a single large reserve (SLR), indicating that theoretical considerations can support or oppose the setting up of a SLR (after Higgs, 1981)

For Reserve <1	*Species-area Curve*	*Against Reserve <1*
Species lost by fragmentation	Irreversibility	Species lost from specialized habitats outside large reserve
(a) Better buffering	Catastrophes	'all eggs in one basket'
(b) Easier recolonisation		
Several, e.g. less interference, less eggs per area	Management	Several, e.g. easier to set up, less likely to be developed
Proportionaly more non-edge habitat	Edge Effects	If the edge species are interesting, more in small reserves
Fewer extinctions mutually	Extinctions	Preservation of exclusive groups of species

The above diagrams incorporates some geometrical rules for the design of nature reserves on the basis of some conventional biogeographic theory. The designs on the left (in black) all result in lower spontaneous extinction rates than the corresponding designs (outlined) on the right. Both the left-hand and the right-hand designs have the same total areas and assumed homogeneous environments.

A. A continuous reserve is better than a fragmented one because of the effects of distance and areas.

B. A round design is the better one because of the peninsula effect (MacArthur and Wilson, 1967).

C. A close grouping is better than a linear one because of distance effects.

D. If the reserve must be divided, extinctions will be lower when the fragments are connected by corridors of natural habitat, no matter how thin the corridors.

Another principle, not incorporated in this figure, is that whatever the design of a given reserve, its extinction rates can be greatly reduced by the proximity nearby of similar reserves.

Points most forcibly. One, the catastrophe theory, not only reinforces the short-term sensitivity of all ecosystems to sharp environmental changes or disasters but, second, it also puts island biogeography theory at risk because of the possible random or periodic abbreviation of the assumed time-scales of its application, what an immense opportunity for research is now afforded by the birdless Christmas Island.

NEW DIRECTIONS AND APPLICATIONS

Biogeography is in a critical re-emergent stage in both the geographical (Watts, 1978) and biological sciences (Taylor, 1984). Whiles! major theoretical reappraisals in the latter group should evolve from current controversies over the origins and patterning of the distributions of biota over the earth, the continuing maturation and eventual convergence of the numerous thematic studies within the former group, will enable the established of new integrated methodologies within physical geography, within biogeography itself and also within geography as a whole. The calibration of man/land linkages in mutually compatible terms will rebridge the current intelectual void (Johnston, 1983) between two major focci of the subject.

However, concerning the reality of the scope of biogeography as currently taught and researched in departments of geography, it was Hill (1975) who first argued that the concentration on palynology and cultural biogeography had developed a historical perspective which served only to alienate biogeography from many of the contemporary trends in physical and in human geography. Later, Edwards (1982) constructively analyzed what was by then an increasing dominance of palynological work in geography departments but deplored, with some justification, its lack of innovation in ideas, methods and techniques. Following the strictures of haines-Yound and Fetch (1980) but responding, to the earlier exhortations of Moss (197J), physical geography as a whole requires to develop deductive strategies which go beyond the observation, collation and analysis of field-based and laboratory-derived data. A palaeoecosystematic approach, as demonstrated by Taylor (1980), is eminently biogeographical in concept and application but requires the cross-fertilization of ideas on contemporary meso-climates, hydrologies and soils. A more balanced and mature perception of environmental relationships emerges as well as the place and response of prehistoric (and historic) man within them. Archaeological and historical correlations over space as well as time cannot but gain from such appraisals. As Edwards (1982) also argues, the medium of pollen counting has other 'applied' rewards in that the calibration of rates of change in past ecosystems allows for the building of models to predict probably directions and rates of change in modern ecosystems (Bradshaw, 1983). This important principle and its application should become the conventional and repetable basis for the determination of the conservation status of specific habitats and the time-scale of conservation periods. In a constantly changing pattern of both natural and man-made land-usage, strategies of alternating conservation and usage may well be more sustainable and should not be dismissed as satisfying neither side of the argument.

INTEGRATIVE, BALANCED APPROACHES IN LANDUSE ECOLOGY

Provided it develops and attacks its own research frontiers, palynology will continue to dominate biogeographical programmes in geography departments in the immediate future. But the full development of biogeography as a competitive sub-field requires broader interests, including its current 'second string2 , i.e. land-use ecology. The injection of biogeographical approaches to land classification systems and to the measurement of causes-and effects of land-use changes and environmental impacts enables (i) a necessary reconciliation of short-term and long-term, nature-derived and man-derived processes, and ecological and economic thresholds, (ii) a maximization of productivity and conservation of ecological resources, and (iii) the final optimization of land-use strategy and planning. This may sound perfectionist and unattainable but such reconciliations lie at the heart of the solution to land-use problems, no matter how pragmatic the targets and techniques adopted for standard planning procedures or adhoc consultancy are often in politically highly inflammable situations, involving complexities of ownership, tenure, responsibility and prejudice.

To quote a few examples, Cruickshank and Armstrong (1971) proved a functional relationship between sub-soil parameters and gross margins for a range of cropping enterprises on a sample of Londonderry farms in Northern Ireland. Maxwell et al (1979) have devised an economic model, including the technique of discount rating, for the allocation of land as between agriculture and forestry in the context of the British uplands, but the elegance of the model is in contrast to the crudity of their classification of land inputs. Tubbs and Blackwood (1971) produced a workable classification of ecological habitats to be protected from development within the Hampshire Structure Plan but the problem of reconciling ecologically-superior, unploughed meadow with economically-superior intensive arable land is not resolved. The report of the MAFF (1966) on land classification techniques was correct in proposing that economic classification per unit area or groups of holdings should be expressed in precise correlation spatially and functionally, with the ecological classification of the land types and area available to a specific economic category of farm area, farm group or farm type. Future research should explore this methodologically of difficult avenue: difficult because of the incomplete, fragmentary or unrepresentative nature of farm data and land data available (Taylor, 1974).

Simmons (1980) has provided details of recent contributions by geographers to the study of modern ecosystems and their management. Notable works are those of Harrison and Frenkel (1974), and Harrison (1975) on vegetation-analysis, Eden (1974) on selected savanna ecosystems, Tivy (1972), Barkham (1973), Warren and Goldsmith (1974 and 1976), and Tivy and Rees (1978) on recreation ecology. With increasing land-use pressures and the imminent expansion of the international scale of tourism, environmental information is sorely needed both for conservation practice and also the successful operation of adjacent or on-site land-use systems, including tourism (e.g. Taylor 1979), who presents a commissioned review of climate and weather factors affecting British tourism, and points the way to the need for similar regional, biogeographical surveys along the lines of those by Coppock and Duffield (1975) in Scotland and Warren and Goldsmith (1974) in the Scilly Islands, for example.

FUTURE REMOTE SENSING TECHNOLOGY

Darch has demonstrated the present and future applications of remote sensing techniques in biogeographical research. Cold (1968), Barrett and Curtis (1976) have made major pioneer contributions in this field. New remote-sensing platforms available for experimentation in the immediate future range from the French Satellite Source, SPOT (operational in 1984 and, offering a pixel resolution of only 10 m^2, of great potentials for vegetation and land-use mapping) to the use of a micro light aircraft as pioneered by Francis, Taylor and Williams (1984) (which would appear to be the ideal platform for the photography and study of small and medium-sized (e.g. 10 m^2 to 1000 m^2 ecosystems). It has already proved superior for the study of erosion forms and processes in blanket peat in central upland Wales. It provides high resolution aerial photography at low cost. Again, low take-off and landing requirements and low flying speed, together with direct pilot and camera control, make the technique superior, in cost-benefit terms, to other available methods of remote-sensing, e.g. conventional aircraft, helicopter or balloon. It has great potential for biogeographical and other forms of field-based research.

The details of remote sensing aspect for the use of biogeographic studies has already been described in the earlier chapter of this book,

CONSULTANCY

In addition to academic establishment and scientific acceptability, biogeography in its applied aspects has much to contribute in the fields of public and private consultancy. Cole (1968), Barrett and Curtis (1976) and others have been involved internationally, for example, with resource and land-use survey for agricultural and industrial purposes. Taylor has advised on peat land resources and development, internationally, agro-climatological problems, land-use strategies, and conflicts between land-use and conservation interests. Other consultancy activities include references quoted above concerning recreation ecology and ecosystem management, etc.

These many and varied developments in applied biogeography complement the extension of academic biogeography in both physical and human studies and in the currently neglected borderland between the two. The re-emergent sub-field of biogeography appears well set to liaise reciprocally also with the biological and environmental sciences to the collective benefit of al practitioners, no matter what their first-degree subject was or what particular name their department carries. There are far too many scientific challenges and pressing problems of environmental monitoring and management to allow intrnecine quibbles on academic territoriality to interfere with progress in pure and applied research. The thrust must be interdisciplinary; the resultant advancements in biogeographical theory and practice will be of benefit to all biogeographers, regardless of their training or affiliation.

ENVIRONMENTAL PROTECTION

Human awareness of congenial environment is not new. From time immemorial people have tried to keep their habitat and nearby surroundings clean and free from harmful elements. But awareness of balance in environment and ecology is of comparatively recent origin.

The environment in which human beings originated and survive has a number of constituents like, air, water, soil, plants-all of which maintain a complex structure in themselves, but these are an inter-relationship and interdependence, based on certain fundamental principles. Survival of human beings at present and in the period ahead is largely dependent upon a natural balance among all these elements surrounding us. We all want to breathe fresh air, use pure water and live in noiseless atmosphere. Unfortunately, we find ourselves surrounded by polluted air, water and noisy world. All these combined together may be called environmental pollution, which has emerged as a major problem all over the world. Let us for the present look at environmental policy in India with regard to air pollution and noise pollution.

AIR POLLUTION

Pure air is vital for life on the earth. It is vital for man animal and vegetation alike. A 'normal healthy person can live about five weeks without food, and five days without water but only five minutes without air'. This shows the importance of air in our life. The story behind air pollution is quite old. It dates back to the period when fire was invented, "But in those days, the smoke, unbumed carbon particles, soot and gases rose in the air and were carried away by the wind". H presented no problem. The automatic mechanism of ail purified it. With increase in population and growth o1 cities, men started to life in close proximity and started to burr fire simultaneously at many places close to each other. Still the problem did not assume unmanageable proportions. But this situation did not last for ever. With the Industrial Revolution of Great Britain came a concentration of industries, and the problem surfaced. John Evelyn, a British reporter, provided in 1661, the "first list of scientific solution to the problem of air pollution. However, the problem then was no1 visible in the less developed and less populated countries, including the U.S.A. Two hundred years later, the American people became conscious of air pollution and articles began to appear in several magazines about the dangers of the 'organic dust' that was polluting the air of American cities. With the passage of time, the threat has spread to the other industrial countries like Japan, Germany, etc. in fact, to the whole world-developed as well as underdeveloped though the magnitude of pollution different.

It is worthwhile here to note what constitutes air pollutants. Broadly speaking, they may be classified under two categories: (1) Solid pollutants, and (2) Gases. The pollutants which find their way into air are fine particles, sulphur dioxide, carbon monoxide, a noxious mixture of fog and smoke, smog reactants, total oxidants, radio-active pollutants and miscellaneous pollutants. Though all of these solids and gases may not contribute to air pollution to the same degree, they are still worth mentioning. The fine particles have larger magnitude than the rest. They creep into air through chimney smoke, stone crushers, volcanic eruption, etc. The carbon particles have the ability to absorb certain gases. When they are breathed into our lungs with air along with some poisonous gases, if may prove dangerous for the human body.

Sulphur dioxide is another dangerous pollutant which enters into our body along with the air we breathe. 'It attacks the lungs and other parts of the respiratory system usually slowing down the changing action of the little hair like structures - the cillia - that line the main parts of the system'. It affects men and animals alike. Plants also suffer from sulphur dioxide. It has been estimated that for every ton of coal that is burned, an average eighty pounds of sulphur dioxide is released into air. The thermal power plants, steam engines and coal, used as domestic fuel, constantly emit carbon dioxide and sulphur dioxide in air.

It would not be out of place here to mention that not only organization and industrialization are polluting air, but also men and animals. In rural and semi-urban areas, there is hardly any proper sewage system and the human wastes are discharged in open space. With the increase in population, more and more human wastes are discharged-making air highly polluted. Mahatma Gandhi advised that people should take with them a khurpi while going to ease themselves and bury waste under the ground. But we do not find anyone following his valuable advice. In many urban areas, the existence of service latrines also pollutes air through night soil areas.

Yet another source of air pollution is roadside dust either released by consumption of fuel in vehicles or dust raised in air due to speeding vehicles. In our country, the roads are not fully metalled. When speedy vehicles run on these muddy and dusty roads, they leave behind them a cloud of dust, which enters the air and goes up into the sky. In many big cities like Delhi, they also affect visibility.

NOISE POLLUTION

The other factor which is noise pollution we have traveled a long way in a noisy world. Noise is nothirg but unwanted sound. The intensity of sound is measured by an abstract unit called 'decibels'. 'Ordinary speech has a loundness of sixty decibels and the normal human can hear sounds over a range of one hundred and thirty decibels'. A sound turns out to be annoying if it is more frequent, intensity and duration exceed the tolerance limit. Many persons have lost their hearing capacity due to loud noises.

At present, the electronic media, like loudspeaker, radio, television, tape-recorders, etc., may be found everywhere. The operators of these instruments have little concern about the annoyance caused to neighbours-not even about the sick and ailing. Religious places, once known for peace and tranquility, have now turned to be major sources of noise pollution.

Constant noise effects our hearing. Exposure to "constant noise may cause our blood vessels to contract, our skin to become pale, our muscles to be shot into our bold stream. This adrenalin produces tension and nervousness."

There is lack of conscious and effective measures to deal with the menace. Though, it is often claimed that our country has adequate legal safeguards, their practical validity is almost nil.

The above discussion examines only two types of environmental degradation. But the problem is multi-faceted and envelops the entire gamut of human life. Prevention o1 pollution of water, control of sewage, checking of marine pollution, are all important for our country.

Who are the creators of pollution? The answer is quite clear. 'The creators of pollution are human beings'. We all known that the number of people in the world is increasing. The more the people, the more the pollution and the harder the solution.

In our country, the protection of environment from different types of pollution is a truly challenging task. It involves proper management of land, water and soil resources, protection of disappearing species of animals and plants, natural eco-system, provision of basic needs to the vast population without damaging our natural environment and cultural heritage. Prior to implementation of the Sixth Plan there was no concrete programme in this direction. The Sixth Plan for the first time included environmental planning in its frame-work. It also admitted the unfavourable impact on environment from some of the development projects.

The Seventh Plan stressed environmental planning more emphatically. It recognized that 'the environment today is under severe threat from the pressure generated by growth of human population, poverty and misuse/unplanned use of natural resources; and further added that economic growth cannot be achieve in a sustainable manner by environmental erosion. 'The basic approach to the Seventh Plan would.-„ be sustainable development in harmony with" the environment.' The documents further states that 'environmental planning/protection/ improvement requires a coordinated highly decentralized approach involving the co-operation and active participation of every segment of society and most importantly of the political leadership.'

The above discussion sums up, in a nutshell, the global problem of environmental pollution which would throw our very existence in peril, unless proper and timely remedical action is initiated in right earnest. No nation can sit tight over this problem. *Pollution respects no national boundary.* Its extent is limitless. Since the problem is global and not confined to a particular area, it also requires global solution. Yet, none can ignore it at the local level. There must be created greater awareness about this problem at every level. A number of international agencies are co-operating with us at different levels It is suggested that the developed countries contribute a larger share towards the expenses incurred in environmental protection. Concrete action in this regard may proceed on the lines stated below:

1. More and more people should be made aware of the dangers inherent in environmental pollution.

2. Universities, colleges, schools and research institutions should work out a curriculum regarding protection of environment.
3. Existing legislations should be reviewed and updated in view of the changed situation.
4. People should be encouraged to take interest in social forestry.
5. Co-operation should' be extended to voluntary organizations by governmental departments and other bodies concerned with environmental protection.
6. Publications, highlighting the benefits of environmental protection, should be widely circulated among people.

The list presented above is not exhaustive, but only indicates an approach. A comprehensive planning both at the micro and macro levels is the need of the hour.

ECOSYSTEM

Earth is considered as the living planet of the solar system. It is endowed with a rich variety of life forms and large number of living organisms governed by the laws of nature. The interdependence of the various life form-starting from the unicellular primary producers to the complexly built higher plants and animals-is a unique feature of this green planet. Thus, our natural resource development and conservation of these resources are equally important for our survival and well being.

Man, the highest ovalved social animal, has undergone a stepwise evolution and development. For the present need, he destroyed the environment beyond a desirable limit and pushed it to the danger zone. The socio-economic progress due to rapid industrialization has also left us bewildered spectators to the expanding concrete jungle, proliferation of pollution, indiscriminate deforestation and destruction of ecological balance. As a result, today we feel the need to break away from our modern day life-styles and find solace in the lap of nature where exists a healthier, safer and more congenial environment.

There has been a trade off between environment and development in which development has been achieved at the cost of imbalancing the environmental quality. The industrial revolution initiated the dream of Man's total victory over nature and signaled the beginning of the end of humanity. The sustainable utilization of resources are required as they have a bearing on our future survival. These developments will help in improving economic development where local environments and biosphere are protected.

Water occupies 75% of our land surfaces which we depend upon to carry out our metabolic activity. The water body is polluted by industrial effluents, sewages and human wastes, etc. Thus it causes serious threat to aquatic life and effect their habitat. On studying e.g. the Cauvery basin, it is understood that these industries have drastic effect on the ecology of Cauvery. Spawning of Mahaseer and trout is affected, as a result these fishes have dwindled. Vast streches of the 600 km long Ganga river continue to remain highly polluted due to industrial activity. The Narmada valley project is a typical case of government priorities towards industries over the environment. For the sake of hydro-electric generation, large areas of cultivable fertile lands are being inundated and thousands of people are being displaced. Vast regions of virgin forest lands are cleared in many countries for cultivation of cash crops. The coffee and rubber plantations of India and Malaysia, and the rubber, sugarcane and rice plantations of Brazil are typical examples of such degradation.

In tropical country like our, the mangrove estuaries are the most productive natural system and, as such, ideal for feeding, breeding and nursery grounds for many fishes and crustaceans of economic importance. The major commercial sea food resources include penaeid prawns, fresh water prawns and marine fish, etc. They serve as a crucial habitat for boosting coastal aquaculture. Also, the area gets considerable potential for wildlife tourism and acts as a barrier to coastal erosion. Thus the rich decline habitat is to be conserved for its diversity and richness on the possibility of developmental activities like prawn farming, pisciculture and other allied aquaculture forms. Further afforestation and natural improvement are to be promoted which would benefit the economically poor individuals.

The Gulf war threatened aquatic species due to the explosion of atomic bombs and explosion of scud rockets which carry tones of explosive material, causing air pollution. Due to explosion of oil wells in Saudi Arabia, the oil float over the water formed the thick film on the surface and prevented diffusion of oxygen supply to the aquatic medium resulting in the destruction of aquatic flora and fauna. Further, the dumping of domestic and industrial waste accelerates the environmental degradation at all levels. In developing countries, the inputs of heavy metals has been increased into the aquatic environment. This has disturbed the aquatic ecosystem. Soil fertility has been reduced due to application of chemicals and there is a decline in agricultural productivity. Hundreds and thousands of tones of pesticides, insecticides, weedicides, herbicides, etc. are accumulating in the environment, thus polluting the air, water, land and also enter into the food chain accumulating in the body of the organisms. Thus urbanization, industrialization and intensive farming wastes need adequate disposal and treatment. Thus as a whole, new range of eco-friendly technologies will have to be developed and the existing ones either effectively adopted or discarded. Thus, there is a need for better soil, water and fertilizer management.

In India, the greatest pollution centres are seen in the industrial townships along the Indo-Gangetic plain. The tanning industry is one of the main sources of environmental pollution in Tamil Nadu, Uttar Pradesh, West Bengal, Rajasthan, Karnataka, Punjab, Andhra Pradesh and Bihar. Due to the complex nature of effluents produced by the processes in tanning, this industry will have to take more congnisance of steps for making the environment cleaner. The problem are created to a great extent because of the pressure to produce raw materials for modern industry.

The expanding population forced us to utilize the resources at a higher rate and cause environmental destruction. As a result of this, hundreds and thousands of animals and plant species are lost forever, each year. This has resulted in the depletion of vast amounts of carbon gases absorptive capacity. For our survival, we depend on fresh air, water and food which we

.take from our environment and in turn we give some by products to the environment. The air medium which gives us oxygen as a by-product is being polluted by the smoke released from the industry and motor car.

1. Conservation and Protection of Ecosystem

We reduces the concentration of oxygen and increases the concentration of carbon monoxide and carbon dioxide which cause a respiratory disease namely Anoxia in our body. There has been a 26 percent rise in CO_2 in the atmosphere over the pre-industrial revolution level, the source being 1.8 billion tones of CO_2 that we spew into the air every year by burning coal and driving cars. It is predicted to raise the average earth's temperature of one to two degrees in the next 25 years resulting in sea-level rise.

Acid rain has been defined as rain that is unnaturally acid a a result of pollution of the atmosphere with oxides of sulphur and nitrogen from the burning of coal and oil. In recent years, it has caused massive damage to trees, crops, plants, polluted rivers, lakes and springs and damaged human health as well as wild life and also defaced some of the most beautiful and cherished monuments. According to the World Resources Report for 1992-93, trends in nitrogen oxides emissions show increase in near by every city. The effects include damage to lung tissues, stinging eyes, coughing and chest discomfort, increased asthama attacks and. treated susceptibility to infection.

Global ozone depletion is not the only factor contributing to the change in the climate of the earth's atmosphere but also the heat trapping green house gases mainly CO;, produced by fossil fuels, petroleum and coal. The overall reduction in Ozone layer is now estimated to be approximately 8 percent. India has the highest percentage of degraded land in the world due to degeneration of forests at the rate of 2.8 percent annually. As a result, it has very little vegetation to hold the soil in place when it rains and precious top soil is washed down, damaging it further. Forests act as global sinks and as a pressing need of today we have to regulate forest exploitation. Thus we can afford to think about deforestation and still hope for development and conservation.

Now the greatest crisis is the depletion of ozone layer or the green house effect. According to the Urban Environment Institute, the developed countries are in a mad race to exploit all available natural resources. As per the available data, earth has become warm because it has lost 2 percent of the protective shield in the last two decades. Depletion of the ozone layer is the reason given for warming of the earth, as 1 percent of reduction in ozone increases UV radiation by 2 percent. As a result of this, nearly 6000 people are dying of skin cancer every year. In Australia and Newzealand, it is upto 7 percent. People in Bombay, Delhi and Calcutta are also reported to be affected. More than 50,000 people are reported suffering in Bombay alone.

Proper maintenance of fridges which contains CFC's is important. India has taken major steps in phasing out CFC's used in refrigerators and freezers to HCFC-22 transitory substitute with a low ozone depleting potential (ODP). The earth summit meeting officially known as the U.N. Conference on Environment and Development (UNCED), held from June 3rd to 14th at Rio De Janeiro (Brazil) was the world's largest gathering of the heads of States and their representatives of 178 nations. The global warming was the international issue. During this meet various developmental aspects were proposed to control the exceeding pollution. The representative nations including India unanimously approved and signed the document known as Agenda-21 to protect the atmosphere from global warming.

A global effort is needed to bring within the easy reach of al, developing and the developed countries, the technologies that exist and are yet to be developed to combat pollution and environmental degradation. Thus, there is a friendly need for the prospective long term integrated plan for industrial development and control of environmental pollution.

2. Conservation Strategy

United Nation's conference on Environment and

Development in Rio de Janeiro in 1992 signaled a major shift in the attitude of governments towards the Environmental issue, bringing it to the centre of the international agenda. The conference was a gathering of the entire community of nations, represented by their heads of States or Governments. This made it the large summit conference ever, the first "Earth Summit" and potentially the it was most important.

In this context let us have a look at the Environmental problems faced by the nations and the strategies to be adopted.

GLOBAL WARNING

Global climates is changing due to the accumulation o greenhouse gases in the atmosphere. Greenhouse gases let sunlight through but trap some of the heat radiating back to space (hence the name). As a result, the world is getting warmer. If current emission trends continue, earth's average temperature is expected to increase by an average of 1.5-4.5° C (probably 3-8° F) above the pre-industrial level by the year 2030. At higher latitudes, winter temperature will probably increase by at least double the global average (Greenland could have the climate of Ireland). This is the same amount of warming which occurred after the last ice age-but about 35 times as fast. Some of this warming-an average of 0.5°C could alter earth's climate more than it has ever been doing during the 10,000 years. If nothing is done to stabilize the green house gas content of the atmosphere the additional amount of warming to which the world is committed will increase and the rate of warming will accelerate.

In response, climate and ecological regions will shirt (c 1° C change in temperature is equivalent to a change in latitude of 100-150 km), precipitation patterns will change sea-level will rise and inundate low lying coastal areas; and storm intensity will increase. The timing and magnitude o these changes is uncertain; but they will be continuous-for as long as global warming is continuous-and irreversible.

DEPLETION OF STRATOSPHERIC OZONE

The stratospheric Ozone layer prevents the most dangerous

ultraviolet rays from reaching the earth's surface and filters out about 70-90 percent of the wavelengths that cause sunburn, snow-blindness, eye damage, and skin cancer This shield is being depleted by Chloro-fluorocarbons, NO_2 halons and other gases.

Ozone depletion over south pole has affected area; nearby Australia for years, catapulting the country to the top of the world statistics for skin cancer. Each year the sun's hazardous ultraviolet rays slip through the thinning Ozone layer and cause 140,000 cases of skin cancer-nearly 1000 of them fatal-in a population of only 17 million.

ACID RAIN AND PHOTOCHEMICAL OXIDANTS

Acid rain kills aquatic life (20 percent of Sweden's takes are now fishless or about to become so, and in Norway, fish are extinct in 13,000 Km^2 and endangered in another 20,000 Km^2), pollutes water, acidifies soils and damages buildings and materials Photochemical oxidants harm crops and natural vegetation (depressing crop yields). 5.10 percent in USA, a toss of $ 1-2 billion a year, and are the main ingredients of urban smog, damaging human health in wake. The combination of acid rain and photochemical oxidants is believed to be the chief agent in the decline of forests in Europe and North America. The sulphur dioxide (SO;,) and Nitrogen oxides (NO;,) in acid rain come from fossil fuel burning (mainly in power plants and vehicles); and fossil fuels are the main agent in the production of photochemical oxidants (formed by sunlight triggering reactions among nitrogen dioxide, carbon dioxide, oxygen and hydrocarbons).

DESTRUCTION AND DEGRADATION OF FORESTS

Every year, 12 million hectares of tropical forests are cleared for agriculture (completely, or as part of the shifting cultivation cycle), and 3.8 million hectares of tropical woodlands are cleared or degraded for agriculture or fuel wood. Another 4.4 million hectares a year of tropical forests are simplified by logging, much of it unsustainable. Temperate and boreal forests are being fragmented and simplified, chiefly by logging (much of it is unsustainable) and urbanization. In addition, almost 15 percent of the timber volume of 17 European countries has been moderately/severely damaged by air pollution. Population growth, poverty and failures of public policy, are at the root of tropical deforestation. Similar failures of public policy, together with uncontrolled use of fossil fuels, underly the degradation of temperate and boreal forests.

EXITINCTION OF SPECIES AND GENE POOL

Some 3.325 plant species and 631 animals species are recorded as endangered with extinction; and additional 15,368 plant and 2.357 animal species are recorded as vulnerable species extictions are believed to be occurring more rapidly than ever before, with an estimated 5-15 percent of the world's species likely to become extinct between 1990 and 2020, and up to 25 percent by 2050. Human beings are now the main agents of extinction, causing it by offering habits (chefly forests, but also fresh waters and wetlands), over exploitation and introducing exotic species to places where they out compete or eat away the native species.

Extinction of gene pools are even more widespread than of species; even abundant species are experiencing genetic erosion. Wild gene pools are destroyed by the same process as wild species. Domesticated gene pools are lost through the replacement of traditional crop varieties and livestock breeds by more modern ones.

DESTRUCTION OF AGRICULTURE RESOURCES

Land degradation (diminution of the land's biological productivity and desertification (degradation of dry lands) are believed to be widespread and increasing, but hard data are few. The best estimate at present is that 61 percent of the world's dry lands is decertified to some extent. An estimated 6-7 million hectares of agricultural land are now made unproductive each year because of erosion - more than twice the rate in the past three centuries. Water logging, salination and alkalinization reduce the productively of an additional 1.5 million hectare each year in addition between 1980 and 2000, an estimated 1.4 billion hectares will be lost to city growth, poverty and inequitable land distribution: and in developed countries to overproduction (stimulated by subsidies and other economic incentives). Efforts to protect farmland from urbanization generally succumb to economic and political pressures.

WARS AND MASS DESTRUCTION

Wars, growing military expenditure, and the proliferation of nuclear and other weapons and mass destruction, pose the starkest threats to human survival. Enough nuclear weapons exist to destroy the world several times over, chemical and biological weapons are yet another menace. Since the end of World War II, there have been 119 major wars fought in 65 countries and territories, killing more than 19 million people (civilian and military). (These statistics are before Gulf War).

Environment damage (such as habitat destruction and mining of farm lands) has impaired the lives of millions more. Wars are likely to increase, because non-military threats to security are growing (notable environmental stresses and resources scarcities).

ECONOMIC INEFFICIENCY

Economic inefficiency contributes to ecological unsustainability. Subsidies have encouraged inefficient use of pesticides and fertilizers (so that the costs of their use outweigh the value of the extra yield). Irrigation subsidies reduce incentives to manage water and operate and maintain irrigation systems efficiently. Deforestation and land degradation have been promoted by subsidies for cattle ranches that would not have been economically viable without them. Pricing policies have favoured expansion of crop production at the expense of hill forests, increasing rates of soil erosion 6-10 times.

CAUSES OF UNSUSTAINABILITY HUMAN POPULATION GROWTH

World population (5 billion) is growing rapidly and will double again by late next century, unless a concerted effort is made to reach replacement-level fertility by 2010. Most countries with higher population growth rates (2 percent per year or more) already have great difficulty in meeting their needs for food, water, health care, sanitation, shelter, jobs, energy and productive land and are destroying their environments in the process. Their plight will worsen until the growth rates are substantially reduced. Rapid urbanization enhances these problems. In addition, even small increases in the populations of countries that have a large impact on global processes (such as the USA, CIS and China which account for half of all industrial CO;, emissions) can have a significant effect on the entire world.

STRATEGIC DIRECTIONS

The key to preventing global warming above the unavoidable level is to stabilize and eventually reduce emissions of the main greenhouse gases: Carbon dioxide (CO_2), Chlorofluorocarbons (CFC), Methane (CH_4), 'Nitrous oxide (N_2O) and ground level Ozone (tropospheric O_3). CO_2 accounts for about half of global warming; the other gases account for the remainder.

To maintain CO;, emission at their current level and at the same time allow developing countries to increase their energy consumption as part of their development effort, world average per capita output would have to be reduced from 1.3 to 0.9 tones, and countries emitting CO;, above the world average per capita level (for example USA 4.9 tonnes, Canada 4.1 tonnes, Russia 3.6 tones, Japan 2.2 tonnes) would have to reduce emissions to 0.9 tonnes per capita per annum. Africa, South and South-East Asia and Latin Amrica are currently emitting two-to three times more CO_2 from deforestation than from energy consumption.

To achieve temporary stability, reduce annual emissions of CO_2 due to fossil fuel combustion from the current (1986) 5.5 billion tonnes to 2.0 billion tonnes by 2060 (reduce 500 million tonnes/decade). Thereafter to prevent additional CO_2 emissions will have to be reduced still further. Shift fossil fuel use from coal to oil to natural gas; and shift from fossil fuels to other forms of energy production; preferably solar, wind, small-scale hydro, some bio-energy. Improve energy efficiency by 1.5 percent per year. Reduce energy consumption, ensure that bio-energy consumption does not exceed bio-energy production (fuel wood burned is replaced by the same amount of new fuel wood planted). Emissions of sulphur dioxide, nitrogen oxides and carbon mono oxide have to be cut. Phase out fully halogenated CFCs by the year 2000 and phase out other major Ozone depleters or restrict them all to close cycle use by 2010 (better even earlier).

Reduce the amount of waste generated, transform an increasing proportion of materials used into products; recycle the materials once the products cease to be useful; and ensure safe disposal of residual toxic wastes. Promotes public over private transport, and increase-energy efficiency of all forms of transport.

Cut annual CO_2 emissions caused by changes to vegetation and soils from current (1980) 1.7 billion tonnes to 10 million tonnes by 2060. Reduce the rate of tropical deforestation from 11.1 million hectares/year (1980s) to 50,000 hectares/year by 2060 (reduce by 1.6 million hectares a decade). Plant trees, reforestation of two million km^2 would result in the annual storage of 1 billion tonnes of carbon until the new forest reaches maturity. Forests have to be protected by providing alternative sources of timber. Protect aquatic systems and cropland by rehabilitating degraded land.

Reduce species extinctions and establish a comprehensive protection of the major genetic varieties of plant and animal domesticates and their wild relatives. Adopt sustainable agricultural practices, including minimal burning of crop residues and restrained use of nitrogenous fertilizers.

Stabilize human numbers by 2060. The earliest by which replacement-level refertility cold be reached is 2010, in which case world population would stabilize at 7.7 billion by 2060. This assumes that the 77 countries with total fertility rates (TFRs) of 4.2 and above will have them by 2010 all countries should have TFR 2.1 or less.

Governments should eliminate energy subsidies and emphasize energy conservation and least-cost energy investment strategies.

Environmental impact assessment (EIA) should be applied to investments (products and projects) that are likely to cause significant environmental and socio-cultural impact and/or have not been specifically provided for by the planning process. EIA should also be applied to policies and programmes, especially major macro-economic, finance and sect oral policies that are likely to result in significant impact on the environment. Cost benefit analysis (CBA) should be integrated into EIA.

FORESTS

The forest is a biological unit having a vast social organization of living communities at work. This special organization includes not only trees but also many other living organisms from the plant world, viz. shrubs, herbs, mosses, lichens, algae, fungi, bacteria and animal organisms including the mineral complex entity made up of different biological units that have come into being as a result of the combined action, reaction and co-action of a variety of organisms with complex factors of the habitat. The flora and fauna of the forest are interdependent on each other. How do the birds destroy the harmful pests? China, learnt this lesson after widespread loss of harvest due to the pests, which multiplied after the elimination of birds by the State in an attempt to save the crops. Famous bird-watcher Salim Ali proved that an owl kills at least three rats in a night and a pair of mice creates a family of 700 in a year. Five rodents eat one person's food. This is just an example of interdependence in nature.

India is extremely rich in its ecology which is varied with genetically diverse forest resources and is one of the world's top twelve nations having mega diversity in terms of biological resources. The plant wealth found in India's forest are made up of 45000 species of trees, shrubs, herbs and climbers which account for about 12 per cent of the global plant wealth. The flowering plants alone number21000 species and almost a third of these are endemic, located mainly in 26 endemic centres of India. India's forests are the home of over 75,000 species of animals of which about 372 are mammals, 2,000 birds, 1,693 fishes and as many as 60,000 insect species.

Forests are renewable resources and they contribute substantially to the social and economic to development of the country. They have major role to play in enhancing the quality of our environment. The history of forest is linked with the history of civilization. The 4000 year old *Agnipurana* mentions that a man should protect trees to ensure material prosperity and religious merit. 2500 years ago, Gautam Buddha preached that a man must plant trees every five years. The great epics *Ramayana* and *Mahabharata* give attractive description of forests like Dandakaranya, Mandavana and Khandvan. The Supreme God of Indus Valley was supposed to live under *pipal* (Ficus) trees. *Pipal* and *Babul* plants were believed to have descended on earth from heaven. The people in ancient times lived in harmony with their ecosystem, which was formed by the forests. They did not cut the trees recklessly and the forests produced more than enough for everybody. The first indication of forestry administration is found in 300 BC during Chandra Gupta Maurya's reign, when a Superintendent of forests was appointed to protect forests and wild life. Nund Rishi the saint of Char-a-shreef preached that there would be enough food only when there were forests. From top of the hill, he cold see the fertile valley down below and realize that the miracle was due to fertile soil produced by the hill forests. Similarly Jamboji, the founder of the Vaishnoi sect in the desert of Rajasthan, was preaching that to survive in the desert, green trees should not be felled and no animals and birds be killed. The Vaishnoies have kept alive this tradition of saving the Khejdi (Accacia) trees even at the cost of their lives. Modern science too recognizes that forests are mothers of the rivers and factories of soil manufacture. For the British, Indian forests were an inexhaustible source of durable and ornamental timber and other forest products. Teak forests along the coast of Malabar were over exploited to meet the requirements of the British Navy. The Sandalwood trees of South India were exploited for the European markets. The two world wars were also the periods of great devastation of Indian forests. Forests were cut recklessly to meet the increased demand. As a result, rich productive forests vanished, causing an irreparable damage to the ecosystem and to the Indian people, specially the tribals. Unfortunately, the forest destruction did not stop even after the British had left and it is estimated that India is losing about 1.5 million hectares of forests annually.

Forests have a significant role not only in ensuring the environmental stability but also achieving economical benefits. Forest is not just a group of trees, but is an ecosystem in itself, comprising all the living and non-living components. The main living components of a terrestrial ecosystem are plants dominated by trees, forming the consumer element and decomposers of the micro organisms, Soil, water, air and sunshine form the non-living components of a forest/ terrestrial ecosystem. These components interact with each other and involve the ecological energy cycle which consists of two other cyclic processes, namely water cycle and matter (organic and inorganic) cycle. These processes maintain the dynamic equilibrium between the living components and non-living components within an ecosystem. Any imbalance or deviation in this process will lead to a total collapse of the ecosystem. Droughts and floods are the two most important consequences of the imbalance in forest ecosystem caused by the indiscriminate felling of trees. The forest ecosystem fulfils extremely important protective, regulatory and productive functions both for the well-being and development of society.

The importance of forest in the ecosystem can never be over emphasized. Forests have numerous roles to play both natural and man made. Natural functions involve protective and regulative services, while man imposed functions relate to production and socio-ecological services. Plants are valuable for us in many ways, besides protecting and improving the environment in which we live. All attempts of the Government to conserve this resource appear to have isolated the resource from the people as far as their responsibility, towards maintenance and development of the resource is concerned.

The alarming increase in human population, will demand at least four times more energy than today by the year 2040 and the projected increase in the use of industrial wood 13 fold. Where will the huge volume of wood required for energy use—solid wood products and paper making come from? To thinking people around the world, wood from natural forests is becoming an unacceptable answer. A recent report of the Food and Agricultural Organization says, the demand and consumption of forest products has risen so steeply that large investment would have to be made for future use. It recommends private initiatives in the industry. A world think-tank, headed by Dr. William Sultan, Director of Research and strategy at Fletcher Challenge Forests, New Zealand, advocates a bold and novel concept. Dr. Sultan makes two broad based sunrises (1) A major portion of any increased wood supply, must come from newly created plantations (2) the intiative and capital to grow large scale plantations must come from business sector.

To meet the unsatiated demand of the domestic market, it is essential to redefine the objectives of forest management in the context of the national development. Thus, there should be a change from the present conservation oriented forestry to a more dynamic programme of production forestry. Wood remains one of the most basic needs of man, with large scale uses in construction of homes, ships, furniture, sleepers for railway tracks as well as fuel with industrialization and urbanization, forests have been indiscriminately felled all over the world. The earth loses almost forty millions hectares of forest area with no replacement, adding to an ever increasing shortage of timber India us having the best agro climatic conditions viz. tropical, sub-tropical and temperate climatic zones where diversified tree species can be planted thus increasing the production with elite management practices to have maximum biomass. This would go a long way in conserving the ecosystem of the country within a short span of time.

The estimated cost of such national level plantation efforts comes to several thousand crores. Such an investments surely beyond the government resources which are already under constant pressure to increase social spending. However, the magnitude of investments required to establish plantations is within the scopes of the business sector. For this purpose production of forests should be increasingly privatized and involvement of people must be from the initial stages of plantation. This further envisages that the state forest department should have a broader approach in forest management activities and involve people at various decision making levels. The present day forester no doubt talks of involving people in the protection and management of forests, but the people at the people grassroots level feel alienated. Such a situation does not augur well in the forest management and immediate corrective measures needed to be undertaken. Many a private companies with dedication have undertaken mass area plantations in various parts of the country. Although this is mostly to cater the needs of the industries, it would also go along way in adding to the quantum of forest products available to the people at large, that is why private sector companies are attempting to raise captive plantations to augment raw materials for industries. Thus, their sphere of activities encompasses, providing soil cover and thus reducing the pressure on biosphere and side by side provide employment opportunities to the rural poor and above all involving the people at the grassroots level in restoration of the environment. Efforts need to be made by the government both at the centre as well as at state levels to involve all possible agencies in a massive tree planting efforts based on sound management practices accompanied by latest technologies. Efforts are also needed to be made to encourage such investments by offering incentives and support. Such an approach will go a long way in transforming the rural masses in maintenance of the ecological balance and thus reducing the stress on biosphere. Time has come now for the people of the country to rear a tree like a child and thus justify the "ADOPT A TREE" campaign to save and conserve the environment.

JOINT FOREST MANAGEMENT

The new participatory management system being developed by some forest department and village communities to jointly manage forests is a new and promising direction in forests management that offers hope to protect degraded forests which will regenerate and produce long term benefits.

India has only about 37.8 million hectares of closed forest cover with crown density of over 40 percent which is about 11.5 percent out of total geographical area of country is about 74.88 million hectares (22.7 per cent of land area of country). This shows the poor status of our forests despite the National Forest policy of 1952 which envisaged to raise the forest area and its cover to 33 per cent of geographical area of the nation, as a national target. The country has aboul 36 million hectares of degraded forest lands. National Remote Sensing Agency reported loss of about 2.89% area of country of forest cover just in a span of five years between 1972-1975 and 1980-1982.

While forest area is about 75 million hectares, the area under agriculture is about 155 million hectares, almost double. Agriculture contributes about 48 per cent of gross domestic product of the country, while forest contribute only 1.6 per cent to GDP. Agriculture accounts for 75 per cent ol the rural working force, while forestry accounts for only 0.2 per cent.

The silviculturally permissible production limit of wood is about 12 million cum a year while the demand of wood from wood based industries is about 28 million cu. m a year, About 40 million cu. m fuel wood can be extracted annually on sustainable basis, while the demand of fuel wood is about 235 million cum a year. About 434 million tonnes a year ol fodder can be sustain ably extracted from grasslands, forests and from agricultural lands, while demand of fodder is about 882 million tonnes a year.

Thus due to over exploitation of forests, Indian forests are shrinking and productivity dwindling. These forests are facing many threats. These threats affect biodiversity, species composition, forest community structure, composition physiognomy, stratification vitality, trpohic structure energetics and dynamics (succession).

Preservation of forests is vital for health of a planet and economy of nations. The forests are home to million of people providing a diverse range of products such as timber fuel wood, fibers, fruits, seeds, mushrooms, resins ornamentals, ıubber and animal proteins.

Forests play a key role in regulation and conserving water, ameliorating local climate and preventing floods and soil erosion. India's existing systems of forest management are failing to sustain natural forest resources are depleted, village communities dependent upon them are impoverished.

NATIONAL FOREST POLICY

India's forest policy originated in the last century (1894) at a time when the colonial government had priority on state custodianship and commercial exploitation. These objectives persisted overtime and are totally inappropriate as India's populations is still rural. However 1894 and 1952 forest policy resolutions did lay emphasis on the provisions of basic needs such as small timber, fuel wood and fodder for villagers. Secondly, the forest departments have failed to protect vast tracts of forest lands, resulting in dwindling forest cover in spite of various forest acts. Such acts need to be strengthened further. Thirdly, awareness of our environment and our impact on it have perhaps come of age. We are beginning to move towards concepts of sustainable development, a concept for biosphere as a whole. The concept of sustainable development ushers not only in protecting natural resources but also conveys dictum of conservation and protection culture.

This led to major shift in forest policy of Government of India. In 1988 National Forest Policy was formulated by the Government of India, which stressed people's involvement as one of the essentials of forest management in the development and protection of forests and the village communities should be motivated to identify themselves with the conservation of forests from which they derive benefits. The requirements of fuel wood, fodder, small timber such as house building material and other minor forest produce of the tribals and villagers living in or near the forests are to be treated as first charge on forest produce.

COMMUNITY PARTICIPATORY MANAGEMENT

The National Forest Policy of 1988, Ministry of Environment and Forest, Government of India issued guidelines to all state forestry departments in 1990, to ensure participation of communities and NGO's in the management, regeneration and protection of degraded forest lands. The highlights of guidelines are:

1. **Developing partnerships**: Between village communities (beneficiaries), the voluntary agencies/NGO's and forest

departments. NGO's may serve as motivating force between communities and forest departments.

2. **Plants-10 year working scheme**: Plants of short duration of about ten years may be useful. Plant about forest management and technical operations should be developed by foresters in consultation with village communities.
3. **Plants to be grown**: Trees for fuel, fodder and timber should be grown. In addition fruit trees, legumes, grasses, medicinal plants should be grown which would meet requirements of local village communities, help enrich the degraded lands and conserve soil and water.
4. **Access and benefits**: This must be given to village communities undertaking regeneration activities with equal opportunity to all, based on willing participation. The benefits of people's participation should solely be derived by village communities only and these should not go to commercial or other interests.
5. **Rights to usufruct**: All non wood forest products-grasses, tree branches and minor forest produce; percentage share of final tree harvest should go to communities subject to successful and satisfactory protection.
6. **Use rules**: Strict adherence to rules about no grazing or harvesting trees before maturity.
7. **Funding**: Forest department may meet the cost of Joint forest Management programmes from funds under social forestry programmes for preparation of land, raising nursery, and for protection of trees. The village communities may also seek additional funds from other agencies.
8. No ownership or lease rights of the forest lands should be given to communities or to the voluntary agencies/NGO's.
9. Forest land should not be assigned in contravention of the provisions of the Forest Conservation Act. 1980.

ENRICHMENT PLANTING

Enrichment planting is used to enhance forest productivity by planting valuable plant species in gaps within the natural forest. Most state forest departments developing Joint Forest

Management programmes target at 10-25 per cent of the regenerating forest for enrichment planting. Choice of plants is made by village communities and foresters jointly. The species planted in comparatively open areas may be fodder grass, fiber plants, bamboo, timber trees or fuel wood trees. Under the forest canopy shade tolerant mushrooms, medicinal plants, etc. may be grown.

NATURAL FOREST REGENERATION

Forest degradation is a gradual process caused by over exploitation such as over grazing, over commercial timber extraction or fuel wood cutting. The forest degradation can be halted and reversed (regenerated). The first set up in effective regeneration requires strict control on grazing and cutting of green trees and shrubs. Village communities can develop methods to control grazing through social fencing and stall feeding. Miroplants should be developed to assess fodder requirements and identify ways to meet fodder requirements through regeneration and enrichment grass planting. Once the strict access controls have been achieved, a number of silvicultural practices can be initiated to regenerate plants and increase productivity such as clearing of dead materials, cleaning of stool, coppice regeneration, multiple shoot cutting, enrichment planting of trees, grasses and herbs in gaps.

JOINT FOREST REGENERATION MANAGEMENT

In recent years successful Forest regeneration has been achieved through Joint Forest Management programmes in some parts of various states - West Bengal, Haryana, Orissa, Himachal Pradesh, Gujarat, Uttar Pradesh, Jammu & Kashmir, Tamil Nadu, Andhra Pradesh, Bihar, Karnataka, Madhya Pradesh, Maharashtra, Punjab, Tripura, Rajasthan, etc. In these states, more than 10,000 groups of village communities are partners in joint Forest Management of forest ecosystems covering more than one million hectares. Fourteen states have issued Joint Forest Management facilitating notification to-date.

Joint Forest Management in West Bengal accelerated regeneration of over one lakh hectares of degraded Sal forest in the south-west through community protection, grazing bans, stool cleaning, multiple shoot cutting and enrichment planting.

In Haryana in the Shivaliks, Joint Forest Management led to regeneration of degraded Acacia trees and grasslands. Social fencing imposition by village communities for five years resulted in 10-40 times production of fodder grass, 2.5 times the natural *bhabbar* (fibre) grass, average rainfall run-off decreased drastically from 40-80 per cent to just 3 per cent. Enrichment plantation of *bhabbar* grass increased its production by 20 times per hectare. Village communities doubled profits from *bann* rope making.

A recent analysis of lands at imagery indicates that nearly 30 million hectare of degraded forest has the potential to regenerate naturally forded protection by village communities. Also the costs of regenerating forest lands per hectare is only five per cent of cost for plantation establishment per hectare. The potential return from joint forest management to regenerate these degraded lands is very high, chiefly (1) Rapid increase in growth of plants enhances supplies of fuel wood, fodder, minor forest products, (2) Increase in employment opportunity for rural people, (3) Increase in income through high forest productivity including minor forest produce. (4) Improved vegetative cover resulting in soil and water conservation, and (5) Reduced conflicts between foresters and village communities.

GLOBAL PROBLEMS AND SOLUTIONS

Interplay of economic forces and the velocity of technological changes have terminally eroded the traditional concepts like sovereignty, security, geo-politic and economic progress. Poised at the end of the century, the world today is under going a revolutionary transformation. With the end of the cold war, we are left with a world that is more fluid, fragmented and multipolar than ever before. We are confronted with problems not only related to global security but also human security.

The threat to human life can come from militarism, expansionism, ultra nationalism, ethnic chauvinism, religious extremism and environmental pollution etc. In a 'borderless world', to use Konichi Ohmae's expression, drug dealers can plunder money in a fraction of time, it takes their to detoxify across the end. A person suffering from AIDS/HIV can carry the incurable disease to any part of the world. Global problems of this nature require global solutions. With integration of global economy, no government can solve these problems independently. In today's world, it has become almost impossible even for the most dominant states in internation affairs to set their own agendas and manage their own affairs unaffected by external events and 'exogenous ambiguities'.

The UNO declaration on the 'Right To Development', World Conference on Environment, Convention on 'The Right To Child', Emerging Consensus On The Rights Of The Indigenous Peoples, the World Summit On Social Development testify to an explosive proliferation of welfare ideology at the global level.

Earlier the welfare state was mainly concerned with the individuals and groups suffering from proverty, unemployment, sickness or other vicissitudes in life. An important development which has taken place in recent decades is the increase in the problems which are faced by the society as a whole-the problems arising out of energy crisis, feeding an ever growing population, controlling restless youth, rising consumerism and rising expectations. The discords and conflicts of modern day complex societies cannot be resolved by better housing, social services and a higher standard of living.

Even in advanced economies, despite significant improvements in living standards, evils such as violence, delinquency and crime continue to exist. We can not ignore the negative aspects of economic growth and development also which lead to unhappiness, frustration, alienation and disparities. Nor can we really calculate the 'loneliness and solitude' felt by millions of men and women in developed societies in terms of GNP, HDI or PPP.

In the developing societies, we find that the one-fifth of the world's population is going hungry every night, one-fourth is lacking access to the safe drinking water and one-third living in perpetual state of subject proverty. Not only the poor, but the rich are also affected by ever growing human distress owing to weakening social fabric as a result of excessive materialism, excessive individualism, excessive mobility and excessive disparities in income. It has become a matter of political correctiveness to talk about the human security. Since most of the problems are not confined to national borders, collective action is needed across the world. Only a global perspective can foster greater concern for the problems of hunger, disease, ignorance, homelessness, political instability, economic crisis, social disntegration, ecological degradation, terrorism, and decline in ethical values.

The UNDP in its 1994 report came out with certain valuable suggestions to foster economic partnership among the nations to promote social development at the global level. One suggestion is to introduce trade able permits for various forms of pollution. According to it, as much as five per cent of the GNP of advanced economies can be transferred to the poorer ones in this way.

Another proposal is to divert the peace dividend, 20 per cent of the amount saved by the advanced economies and 10 per cent of that saved by the developing countries through a 3 per cent cut in expenditure on military, to global welfare. Another proposal is to introduce a global tax on the use of non-renewable energy. James Tobin, the Nobel laureate, has recommended a 0.5 percent tax on all speculative movements across the world. Under it, all states are required to spend at least 20 per cent of their public spending in providing for the basic needs.

Infect, in view of the prevailing economic disparities between the developed and the developing world, the advanced economies owe an additional responsibility. A mere 1 per cent increase in the savings of the richest few countries when transferred to the poorest ones, can increase the latter's rate of investment upto 50 per cent, without affecting the well-being of their own citizens.

The well-being of an individual no longer depends on the fulfillment of his or her physical needs. Rather, it depends on the fulfillment of psychological needs as well. What really matters is the enhancement of human capabilities rather than the promotion of aggregate growth. There can be an inverse relationship between an individual's income in terms of money and his or her leisure hours. Higher the income in terms of money, there is less leisure and, therefore, lower utility.

The myth prevails among the citizens of the advanced countries that foreign aid is the major diversion of their resources. In fact, if all foreign aid were stopped, there would hardly be a gain of 0.3 per cent in their own safely net. While most of the advanced welfare state are spending approximately 15 per cent of their combined GNPs on social development for their own citizens, they are spending only 0.3 percent of their combined GNPs on human security at the global level.

Even if at all the 20:20 compact is agreed upon in Copenhagen, Summit on Social Development much inequity and poverty would still remain. To meet this deficit, a global tax of 0.1 per cent could be levied on the richest countries with per capita GNP of US $ 10,000 and above. Unless and until a global fund is created, the programmes and policies aimed at social development at the global level cannot be implemented.

On the threshold of 21st century, when we talk of our common future, world heritage, sustainable development, preservation of environment and the valid interests of the future generations, how can we neglect those who are forced by circumstances beyond their control to live dismal Ivies today? The ethics of universalism demands not only intra-generational equity but also inter-generational equity.

If income redistribution is justified in advanced welfare states as a contribution towards human development, the same argument can be extended to support income redistribution from the developed world to the developing. This is certainly not the debate but a humble beginning.

FIRE : A NATURAL EVENT

Fire wasn't invented by man. Fire existed before man even lived on earth. A fire could start for serval reasons, such as a volcanic eruption or else a lightning strike. Of course, in cold or damp regions, covered in tender green vegetation, spontaneous fires must have been less frequent. In hot, dry areas, on the other hand, inhabited by dry, woody plants, there was a good chance of fire catching and taking hold spontaneously. In these cases the fire might burn for days and days and must have devoured the vegetation over large areas before being stopped by some kind of natural barrier or put out by the rain.

Even today some fires are produced by these same natural causes. In the Yellowstone National Park, in the United States, lightning causes an average of 22 fires every year and the trunks of old fir trees show the scars left by repeated fires, with an average of one every 30-60 years. Fire has probably been a regular visitor to Yellowstone for hundreds of thousands of years, as it's a volcanic area where there were large eruptions in the past and where there are still a great number of fumaroles, or smoke holes, solfataras, or sulphur vents, thermal springs and the well known, spectacular geysers. Most of the region is covered in pinewoods made up of a species of pine *(Pinus contorts)* which has two kinds of cone: one that opens in the normal way on ripening and one that stays closed and protects the seeds in case of fire, only opening when subjected to a high temperature. In this way the survival of the species after the fire is ensured. On the other hand, if many years go by without a fire, this pine tends to disappear because the seeds have difficulty germinating in the shade of the older trees. This is why National Park officials let fires burn in some areas, while watching to make sure that they don't escape towards other areas where they could do damage.

Many parts of the world show this tendency to spontaneous fire because of their dry climate and highly inflammable vegetation. By studying the layers of ash that have accumulated in the sediments of lakes, we can see that for thousands of years coniferous woodland has suffered fires about every two hundred years. In the Mediterranean region there are also spontaneous fires in summer, the hottest and driest time of year, when thunderstorms with lightning are frequent. Similarly, in prairie and savannah regions the abundance of dry grass in the dry season facilitates natural fires.

In all these regions the vegetation can stand periodic fires of a certain frequency, since the species that make it up have methods of self-protection and regeneration.

The consequences of a fire aren't always the same. The seriousness of a fire from the point of view of its ecological effects depends on the vegetation, the soil and the local climate, and also on the characteristics of the fire (the moment, intensity, maximum temperature, frequency, extension, etc.). So different fires will have different effects in different places, and the recovery process will vary.

FRESHWATER

It is widely recognized that water is going to be one of the major issues confronting humanity at the turn of the century and beyond. We are facing a crisis as regards the quantity and quality of water supply, but we have yet to experience the full social and political impact of that crisis. The escalation in the global population and the quest for continued development is leading to conflicting pressures on water resources. Such resources are the ultimate recepient of pollution from various socio-economic activities associated with urbanization, agriculture, mining and clearing of native vegetation. Pollution originating from human waste, especially where appropriate sanitation facilities are not available, or are located too close to water supply sources in developing countries, affects both surface water and ground water.

This makes water supply and health perhaps the most important issue for the larger proportion of the global population. Paradoxically, the demands for "sustainable management" and increasing global population require more potable water from a declining available potable water base. Because of their limited size, small islands are particularly susceptible to these kinds of conflicting pressures on water resources.

In the post-UNCED (United Nations Conference on Environment and Development, Rio de Janeiro, June 1992) era, the challenge will be to converge the latest developments in hydrological research with socio-economic and cultural factors as a basis for integrated water development. The need for hydrological science as a foundation for integrated water management can thus only may increase.

It is universally accepted that proper water administration is a critical component of sustainable development in many countries-that is, developments that meets the needs of both present and future generations. Indeed, water is an essential factor in a large number of productive activities, of which one of the most important is the production of food by irrigation. This activity, on a global level, accounts for two thirds of the water resources used by humanity. A supply of drinking water and sanitation in urban centers are crucial for preserving human health in developed countries and for improving it in developing countries. A large proportion of disease in developing countries results from lack of drinking water and hygiene.

For some decades it has been known that the misuse of water resources is responsible for many important environmental problems. For example, in many industrialized countries both surface water and groundwater are seriously contaminated. This deterioration is a consequence of range of human activities, sometimes in isolation, others over a large area or a long period of time. Among examples of the latter is modern agriculture, whether it uses irrigation or not, as a result of the intensive use made of mineral fertilizers and pesticides. In some cases the transfer of water from one basin to another has given rise to considerable ecological or social problems, such as the drying up of the Aral Sea in the former Soviet Union.

WATER SHORTAGE: EXAGGERATION, REALITY OR BAD MANAGEMENT

Some of these problems have made news and have created the impression that water shortage will be one of humanity's big problems in the coming decades. Sometimes this feeling is due to genuinely manipulative publicity campaigns to justify the setting in motion of hydraulic mega projects which basically benefit a few large construction companies. The truth is that except for a handful of very specific cases, no problems of water shortage are to be found almost anywhere. On the other hand, cases of bad water management are not rare at all.

Over the last few years, a kind of axiomatic figure of 1000 cubic meters per person per day has frequently been given as an indication of the amount of water any country needs to reach for normal development. The indiscriminate use of this figure makes little sense. We need only remember that Israel has a supply of less than 500 cubic meters per person per day.

In Europe, average water use as a proportion of gross water resources is of the order of 16 percent. In Spain, this proportion is almost doubled, which is hardly surprising since it is the driest country in Europe. Israel uses 110 percent of its resources each year; this is explained by the fact that part of the water used for urban needs is recycled for agricultural use.

In some dry countries, for example in the Near East or in the Persian Gulf, water use has been or could be the cause of conflicts. However, most authors agree that water problems in these countries could be suitably and fairly simply resolved were it not for the existence of other more important political problems.

BASIC PRINCIPLES FOR GOOD WATER MANAGEMENT

Good management of water resources - and of almost all other natural resources - must be based on the principles of solidarity, 'subsidiarity' and participation. The physical reality requires that these resources be considered a common heritage of humanity both now and in the future. By 'subsidiarity' we mean that water management should be as decentralized as possible: what one person or any minor social group can do should not be done by a higher authority. For example, what a local government can do should not be done by a regional, state or federal government. Participation consists in water users playing as large a part as possible in decisions affecting water, in keeping with each country's social and cultural structure. Obviously this participation calls for certain cultural and technical knowledge - a hydrological education - on the part of those users. The "Comunidad de Regantes de la Acequia Real" (the community of growers authorized to irrigate from the royal irrigation channel) of the Turia in Valencia (Spain), which has been operating for seven countries, is a participation. Every Thursday throughout the year the Water Tribunal of this Community meets in the Portico of Valencia Cathedra. Seven judges are chosen by the water users themselves and are empowered to resolve their conflicts; their decision is final.

The need for participation by users is even greater in the exploitation of groundwater. In this case, users tend to extract water independently of one another. They often fail to realize, until there is a serious economic or environmental impact, that their pumping affects other people who rely on the same water supply as has happened, for example, with the groundwater reservoir or aquifer of Western La Mancha (Spain), whose exploitation has left the National Park of Las Tablas de Daimiel in a state of "ecological coma".

Water shortage is rarely a serious problem: in fact, in some cases the problem is exaggerated to justify the construction of large works usfng taxpayers' money. On the other hand, the contamination of surface and groundwater tends to be a problem which rarely receives adequate treatment. Successful water management should be based on three basic principles: solidarity, subsidiarity and participation. The specific way in which these principles are applied will vary from one country to another, but the effectiveness of water management will depend in large measure on the hydrological education of the general public.

MARINE RESOURCES

Resources are of two basic types; the renewable and non-renewable and could be further classified with specific reference to the nature of a resource. Both renewable and non-renewable resources are available in large quantities in the ocean. The sea is being used as a reservoir of food since ancient times. Presently most of the fish catch come from Asia, the production level being 73.4 million metric tonnes, leading nations being Japan the USSR, China, Peru, Nonway and the USA. It is well known that hydrocarbons by far the most valuable are found in very substantial quantity under the bed of the sea. At present about 20 per cent of world's petroleum products come from the sea, and may reach 50 per cent by the year 2000 A.D. Tides, waves and currents, besides others like thermal difference, salinity gradient etc. could become immense sources of energy. They will also be useful for the multipurpose economic development of the poor tropical and subtropical countries lacking hydrocarbon deposits, provided appropriate technology is available to them.

Sea floor mineral deposits include all unconsolidated sediments lying on the floor. Present commercial production comprises of sands, gravels, corals, lime shells and relatively small quantities of tin, titanium and iron Potential sea floor mineral resources are, however, immense and comprise of both oozes and clays, phosphorites and manganese modules, and the newly discovered polymetallic sulphides and cobalt crusts.

MARINE ENERGY

The world oceans hold a vast store of non-renewable energy resources in the form of oil, gas and coal deposits.

The oceans, covering about 71 per cent of earth's surface, receive major portion of solar radiation reaching on our planet. This energy, because more of it reaches the equatorial region than the polar region, produces an atmospheric circulation pattern that in turn causes an oceanic circulation. However, a long range welfare depends not on the total amount of energy available, but rather on the maximum rate at which it can be continuously extracted, particularly, the renewable ones. Extracting energy from the ocean represents an additional ocean use activity which will have to compete with fishing oil exploration and drilling, ocean mining, navigation and military uses of the available ocean space, especially in the case of coastal waters. Coastal inlets are best for deriving tidal energy. In the same way near shore tropical and subtropical ocean waters are best for vertical temperature gradient, i.e., for the Ocean Thermal Energy Conversion (OTEC). Areas of the strong persistent currents, such as the western boundaries of the oceans are most suitable for extraction of energy from ocean.

OTEC utilizes the temperature difference existing between

warm surface sea water of around 28-29°c and the cold deep water of around 5-7°c which is available generally at a depth of 800 to 1000 meters in the tropical waters. According to the feasibility studies, the OTEC power is economically competitive with fossil and nuclear power sources. A new plan for OTEC use involves a 'grazer' and it does not produce electricity by immediate energy conversion but transforms the ocean energy by producing methane hydrogen and ammonia. An optimistic estimate of available power envisages between 100 to 300 quades, whereas the current world power use comes about 250 quades per year. Estimated global power potential from OTEC alone is about 10 million MW, approximately 10 times the total world electric power production today. The total OTEC potential around India's southern coasts is estimated to be more than 50,000 MW, i.e., about 15 per cent of our total installed power generation capacity.

Energy from the ocean waves is potentially available, almost everywhere at the sea. There are many systems which propose to harness the energy of the waves. The simplest system consists of letting the energy of the waves be released as an up rush of water on a steep rump that falls into a reservoir. UK, Japan are the pioneers in the wave energy development, while Sweden, Norway, the USA and India have started Research and Development (R&D) activities on large scale. It is estimated that the global wave energy potential is 60 to 80 MW/m. Even at a given place, the energy availability varies during the different hours of the day, and in different months. Along Indian Coast it may lie anywhere between 5 KW/m and 15 KW/m. For a total Indian Coast, the wave energy potential is around 60,000 MW. The total tidal resource of the oceans has been estimated at $3x10^6$ megawatts, of which only 2 percent is suitable for harnessing. This is a significant amount since it represents nearly 5 per cent of worldwide power generation (1980) from all sources. The first commercial production, in 1966, was by the Rance Plants of France, with peak annual output of 2.40 megawatts. Russia, Canada, The USA have entered the final era of production, while Australia, Argentina, Korea and India have prepared the working plans, In India, possible sites according to 1966 survey are the Gulf of Kutch, the Gulf of Cambay and Sunder bans in West Bengal, having annual average tidal range of 11 m., 6 m and 3.5 m respectively, and possible installed capacities of 7300 MW. 1000 MW and 15 MW with respective costs Rs. 1925 crore, Rs. 600 crores and Rs. 15 crores, Possibilities of the tapping of ocean currents to provide new sources of energy are maximum on the western parts of oceans, examples being the Gulf of Stream in the Atlantic Ocean and Kurooshivo in the Pacific Ocean. Wind harnessed directly and under favorable conditions has a much higher energy density than the sun. India is still in the process of estimating of offshore aeolian energy resources. An imported wind generator has been installed for the first time in India to operate a light house at Kanai Creek (Guajrat) with a power output of 300 wotts.

The energy from Salinty Gradient is represented by the cosmetic pressure difference between the sea-water and the fresh water which is very high. Salt domes are often located near shore or under the sea floor, dissolved salt pumped to the surface and interlaced with sea water could be a source of salinity power. Still another source of energy are the salt pans in arid areas, by limiting sea-water access and utilizing solar evaporation, a hyper saline brine can be interfaced with the sea-water. In India, Sunder bans and other deltaic and esturine points are potential places for generation of energy from the salinity gradient in near future.

The magneto hydro-dynamic generator (MHD), uses geotrophic currents and long strip that is wound with a flat wire, the following current produces an electric current of 5 mho/m. Marine Biomass while wet, undergo anaerobic decomposition, thereby producing gaseous mixture of CO^2 and Ch with the possibility of using residues as an excellent fertilizer. Two main marine biomass energy resources being (1) the giant sps Macro cystic Pyrifera and (2) Garcitaria hilvaniae. Changes of biomass power being competitive with coal gasification are bright. Geothermal energy is associated with rift zones and volcanic activity, but currently it appears that only in coastal and insular situations would tapping of such energy be warranted economically. Thus the self domes inside shallow oceanic waters are a good source of Geothermal Energy. Retrieval of Uranium dissolved in sea-water should be a major source of energy Japaness Metal Miring Agency has developed experimental factories to harness this energy.

FRESH WATER FROM SEA

Oceans, ice caps and glaciers constitute 97.2 per cent and 2.15 per cent of world's fresh water supply, respectively, Fresh water is one of the most valuable resources extracted from the sea, especially for the countries where land water availability is very difficult and costly. Another comparatively different possible source of fresh water is icebergs. Icebergs, the best come from Antarctica would be towed by some mechanism to the areas where water is needed. The most publicized such area is Saudi Arabia, others being California and Australia.

There are alternative additional fresh water sources (acquifers and spring) underneath the continental shelf, that could, when tapped, provide coastal settlements with a valuable resource. Sites already located for such springs include several areas of the Mediterranean and possibly the Romanian coast of the Black Sea in the Pacific, Japan, Australia, Guam, Samoa and Chile, and the California coast of the United States; in the Atlantic, south California Florida, several locations in the Gulf of Mexico, the Mexican Yucatan peninsula, the Bahamas, Barbados and Cuba, According to one estimate by 1978 fresh water production from the ocean alone worth $250 million annually, with an estimated product of 4 million m^3 per day.

MINERAL RESOURCES

The ocean has been repeatedly labeled as the last frontier, and claims have been made that metals can be hailed from the sea at 50-70 per cent of the cost of launching: that sea ores are often highly concentrated: and that shelves are rich in petroleum, natural gas, tin, phosphorite, diamonds, sulphur and iron, Manganese rich nodules have been hailed as a bonanza that would help the economy of developing countries. But still ocean mining has to cope with some problems like availability.

Mineral exploration will undoubtedly be influenced by recent developments in the plate tectonic theory. Three types of environment are areas of major igneous activity:

1. Spreading plate boundaries; 2. Subduction Zones; and 3. Hotsports of rising manle rock. Ore deposits have been shown to be associated with each of these zones.

Mineral deposits of economical interest are quite different from the surrounding sea-floor materials; this allows their spotting and identification based, for example on density, seismic velocity, magnetism, electrical and thermal conductivity, indeed polarization and chemical properties.

Mining beneath the sea-floor, includes (a) Petroleum (b) Natural Gas; (c) Coal; (d) Limestone; (e) Tin; (f) Copper; (g)

Nickel; (h) Iron, and (i) Sulphur. Chief prospects for petroleum deposits are youthful margins where some basins contain thick accumulations of sediments. Oil may also occur at convergence zones and near translation faults. Asia remains the continent with greatest promise of discovery. Mining on the sea-floor includes (a) Phosphorite; (b) Sands and Grevels; (c) Iron beaming sands (d) Diamonds; (e) Gold, Platinum, Osmium, Peledium, Titanium and other Benvy mineral places; (f) Copper, Jead Zinc, Vanadium (g) Banium, Zirconium, Tin, Sulphur, Bartes; and (h) Manganese noduiles containing mainly Cobalt, Copper, Nickel and Manglese) (i) muds and oozes and red sea metalliferous muds; (j) Polymetallic sulphides.

PETROLEUM

The world uses petroleum per year, or about 5 berrels per persons per year. Of this, about 4 billion barrels come from marine sources and this fraction is increasing. Further, most marine wells have been drilled in less than 200 m of water from fixed platform, although in some cases it has been from 500 meters to 6 Km of depth; Upto'1980, the offshore and on-shore oil fields have yielded about 30,000 oil fields, less than 8 per cent of which (24) have reserves more than $68x10^6$ metric tonnes (500 mbbl.). The aggregate of oil bearing offshore sedimentary areas of the world is $50x10^6$ Km^2, i.e., 14 per cent of the total ocean area. New discoveries of oil have been made at the rate of some 2x109 MT per year over the last 5 years. This represents some 66 per cent of current world consumption, i.e., 3x109 MT per year. New oil findings of sufficient magnitude to sustain demand beyond the year 2000 would have to be made at twice the present discovery rate.

EEZ of India, according to present estimations, contains potential oil reserve around 1 billion tonnes and natural gas of around 271 bcm. Proved oil reserves being 510 MT. The 1982 crude oil production was 2.11 crore tonnes. In Gujarat, drilling tests have established the oil fields in Ankleshwar (annual capacity 73 m tonnes) and Cambay basin of Piran Island, the probable reserve being around 60 million tones. The success achieved in 1980 in Bombay High has surely opened a new chapter in the exploration of offshore oil reserves. The potential reserves in Bombay High is supposed to be 230.95 million tonnes (1980 production being 4.5 m tonnes). The Gandhar discovery, which was made in April 1984 remains however by far the most important since Bombay High about 10 years ago. It is believed to be as large as Ankleshwar.

NATURAL GAS

World proven reserves of natural gas amount to an estimated 90,325 billion Cu m as of Pant, 1984, compared with 88,054 bcm a year earlier. World commercial production of gas in 1983 totalled 1,584 bcm, little different from the two proceeding years. In India, Natural Gas (Chiefly marsh gas with some other gaseous hydrocarbons) usually accompanied the petroleum accumulations. The total reserves of natural gas in the country's boundary was estimated to be 351,91 bcm, the offshore being 270.96 bcm. Production at national level decreased by 24 percent in 1980, i.e. 1975 mem, 1981 and 1982 total production were 19.97 bcm and 24.12 bcm. respectively. The country is fortunate to have discoverd natural gas offshore at Andaman and Nicobar islands, West coast of Gulf of Cambay and Kutch and Bombay High regions. The significant discoveries of gas in 1985-86 were B-174 in offshore Bombay, Narsapur in the Krishna Godavari basin, Karjisarin Gujarat and Kaza in Andhra Pradesh. Both oil and gas have struck at some other locations like Panna East and

B-172 in offshore Bombay, Pakhajan in Gujarat and Tatipale in the Krishna-Godavari basin. The known gas reserves have increased from 68 billion cubic meters to 479 billion cubic meters.

MANGANESE MODULES

Under sea mineral wealth is highly diversified as well as largely untapped. Sea would be a rich store-house of many minerals like coal, tin, nickel, coper, iron, calcium, carbonate sulphur, prosperities, sand and gravels, diamonds, gold platinum, osmium, titanium, barium and zorconium etc. .... Among other possibilities Manganese Nodules (15% Mn 15% Fe, Ni-0-4%, Co 0-4%, Cu -.3%) greatly enriched in iron and manganese, are spherical or acorn shaped ranging between 1 to 20 cm in diameter. They are abundant in areas of low sedimentation rates, such as abyssal plains. One of the highest concentration of those nodules noticed is of the order of 100 Kg./m2,.i.e., 3,000 to 75,000 tonnes/sq. mile. A mining operation would need about 30,000 to 75,000 tonnes/sq. mile. Estimates are that as much as 25 per cent of the sea floor is covered by nodules and that over 1.5 trillion ($1.5x10^{12}$) tons are in the Pacific alone, especially in the siliceous ooze area. In Pacific, these deposits lie north of the equator in a broad band between 603°N and 20°N and extending from 110°W to 180°W covering over 11 million sq. kms. .The nodules of a Atlantic and Indian Oceans are generally characterized by having copper, nickel and cobalt below those generally considered economic. It should be noted that the United States has been the prime mover in trying to develop and mine the manganese nodules in the deep sea, Manganese nodules in Indian Ocean cover a large area, over 10 million sq. km2. Distribution maps prepared for Mn, Fe, Ni, Cu, Co and Mo indicate that large areas in the basins of the east of the Central Indian Ridge contains nodules with a high percentage of Mn (715 percent), Ni and Cu (70.2%) and these appear to be more promising basins.

POLYMETALLIC SULPHIDES

Considerable interest has been sparked by the discovery of polymetallic sulphides. They occur along the midocean rift valleys and those found near the Galapagos rift system contain 48%

sulphur, 43% iron, 11% copper and smaller quantities of zinc, tin, molybdenum, lead and silver. The sulphides apparently result from submarine hydrothermal precipitation along the northern boundary fault of the rift valley at depths exceeding 2,000 m. It has been suggested that mining the sulphides could be done using the energy of the hot hydrothermal vent waters (360°C). India has located few scattered deposits of polymetallic sulphides in the central Indian ocean.

Muds are deposited at the sea bottom at lesser depths than on the continental platform. Calcareous muds originate from shell deposits and can be used in the production of whitewash, as fertilizer or for its content of calcium, potassium or bareter. Such muds cover about 35 percent of the ocean bottom at depths ranging from 700 to 6000 m with layers whose thickness is estimated at 400 m on the average. These are spread over 128 million km2 and accumulate at the rate of 1 billion tones per year, or eight times the quantity yielded by contemporary land operations. Brown or Red muds are argillaceous and constitute a source of aluminum, iron, copper, nickel, cobalt, and vanadium. Some oceanographers believe that they cover 50 percent of the pacific Ocean and 25 percent of the Atlantic Ocean floors at an average depth of 30,000 m. Muds that contain relatively large amount of shells ore tests (73 percent ore dead organisms are called oozes). The two types being calcareous and siliceous oozes having subtypes viz., (1) Foraminifera Ooze; (2) Diatom Ooze; (3) Radiolarian Ooze; (4) Pterapod Ooze; and (5) Globigerina Ooze.

DISSOLVED SUBSTANCES

Sulphur, potassium, bone, magnesium, salts and bromines, elements in solution in marine water, are also extracted. In fact salt still ranks third in value among the minerals extracted from the sea. Magnesium is more soluble in its salt compound, thus used much in medicine. One of the principle uses of beomene has been in anti-knock compounds in solar salt extraction. However, it can be precipitated directly.

The process has been modified repeatedly and currently, a

sulphur-dioxide process is used only in the United States. Bromine from the sea provides 70% of the world's need in the late sixties. Magnesium is the third most abundant element in the sea, although not yet produced worldwide. It is the most valuable mineral after hydrocarbons, extracted in the USA, where annual $85 million. The other having several plants are Great Britain and Bulgaria. Thick beds ortacdydrite, magnesium salt have been located along Brazilian coast and in the Congo Basin. Today the value of salt gained from the sea reaches over $ 200 million annually and in 1974 worldwide production amounted to about 172 MT. Most operations are based on solar evaporation.

In additions, sea water analysis have revealed quantities of dissolved copper, cobalt, zinc, gold, uranium and deuterium. Concentrations, however, are small, yet these elements could perhaps be recovered as a sole operation of desalinization plants. And, if the world were to switch to a hydrogen economy, the sea would naturally be an inexhaustible source of hydrogen. As for deuterium, an essential element of the fusion process, the oceans contain 25 percent trillion tons of it. Deuterium is most abundant in tropical water. That amount is the equivalent of 75.10 Btu. Heavy water extraction in Glace, bay (Nova Scotia) is utilizing the Gulf stream water arriving from the equatorial Atlantic.

BIOLOGICAL RESOURCES OF OCEAN

No doubt, the world population is growing exponently. Further, the combination of heavy and increasing consumption with fixed finite resources, spells disaster. Sea food is an excellent source of animal protein, Good management of world fisheries could increase sea food production two or three fold. Phytoplanktons (floating, generally microscopic plants) are the principal plant in the ocean and are at the base of the food chain. The world wide production of organic material by phytoplankton shows four zones within the ocean: 1. Upwelling areas, such as off Peru, California, and West Africa, where production is very high. 2. The shallow water of most continental shelves, which have high production. 3. The Antarctic Arctic and equatorial water, which generally have moderate productivity because the water is mixed by currents and winds; and 4. The deep-ocean areas far from land which have essentially biologic deserts.

The distribution of zooplankton, which feed on the phytoplankton is similar likewise, location of the world's major fishing areas follow the pattern of the phytoplankton production of organic material especially for the near shore parts of oceans. World's coastal areas contain 50 percent of the global commercial harvest, the upwelling areas in 49 percent of harvest and other open areas in deep sea produce less than 1 percent of the global commercial harvest, the areas of the zones being 9.9 percent, 0.1 percent and 90 percent of the ocean area respectively.

About 70 million tons of sea food (2 percent of the total world annual food production, nearly 4 billion tons) is being harvested per year, which amounts to about 15 percent per person. About 90 percent of this is fish, the rest consisting of molluscs, crustaceans and whales. The world catch of fish for 1976 was (161.6 billion pounds) 73.4 million metric tonnes. Most of this catch came from off Asia and was mainly used for food. The most common catch was the small heriling, anchovies, etc. Japan caught the highest having 14 percent of world's share, followed by the USSR 13.8 percent, China 9.4% Peru 5.9 percent, Norway 4.7 percent and USA 4.1 percent are now; to 'herders'. As a result fish constitutes about 1 percent of our total diet on the average, or about 17 percent of the animal protein. There are big geographical variations in this. For example, in the US fish are only about 5%. While Japan and Iceland have annual per capita consumption of fish and shell fish, estimated live weight equivalent around 68.8 kilograms and 66 kilograms, respectively. India has only 2.9 kilograms per capita, consumption.

Recent estimated world production offish, shellfish and seaweeds by Acquaculture show that fish product was 3980492 metric tone [China (2200000), India (490000) metric tonnes)]. Shrimps and Prawns being 15663 metric tonnes (India leading with4000 metric tonnes), Oysters 591386 metric tonnes (Japan 229, 899), Mussels 328517 metric tonnes (Spain 160,000); Clams

38851 (Korea 249201), Scallops 62600 (Japan 62600), cockles and other molluses 29987 (Malaysia 28000), Seaweeds (1,054793 metric tonnes). Further, it is estimated that world wide aquaculture production could reach 50 million metric tons. Besides, closed cycle aquaculture practiced in near shore areas such as bays and estuaries, open-ocean aquaculture will allow access to larger and some varied sources of food and generally solve the problem of accumulation of waste products. Other important techniques being ocean ranching, alternatives to current feeding practices and recycling of nutrients along with other better fishery management methods. With all those advanced techniques, a total harvest approaching 200 x 10^6 metric tonnes is conceivable in the near future, thus forming 10 percent of annual protein world's need. In India about 150 million people live along the coast and over 1.4 million people derive their subsistence through activities related to the sea. i.e., mostly fisheries. According to 1985 National Institute of Oceanography (N10) report the total annual fish catch from sea in India is about 1.4 million tonnes but the potential is estimated to be about 10 million tonnes. About 1.94 million hectares of brackish water is available for aquaculture out of which 30,000 hectares is used at present. These yield about 80,000 tons of products annually.

For Indian Ocean, the generally accepted limit of potential yield is about 15 million tonnes. The present catch according to FAO (1980) estimated is around 3.5 m tonnes of which 1.4 million tonnes are caught by India alone. Of these 3.5 million tones exploited fish catch Indian Ocean, 44 percent constitutes pelagic resources, 14 percent demersal and 11 percent crustaceans. It means that at present level of exploitation the annual yield of demersal fishely resources including finishes, crustaceans and mollasces from the Indian ocean, is less than 1 million tonnes. The present level of exploitation is less than 16 percent of the harvestable resource.

EEZ 2.02 million sq km of India includes roughly 0.2 million sq km under less than 50 meters depth, 0.4 million sq km between 50-200 meters depth over the shelf, and hence 1.78 million sq km remained for the offshore fisheries, 50 percent of the sustainable fishing yield of India's EEZ, about 4.5 million tons, lies in the inshore zone of less than 50 meters depth, i.e., only in 9 percent area of the EEZ. It may be thus command that this inshore zone potential of kilogram per hectare yield is 10 times more that of offshore zone, the later having total potential of 3 million tonnes.

In India, under biological oceanographic studies in EEZ and more in nearby coastal zone, much emphasis should be laid on ecology, distribution and benthos, spatial and temporal variations in the rate, magnitude and total biological production, estimation of potential and harvestable yield, environmental perturbation on biota and collection of base line information for biotic and a biotic components in near shore environment for developing marine parks and sanctuaries. These programmes indeed, will require regular monitoring of about 400 stations. As one of the major achievements in the field of fisheries, the Government of India has recently acquired one Danish multipurpose fisheries and oceanographic research vessel SAGAR SAMPADA for exploration and estimation of resources in EEZ of India and the contiguous high sea.

■■■

Bibliography

Abercrombie, M.L.J.	1960	The Anqtomy of Judgement, an investigation into the process of perception and reasoning, Hutchinson, London.
Allan, J.A.	1978	The Contribution of LANDSAT imagery to reconnaissance soil mapping in North-West India: in collins, W.G. and Van Genderen. J.L. Remote Sensing applications in developing countries, 43-47. Remote Sensing Socienty Reading.
Anderson, J.R., Hardy, E.E, Roch, JT. and Witemr R.E.	1976	A land use and land cover classification system for use with remote sensor data. US Geol. Surv. Prof. Paper 964, Washington
Avery, T.E.	1977	Interpretation of aerial photoraphs, 3rd edition, Burggress Publ. Co. Minneapolis.
Bharucha, F.R. Ball, I.R.	1957	A textbook of Plant Geography, of India.
Ball, I.R.	1975	Nature and formulation of biogeography hypotheses. Syst. zool. 24, 407-30.
Ball, I.	1981	The order of life towards a comparative biology. Nature, Land, 294, 675-76.

Brian Seddon	1971	Introduction to Biogeography Gerald Duck worth and Co. Ltd., London, U.K.
Briggs, John C.		Global Biogeography.
Briggs, John C.		Biogeography and Plate Tectonics.
Brown, J.H. and Gibson, A.C.	1983	Biogeography C.V. Mosby, St. Louis.
Brundin, L.	1968	Application of Phylogenetic Principles in Sustematics and exolutionary theory. In Current problems of Lower Verterbrate Phytogeny (ed. T. Orvig) Nobel Symposium, U. Stockholm PP. 473-95.
Bull, R.M.	1967	A Study of the large Newzealand weevil, Lyperobius huttoni pascoe, Victoria University of Wellington, New Zealand.
Buffon, G.L.L Comte de (1749-1804)	1954	Histoire Naturelle, Generaleet Particuliere, 44 vols. Limprimerie royale, Paris, Paris.
Cain, S.A.	1944	Foundations of Plant Geography, Har per & Row.
Carneirio, CMR	1980	The Brazillian forest cover monitoring programme, Int. Soc. Photogram. Int. Archives Photogram. XXIII, B7 Comm 7,132-141, Hamburg.
Charles Southwick	1961	Ecology and the Quality of our Environment.
Charan, A.K.	1992	Plant Geography, Rawat Publication, Jaipur.
Chauhan, T.S.	1992	Desertification in the world and its control, Scientific Publishers, Jodhpur.
Cleveland, H.	1977	Resource sensing from space prospects for developing countries; National Academy of Science Rept. 23, Washington.
Collinson, A.S.	1977	Introduction to world Vegetation, Geoge Allen and Unwin, London.

Colwell, R.N. (Co-ordinator) 1971 Monitoring earth resources from aircraft and spacecraft, NASA Sp-275 Washington.

Comfort, A. 1987 What real world? (Review of Philosphy and the brain by J.Z. Young) The Guardian (January 23) 11.

Corner, E.J.H. 1963 Ficus in the Pacific region, In Biogeography (ed J.L. Gressitt) Bishop Museum, Honolula, Hawali, PP 233-45.

Cracraft, J. 1974 Phylogeny and evolution of the ratite birds. Ibis 116, 494-521.

Craw, R.C. 1983 Panbiogeography and vicariance cladistics are they truly different? Syst. Zool. 32 431-8.

Craw, R.C. 1983a Panbiogeography and vicariance cladistics are they truly different? Syst. 2001. 32 431-8.

Craw, R.C. 1985 Classic prcblems of Southern Hemisphere Biogeogfraphy Re-examined: Panbiogeographic analysis of the NewZealand frog Leiopelma the ratite birds and Nothofagus, Z. Zool. Syst. and Evolutions forsch., 23, 1-10.

Craw, Robin C. 1999 Panbiogeography: Tracking the History of Life (Oxford Biogeography series No. 11)

Criozat, L. 1952 Manual of Phytogeography, Junk, The Hague.

Croizat, L. 1958 Panbiogeography Vol. 1,2a, 2b, Published by the author Caracas, Venezuela.

Croizat, L. 1964 Space, Time, Form: The biological synthesis, Published by the author Caracas, Venezuela.

Croizat, L. 1968 The biogeography of the tropical lands and islands east of Syez-madagacar: with Particular reference to the dispersal

		and formmaking of Ficus L., and different other vegetal and animal groups. Atti 1st Univ. Lab. Criffogam. Pavia, 1-400
Croizat, L.	1982	Vicariance/vicarism, Panbiogeography, vicarianc biogeography etc.: a classification. Syst. zool. 31, 291-304
Collins, W.	1976	Spectroradiometric Detection and Mapping of areas enriched in Ferric Iron Minerals using Airborne and Orbiting Instruments Columbia University, USA.
Collins, W. and Chiu, H.Y.	1979	Signature evaluation of natural targets using high spectral resolution techniques proc. 13th Int. Symp. On Remote Sensing Environment, University of Michigan, USA.
Collins, W. Chang. S.H. Raines, G.L. Canney, F.C. and Ashley, R.	1980	'Airborne biogeochemical Survey test case results' Abstracts of 6th Annual pecrasymp. Sioux Falls, South Dakota, USA. April, 1980, pp. 71-3
Cox, C Barry, Peter D. Moore	1999	Biogeography: An ecological and evolutionary approach.
Darwin, C.	1859	On the origin of species by means of Natural selection John Murray. London, U.K.
Darwin, C.	1859	On the origin of species by means of Natural selection or the preservation of favoured Races in the struggle for Life, John Murray, London.
Davis, J.H.	1950	Evidences of trans-oceanic dispersal of plants to New Zealand Tuatara, 3, 87-97
Darlington, Phillip J. J.R.	1957	Zoogeography: The Geographical Distribution of Animals. Museum of Comparantive Zooloy. Harvard University Prers.

David Watts 1971 Principles of Biogeography: An introduction to the functional mechanisms of ecosystems, McGraw Hill, Publishing Company Limited, U.K.

Doyle, F.J. 1978 The next decade of Satellite remote sensing photogram : Engn. Remote sensing 44,155-164.

Estabrok, G.F., Johnson, C.S. and Mc Morris, F.R. 1976 A mathematical foundation for analysis of cladistic character compatibility. Math. Biosci., 29, 181-87

Fridriksson, S. 1975 Surtsey: Evolution of Life on a Volcanic Island, Butterworths, London.

Farri, M.G. 1980 A Science in search of a paradigma- Review of the Symposium "Vicariance biogeography: a critique" Syst. Zoo I. 29, 67-76

Farris, J.S. 1983 The empirical basis of Phylogentic Systematics. In Advances in cladistics, I (eds N. Platnik and V.A. Funk) Columbia University Press, New York, PP 7-36

Farris, J.S. 1986 On the boundaries of phylogenetic systematics cladistics, 2, 14-27

Goodier, R. (Ed.) 1971 The application of aerial photography to the work of the Nature Conservancy. The Nature Conservancy.

Gray 1980 Historical Biogeography: Plate Tectonics and the changing Environment.

Gregory, R.L. 1981 Mind in Science; a history of explanations in psychology and physics, weidenfeld and Nicholson, London, U.K.

Harley, J.B. 1975 Ordnance Survey maps: a descriptive in annual. Ordnance Survey. Southamption.

Hancock, John 1986 Biogeography Rana Mattershead, Basil Blackwell, U.K.

Heads, M. and 1984 Bibliography of the scientific work of

Craw, R.C. Leon Croizat 1932-82. In Croizat's Pan biogeography Botanica (eds R.C. craw and G.W. Gjbbs), Victoria University Press, Wellington, as Twatara, 27, 67-75

Henderson, I 1985 Systematic Studies of New Zealand Trichoptera and critical analysis of Systematic methods, Victoria University of Wellington, New Zealand.

Henning, W. 1950 Grundziige einer Theorie der Phylogenetischen Systematic, Deutscher Zeutralxerlage Berlin.

Henning, W. 1966 Phylogenetic Systematics, University of liinois, Urbana.

Hendy, M.D. 1982 Branch and Boundalgorithms to determine minimum evolutionary trees Math. Ent. 10, 221-329

Holkenbrink, P.F. 1978 Mannual on characteristics of LANDSAT Computer compatible tapes protuced by the EROS Datta Centre digital image processing system U.S. Geological survey, Washington D.C.

Horler, D.N.H., Barber, J. and Barringer, A.R. 1980 Effects of heavy metals on the absorance and reflectance spectra of plants, Int. J. Remote Sensing 1 (2), 121-36

Horler, D.N.H., Dockray, M. and Barber, J. 1983 The red edge of plant leaf reflectance Int. J. Remote Sensing Faber, London, U.K.

Howard, J.A. 1977 Satellite remote sensing of agricultural resources for developing countries, present and future: an international perspective in peel R.F. et. al (Eds) Remote sensing of the terrestrial environt, 248-262, Butterworths, London.

Huggett, Richard John 1998 Fundamentals of Biogeography, Routledge.

Hull, D.L.	1967	Certainty and circulation in evolutionary taxonomy. Evolution 21. 174-89
Humboldt, F.H.A. von et.al.	1927	Essai suria Geographic des von et. al. plantes accompagne dim Tables Physique des Regions Equinoxiales, German edition.
Humphries, C.J.	1986	Cladistic Priogeography, Clarendon Press, Oxford.
Humphries, Christopher John Lynne R. Parenti	1986	Cladistic Biogeography (oxford Monographs on Biogeography).
Humphries, C.J. and Parenti, L.	1986	Cladistic Biogeography, Clarendon Press, Oxford.
Lan F. Spellerberg, et, al	1999	An Introduction to Applied Biogeography.
Jablonsk, D. Flessa, K.N. and Valentine, J.N.	1985	Biogeography and paleobiology, Paleobiology 11, 75-90
Johansson, O.	1969	Further developments in producing photo maps is a basis for the economic map of sweeden, Cartogr. 1-6,103-107. Plant Geography, Methuen and Co. Ltd.
Kellman, Martin C. Kirby, R.P.	1977	Remote sensing of Scottish Coastal habitates. T.R.R.U. Rept. 34 University of Edinburan
Kluge, A.G. and Farris, J.S.	1969	Quantitative Phyletics and the evolution of anurans. Syst. Zool., 18, 1-32
Knipling, E.B.	1970	Physical and physiological basis for the reflectance of visible and near infrared radiation for vegetation, Remote sensing of Environment 6, 155-9.
Kuhn, T.S.	1970	The Structure of Scientific Education, 2nd edn. Chhicago University Press, Chicago.
Laubenfels, D.J. de.	1970	A Geography of Plants and Animals,

		Foundation of Geography Series, Wm. C. Brown.
Lee, Y.J.	1975	Reliability of estimating clear cut and uncut nature timber areas using LANDSAT imagery; Pro. 3rd Condian symp. On Remote sensing 265-275. Canadian Aeronautics and space Institute, Ottawa.
Liffesand, T.M. and Kiefer R.W.	1979	Remote sensing and imge interpretation, wiley New York.
Lowtrup, S.	1982	The four theories of evolution, Rev. Biol, 75, 53-66, 231-72, 385-409
Mac Donald, Glen and Glenn M. Mac Donald		Space, Time and life : The Science of Biogeography.
Mac Donald and Hall F.G.	1980	Global Crop forecasting; Soil Sci. Sol. Amer. Prol. 23,164-168.
Mc Dowall, R.M.	1978	Generalized tracks and dispersal in biogeography. Syst. Zool., 27, 88-104
Mc Ewen, R.B., Kasco, W.J. and Carter, V.	1976	Coastal wetland mapping photogramm. Engpg and Remote sensing 42, 221-232.
Mc Coy, E.D. and Heck, K.L. Jr.	1976	Biogeography of corals, sea grasses and Mangroves: an alternative to the center of origin concept. Syst. Zool., 25, 201-10
Mc Manus, J.W.	1985	Marine speciation, tectonic and sea-level changes in Southeast Asia. Proc. 5th Int. Coral Congr, Tahiti, 4, 133-38
Mani, M.S.	1974	Ecology and Biogeography in India, The Hague, Netherlands.
Mielke, H.W.	1998	Patterns of Life, Biogeography of a changing world, Unwin hyman, Boston.
Mielke, Howard	1989	Patterns of Life: Biogeography of a changing world.
Millington, A.C.		GIS and Remote sensing applications in Biogeography and Ecology (Kluwer

International Series in Engineering and Computer Science, 626

Morain, Stanley 1984 Systematic and Regional Biogeography.

Mottershead, Rona 1979 Biogeography Basil Blackwell Limited, U.K.

Muller, Paul et al 1986 Biogeography, Happer & Row, Publishers, New York.

Murtl, P.A. 1972 A guide to air photo interpretation of forest damage in Canada; Can. For. Seru. Publ. 1292, Ottawa.

Myers, A.A. and P.S. Giller ed. 1988 Analytical Biogeography: An Integrated Approach to the study of Animal and plant Distributions Chapman and Hall Ltd., London.

My ets, J.H. 1976 Distribution and Dispersal in Populations Capable of Resource Depletion: A Simylation Model: Oecologia 24:255-269

Nelson, G. 1981 Systematics and Biogeography Cladistics and vicariance, Columbia University Press, New York. Vicariance Biogeography: a Critique Columbia University Press, New York.

Nelson, G. and Platnick, N. 1981 Suystematics and Biogeography/ Cladistics and vicariance, Columbia University Press, New York.

Newbigin, M.I. 1936 Plant and Animal Geography, Methuen & Co. Ltd., London.

Newell, N.D. 1971 An Outline history of tropical Organic reefs, Am. Mus. Novit, 2465, 1-37

Osman, R.W., and Whitlatch R.B 1978 Patterns of diversity: fact or artifact ? Paleobiology, 4, 41-54

Page, R. 1987 Graphs and generalized tracks: quantifying croizat's panbiogeography. Syst. Zool. 36 (1) 1-17

Page, R. 1987 Graphs and generalized tracks: quantifying croizat's panbiogeography. Syst. Zool. 36 (1) 1-17

Parenti, L.R. 1981 Discussion of C. Patterson's Paper, Methods of Paleobiogeography. In vicariance Biogeography : a critique (eds G-Nelson and D.E. Rosen) Columbia University Press, New York PP 490-7

Parry, D.E. and Trevti, J.W. 1979 Mapping Nigeria's vegetation from radar Geog. J. 145, 265-281.

Patterson, C. 1981 Methods in Paleobiogeography. In Vicariance Biogeography: a critique (eds. G. Nelson and D. E. Rosen). Columbia University Press, New York. PP 247-93

Patterson C. 1982 Classes and cladists or inviduals and evolution, Syst. Zool. 31, 284-6

Patterson, C. 1983 Aims and Methods in biogéography. In Evolution Time and Space: the emergence of the Biosphere Systematics Assoc Space. Vol. 23, 1-28

Peargman 1977 Basic Biography, Longman group Limited, London and New York.

Peter A. Furley, et.al. 1983 Geography of the Biosphere; An trodudton to the nature, Distribution and Exolution of the world's life Zones, Butterworths.

Petri, G. 1977 Orthohotomaps; Trans Insp. Br. Geogr N.S. 2. 49-70.

Potts, D.C. 1985 Sea-level fluctuations and speciation in scleractinia, Proc. 5th Internet Coral Reef congr. Tahiti, 4 127-32

Robinson, H. 1972 Biogeography, Macdonald and Evans Ltd., London.

Robert, J.W. Island Biogeography : Ecology, Evolution and Conservation.

Rosen, B.R. 1975 The distribution of reef corals Rep. Underwater As (New Series) 1, 1-16

Rosen, B.R. 1981 The tropical high diversity enigma the coral eye view. In chance, chance and challenge the emerging biosphere (eds

		P.H. Green wood and P.L. Forey) British Museum (Natural History) and Combridge University Press, Combridge. 103-29
Rosan, B.R.	1984	Reef Coral biogeography and climate through the late coinozoic: Just islands in the Sun or Critical Pattern of islands. In fossils and Climate (ed. P.J. Benchley) Geol. J. Spec, Issue, 11,201-62
Rudd, R.D.	1974	Remote sensing a better view, Duxbury Press, North Scituate, Masachussetts.
Schinminke, H.K.	1974	Mesozoic intercontinental relationships as evidenced by Bathynellid Crustacea (Syncarida: Mala Costraca) Syst. Zool, 23, 157-64
Schinmike, H.K.	1973	Grujndfragen der Palaontologie, Schweizerbart, Surttgart.
Schinmike, H.K.	1973	Evolution, System and Verbeiturgs geschichte der famile Parabathynellide (Bathynellaea Mala-Costraca). Mikrofauna des Meeres bodens, 24, 1-192
Sebert, L.M.	1968	Photo maps for resource development in Canada, Can. Cortogr. 5 (1), 50-53.
Seddon Brian	1971	Introduction to Biogeography Gerald Duch worth and Co. Ltd. London.
Sheffield, C.	1981	Earth watch, Sidgwick and Jackson, London.
Sibley, C.G. and Ahiquist, J.E.	1981	The Phylogeny and relationships of the ratite birds as indicated by DNA-DNA hy bridization. In Evolution Todayt, Proceedings of the 2nd International Congress on Systematic and Evolution ary Biology (eds G.G.E. scudder and J.L. Reveal). Hunt Institute for Botanical Documentation, Pittsburgh.
Sinha R.K. ed.	1998	Global Biodiversity, Inashri, Jaipur.

Stehli, F.G. and Wells, J.N.	1971	Diversity and age Patterns in hermatypic Corals. Syst. Zool. 20,115-26
Stevens, P.	1980	Evolutionary Polarity of Character States Ann. Rev. Ecol. Syst., 11, 333-58
Staley, J.T., Lehmicke, L.G. Palmer, F.F. et al	1982	Impact of Mount st Helens eruption on bacteriology of lakes in the blast zone. Appl Environmental Microbiology 43, 644-70
Stomme, H.	1984	Last Iswland, University of British Columbia Press, Victoria.
Taylor, J.A. ed.	1984	Themes in Biogeography, Croom Helm Ltd. Sydney, Australia.
Tixy, J.	1993	Biogeography, A Study of Plants in the Ecosphere, (3rd Fds) Longman Scientific and Technical New York.
Valentine, J.W. and Jablenski, D.	1982	Major deferminats of the biogeographic pattern of the shallow sea fauna, Bull. Soc. Geol. Fr. (Series 7) 24,893-99
Valentine, J.W.	1984	Neogene marine Climate trends: implications for biogeography and evolution of the shallow sea biota. Geology, 12 647-50
Wagner, W.H.	1980	Origin and philosophy of terns. In Recent Advances in Botany, University of Toronto press, Toronto, PP. 841-4
Wallace, A.R.	1876	The Geographical Distribution of Animals, II, Mac Million London.
Watts David	1971	Principles of Biogeography An introduction to the functional mechanisms of ecosystems, McGraw-Hill London.
Welch, R., Pannell, C.W. and LOCP	1975	Map Supplement no. 19, Landuse in Northeast China, 1973; a view from LANDSAT-1; Annals Assoc. Amer Geog. 65, 595-596 (Map Separate)

Willson, A.C. et.al	1985	Mito chondrial DNA and two perspectives on exolution ary genetics, Biol. J. Urn. Soc. 26, 375-400
Williams, R.S. and Carter, W.D. (Eds)	1976	ERTS-1 A new window on our plan et; US Geol. Survey Professional Paper 292, Washington.
Wissmar, R.C., Devol, A.H., Nevissi, A.E. and Sedell, J.R.	1982	Chemical Changes of lakes within the Mount st. Helens blast zone. Science, 216, 175-8.
Wooldridge and East	1951	In The Spirit and Purpose of Geography (Hutchinson 1951)
World Bank	1981	Map of Bangladesh, Land use classification related to land cover reflections obtained from LANDSAT imagery; Resource planning Unit. World Bank Washington, D.C.
Yost, E. and Wenderoth, S.	1971	The reflectance spectra of mineralized tree's Proc. 7th Int. Symp. On Remote sensing Environment, University of Michigan, USA, PP 269-84.
Yost. E.	1975	Multispectral Color Photography for Mineral Exploration by Remote Sensing of Biogeochemical Anomadies, NASA-CR-144811, N77-10606, Washington DC.USA.
Young, J.Z.	1971	An Introduction to the study of Man, Oxford University Press, Oxford, U.K.
Zandee, M.	1985	C.A. F.C.A.: a Collection of APL, functions for cladistic analysis.
Ziman, J.	1968	Public Knowledge, Cambridge University Press, Combridge.
Zsilinszky, V.C.	1966	Photographic inter pretation of tree species in Ontario, 2nd edition, Ontario Dept. of Lands and forests Ottawa.